Solar electricity

A practical guide to designing and installing small photovoltaic systems

Simon Roberts

Prentice Hall
New York   London   Toronto   Sydney   Tokyo   Singapore

First published 1991 by
Prentice Hall Europe
Campus 400, Maylands Avenue
Hemel Hempstead
Hertfordshire, HP2 7EZ
A division of
Simon & Schuster International Group

Typeset in 10/12 pt Century Schoolbook
By Keyset Composition, Colchester

Printed in Great Britain by
Redwood Books, Trowbridge, Wiltshire

Library of Congress Cataloging-in-Publication Data

Roberts, Simon.
    Solar electricity : a practical guide to designing and installing
small photovoltaic systems/Simon Roberts.
    p.   cm.
    Includes bibliographical references.
    Includes index.
    ISBN 0-13-826314-0
    1. Photovoltaic power generation.   I. Title.
TK2960.R62   1991
621.31'244—dc20

                                        90-45440
                                           CIP

British Library Cataloguing in Publication Data

Roberts, Simon
    Solar electricity
    1. Electricity supply. Generation by solar energy
    I. Title
    621.31244

ISBN 0-13-825068-5

7 8 9 99 98

To Severine and the *wafundi*.

Contents

Part Three: Building electronic units

 # Notice

This book is intended to provide guidance in many aspects of installing and using solar electric systems. Since the use of this book and the conditions or methods of installation, operation, use, and maintenance are beyond the control of the author and publishers, we assume no responsibility and expressly disclaim liability for loss, damage, or expense arising out of or in any way connected with such installation, operation, use, or maintenance.

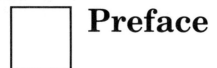

Preface

Solar electricity is the technology of converting sunlight directly into electricity. It is based on photovoltaic or solar modules which are very reliable and do not require any fuel or servicing. Millions of solar modules are in constant use throughout the world, supplying electricity for communications, transport aids, health care, security systems, and many other applications.

Solar electric systems are suitable for any place that has plenty of sun, and are ideal where there is no mains electricity. A small solar electric system in a home can run all the lighting, a cassette player, a television, and other low-power appliances. Larger systems can serve schools, workshops, health posts, and small hospitals.

Some systems are available as complete packages, such as for lighting, vaccine storage, and water pumping. The component parts can also be obtained from a variety of separate sources. However, users and electricians may encounter difficulties when it comes to building, repairing, and expanding their own systems.

Solar electricity is very appropriate for use in developing countries; however, these countries have their own particular problems, among them shortage of foreign currency, long delays for imported goods, and limited access to technical advice.

This book provides the solutions. It contains the essential details about all aspects of using photovoltaic modules in small- to medium-size solar electric systems that have a variety of appliances. The level of involvement of readers can range from users of an existing system to electricians who install systems as part of their work. Here is a list of aspects covered:

☐ Finding out about solar electricity and whether it is appropriate for the needs at a site.
☐ Understanding all the technical details provided by the manufacturers about their equipment.

☐ Putting a system together using parts from a number of different sources and including local materials.
☐ Using and maintaining a system effectively.
☐ Repairing and adding parts to an existing system.

It is not necessary to read the book from start to finish. Readers should dip in according to their needs and interest. Figure 0.1 summarizes the whole book.

Separate chapters in Part One introduce each type of equipment in a system. There are explanations of all the terms used on the data sheets provided by suppliers about their products. Relevant specifications are identified and procedures are given for selecting the most appropriate equipment according to suitability, cost, and other factors. The procedures are easy to follow, with step-by-step instructions. Look-up tables and formulas are clearly laid out and straightforward to use, requiring minimal mathematical ability.

The chapters in Part Two follow in sequence from obtaining information and the planning stage through to running a system. Some users may not be concerned with all these details. For them there are sections within these chapters covering questions to ask the installer and a checklist to ensure that the installation is correct.

Part Three gives construction details for a number of electronic units that are not available as standard items but are very useful in solar systems. Chapter 12 covers all the basic skills required to build them and a number of designs are given for each unit according to the availability of components.

There is a strong emphasis on how to make the best use of parts that are locally available. A variety of solutions is given to suit the range of circumstance that solar systems may be used in.

To help in extracting information, many chapters begin with a diagram which summarizes the different sections in a series of boxes. Page numbers are included in the boxes for quick reference. Many chapters end with a list of questions which bring out the important details and enable the book to be used as a training manual. There are numerous examples throughout and a fully worked example for a whole system at the end.

My hope is that this book will help users to choose a suitable system and get the best out of it. To many people, solar electricity is still very new. Local electricians can overcome this unfamiliarity by installing good systems at low cost and by providing a reliable service to their customers when problems arise.

The concept for this book was a course run in 1984 for Kenyan electricians by Harold D. Burris and Mark Hankins. While I was a teacher on Voluntary Service Overseas, I learned a great deal from Harold's experience at Solar Shamba. My thanks to the Revd Opwora, Augustine Aware, and the staff and students of Namboboto Secondary School, Kenya, for their support and enthusiasm during the installation of my first system.

I must also acknowledge the generosity of many others for allowing me to draw upon their wide experience and for their readiness to read my drafts: James

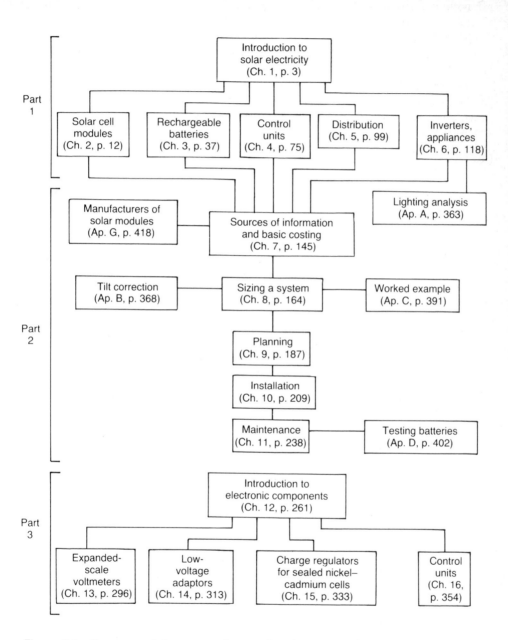

Figure 0.1 Summary of chapters and appendices in this book (Ch. chapter, Ap. appendix, p. page number).

Goodman, Sarah Lancashire, Dave Spiers, Richard Pilkington, Iain Garner, Iain Thompson, Larry Parsons, Richard Prowen, Edwin Bone, Sean McCarthy, Martin Kirkpatrick, Andrew Binnie, Allison King, and staff at Intermediate Technology Power Ltd and Intermediate Technology Development Group. For the sections concerning installation and maintenance, I have also drawn heavily upon the WHO series of books on photovoltaic fridges for vaccine storage. Thanks also to the Brumls, Cookson Group Central Research, and ZED Instruments Ltd for computing facilities while writing the book, and to Sarah for encouraging its conclusion.

Simon Roberts
January 1990

Part One

Technical details

1 | Introduction to solar electricity

What is solar energy?

In general terms, *solar energy* means all the energy that reaches the earth from the sun. It provides daylight, makes the earth hot, and is the source of energy for plants to grow.

Solar energy is also put to two types of use to help our lives directly: *solar heating* and *solar electricity*, the second being the subject of this book. They are sometimes considered to be the same but are in fact based on different processes and require completely different equipment.

Solar heating

This application of solar energy simply makes use of the heating effect of sunlight. It has been used for centuries for drying crops, bricks, and pots and to make salt from salty water in solar evaporation ponds. Solar ovens are made with mirrors that concentrate the sun's heat onto a black-painted box for cooking food.

When most people hear solar energy or solar power mentioned, they usually think of *solar water heaters*, now quite common. Solar water heaters are easily recognized by rectangular black panels mounted at a slight slope and sometimes with a small water tank fixed near to the top end (see Figure 1.1). A pipe is bent back and forth in the panel and water flowing through the pipe becomes hot since the black surface of the panel absorbs a lot of heat when the sun is out. Hot water flows from the panel up to a tank which is insulated to prevent the water cooling down too much before it is used.

Solar electricity

Another major use of solar energy is solar electricity. This is electricity generated directly from sunlight using *solar* or *photovoltaic cells*. The word 'photovoltaic' refers to an electric voltage caused by light.

3

(a)   (b)

Figure 1.1   Examples of solar water heaters.
(a)   Next to a hospital ward.
(b)   On a roof.

Solar cells were first developed to power satellites for the space programme in the 1950s. They are now used on earth and are manufactured by many companies around the world (a list of manufacturers is given in Appendix G).

Most solar cells are made of a form of *silicon*. This is a hard material that is either dark blue or red in appearance. The blue cells are made as thin discs or squares which are quite fragile. The red type of silicon is coated on to glass as a thin film. As sunlight shines on the surface of the silicon, electricity is generated by a process known as the *photoelectric effect*, as in physics.

Individual solar cells can be compared to batteries used in torches and radios in that they produce only a low-voltage direct current. Each silicon solar cell produces about 0.4 V. So just as several batteries are needed in radios and cassette players to build the voltage up, solar cells are connected together (in series) to produce a higher voltage that is more useful. Connected in this way, they are often called *solar panels* but the names used by the suppliers are *solar cell modules*, *photovoltaic modules*, or just *PV modules*.

Applications of solar electricity

Solar cell modules are made in many sizes, depending on their use. The smallest ones power electronic calculators and digital wrist-watches, while arrays of large modules can supply electricity for a whole village. A range of applications is shown in Figure 1.2.

Solar modules are a good source of electricity because they are very reliable, simple to operate, and do not require fuel. However, since they are also expensive to make, these advantages have to be carefully balanced against their high cost before purchase.

(a)

(c)

(b)

Figure 1.2 Examples of applications for solar modules.
(a) Solar-powered calculator.
(b) Street lamp. (Source Siemens Solar GmbH.)
(c) Jack pump that lifts water from a depth of 330 m (1000 ft). (Source Chronar Ltd.)

The main application for solar electricity is in remote but sunny areas that have no mains electricity and where the supply of fuel for generators is unreliable or expensive. Solar electricity is already used in many large projects: pumping water for drinking and irrigation, lighting and signalling in small stations along a railway line, powering telecommunications stations, and providing cathodic protection of pipelines to prevent rusting.

Many appliances in homes and small institutions can be run on solar electricity. Here is a list of examples:

(d)

(e)

(f)

Figure 1.2 Examples of applications for solar modules.
(d) Village power system in Greece. (Source BP Solar Ltd.)
(e) Telecommunications mast. (Source Siemens Solar GmbH.)
(f) Tracking array of 1 MW peak power near Los Angeles (United States) completed in 1983. (Source Siemens Solar Industries.)

Home: lighting, radio, cassette player, record player, television, cooling fan, burglar alarm, small refrigerator.

School: lighting, science laboratory apparatus, slide projector.

Hospital and office: lighting, refrigerator, laboratory (microscope light, centrifuge, colorimeter, and incubator), short-wave radio transmitter and receiver, electric typewriter, calculator, small computer, cooling fan, high-voltage fly killer.

Farm and workshop: electric fencing, water pump, soldering iron, electric drill, sewing machine, other machines with small electric motors.

   All the appliances listed above have low power or wattage requirements so need very little electricity to operate. They are well suited to being run on solar electricity because only a small number of solar modules are required in the system.
   Appliances which produce a lot of heat, such as an electric cooker, clothes iron, or kettle, are all rated in kilowatts (kW) and are not included in the list. It is possible to run them on solar electricity. However, they would need so many solar modules that the system would be very expensive and would not be an economical use of solar electricity. For heating, it is more economical to burn fuel or use sunlight in direct heating, as with the solar oven mentioned earlier.

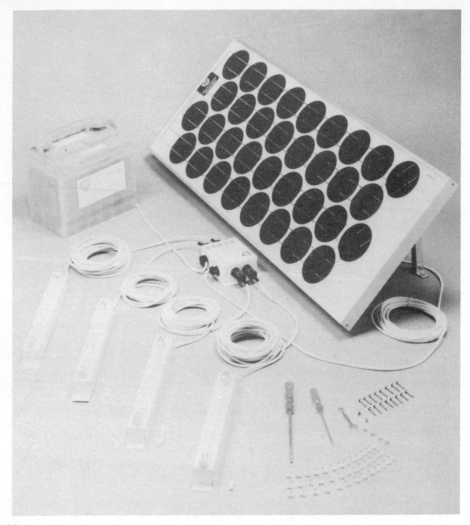

(a)

Figure 1.3   Example of a small solar electric system serving a home.
(a)   Parts laid out. (Source BP Solar Systems.)
(b)   Circuit for system in a home. Parts: **1** solar cell module; **2** rechargeable battery;
3 control unit; **4** distribution; **5** electrical appliances.
(c)   Specifications and typical prices direct from a manufacturer or system supplier
(for 1990).

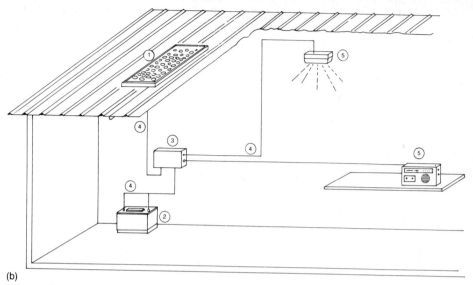

(b)

Component	Specifications	Cost (US$)
Module	Single crystal silicon, 38W_P	250
Mounting hardware	Simple aluminium brackets	10
Battery	Lead–acid, low antimony, 12 V, 85 A h at 100 hour discharge	70
Control unit	Charge regulation, disconnection of appliances during daylight and when the battery is at low voltage	70
Cables and connectors		20
Appliances	Four fluorescent tube lamps, 12 V d.c., 8 W	80
System cost (excluding any transport or other costs)		500

(c)

Parts of a solar electric system

A small solar electric system can be divided into five basic parts, as shown in Figure 1.3(b):

1. *Solar modules* generate electricity from available sunlight.
2. *Rechargeable batteries* are needed to store electricity for later use at night and during cloudy periods. Lead–acid batteries, similar to the ones in cars and trucks, are usually used.
3. Some type of *control unit* is necessary for all solar electric systems. Functions of the control unit include switching the loads either manually or automatically, protecting the batteries and wiring, monitoring the performance of the

system, and giving warnings when something is not working properly.

4. *Distribution* of electricity is as direct current (*d.c.*) and the system voltage is usually 12 or 24 V. These low voltages are much less dangerous than mains voltages (100–240 V alternating current (*a.c.*)) so the wiring is less complicated than in a mains system. However, long runs of wiring in a solar system require thick cables to avoid a large drop in voltage.

5. *Electrical appliances* enable the electricity to be used. Some appliances can be connected directly because they work on d.c. at the system voltage. Other appliances may need a *voltage adaptor* to reduce the voltage or a *power inverter* to increase the voltage and change it to *a.c.*

System voltage

The standard voltage for lead–acid batteries used in cars is 12 V. The wide use of these batteries for other applications means that many appliances are available which operate at 12 V d.c. Lead–acid batteries of 12 V are also a convenient size for solar electric systems. The standard system voltage is therefore 12 V and most solar modules are designed to charge batteries of this size.

Large solar electric systems are sometimes designed for a higher system voltage. The higher voltage allows thinner cables to be used for distribution and this reduces the cost of wiring. Higher voltages are multiples of twelve and are achieved by connecting groups of modules and batteries in series.

For example, a system voltage of 24 V requires pairs of 12 V batteries connected in series so that their voltages add. This means that the positive terminal of one battery in the pair is connected to the negative terminal of the other. These pairs of batteries are charged by pairs of standard solar modules which are also connected in series. The appliances must be able to work at the higher voltage. They are less common than 12 V appliances so tend to be more expensive and perhaps more difficult to obtain.

Example of a system for a home

Figure 1.3 shows how the five parts of a solar system are arranged for a home, with a set of components laid out ready for installation. The details and units used to specify the parts are explained in later chapters.

The prices given in Figure 1.3(c) are only intended as a guide to show the relative costs of each component in a system. Prices of the various parts vary owing to different circumstances, such as whether the parts are locally manufactured or have to be imported. Local prices of imported goods will generally be higher because of extra costs for import, transport, taxes, and the local dealer.

Figure 1.3(c) shows that the solar module is about half the system cost, while the battery, control unit, and four lamps are about equal. This situation is expected to change as methods of manufacturing solar modules continue to improve, bringing reductions in their cost.

For areas with a reasonable level of sunshine, the 38 W_P module (peak output of 38 watts) should generate enough electricity to run all the tube lights for four hours each day. The actual amount of sunshine required for this performance is three peak-hours per day.

Maps showing the variation of sunshine level for many countries are given in Figure 8.4. From these maps it can be seen that levels below three peak-hours per day apply only during the winter to countries at high latitudes. Most tropical countries receive more than four peak-hours per day so the lamps can be used for longer than four hours each day. Alternatively, other low-power appliances, such as televisions, could be run from the system.

During sunny periods, the battery is fully charged at the end of each day. It can then keep the system running through several cloudy days that follow. However, at some times of year there may be long periods with cloud cover. Therefore less electricity is generated by the module but there should be enough to run at least two of the lamps.

The system can be expanded gradually. More solar modules increase the amount of electricity generated. This may be particularly necessary during cloudy days so that lamps can be added and left on for longer each evening. Adding extra batteries provides more storage capacity to cover more days of cloud without having to switch off appliances. If extra appliances are added to the system, extra modules and batteries are both required otherwise the system will not perform as well.

□ *Questions*

1. What are the differences between solar heating and solar electricity?

2. What does 'photovoltaic' mean?

3. Give three examples of the applications of solar electricity in each of the following places:
    (a) Home.
    (b) School.
    (c) Hospital.

4. Some sorts of appliances are not recommended to be run from solar electricity. Give examples of these appliances and explain why they are unsuitable.

5. Name the five parts of a solar electric system and explain their functions.

6. What are the typical operating voltages of small solar electric systems?

2 | Solar modules

When designing a solar system and choosing a solar module, it is necessary to understand a little about how the electrical output of a module is affected by different conditions. Manufacturers usually provide a lot of information about their modules. This chapter explains what the information means and which specifications are important for selecting the most suitable module. The sections of this chapter are summarized in Figure 2.1.

The use of solar modules is quite straightforward. Installation simply involves mounting the module at the correct angle and making connections to two terminal posts on the back. On the other hand, the manufacture of solar modules requires sophisticated equipment and techniques. The manufacturing steps in making a cell are described here only briefly and no details are given about how a solar cell converts light into electricity. Reference should be made to other books on solar electricity for more about these aspects (see Appendix F).

Solar cells

Most solar cells are made of silicon, a material extracted from sand. Other materials can be used to make solar cells but silicon has proved to be most reliable and least expensive for most solar electric applications.

To make a solar cell, the first step is to treat the silicon in order to remove all trace of impurities. Next a very small amount of boron is added to the pure silicon by a process called *doping*. This can be done while the silicon is made into a large single-crystal block by a method called the *Czochralski process*. Thin slices are cut from the block and then heated to about 850 °C (1500 °F) in a furnace, while a gas containing phosphorus is passed over them. The phosphorus in the gas spreads into the surface of the slices and together with the boron gives them the photovoltaic property of converting light into electricity. (In technical terms, a pn junction is formed near the surface between the boron and phosphorous doped areas. See Chapter 12 for details about pn junctions.)

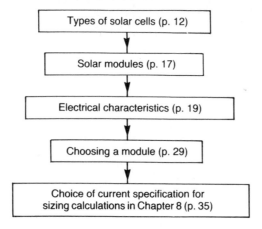

Figure 2.1 Summary of Chapter 2 about solar modules (p. page references to text).

After treatment in the furnace, thin metal strips are attached to the front of the cells and form a pattern of lines (see Figure 2.2(a)). This metal is the negative contact while a layer of metal covering the back side of the cell forms the positive contact. An anti-reflective coating is also put on the front. This helps light to be absorbed in the cell. Each slice of silicon is now a solar cell.

The cells generate electricity as soon as their front surface is illuminated. While generating electricity, there are no moving parts to wear out so the cells do not become used up or damaged in any way. However, it should be noted that the performance of a module does degrade slowly over many years.

Types of silicon

Most cells are made of a type of silicon called *single crystal* or *monocrystalline*, and are made by the procedure described above. Single-crystal silicon can be cut to any shape. Two common shapes of cells are square with rounded corners (maximum length of 100 mm or 4 in) and circular (maximum diameter of 125 mm or 5 in).

Another type of silicon used to make solar cells is called *polycrystalline*, *multicrystalline*, or *semicrystalline* silicon. The surface of these cells looks slightly different from the single-crystal type. Instead of a uniform blue, they have an irregular pattern rather like the pattern on galvanized steel sheets and buckets (see Figure 2.3). Compared to the single-crystal type, these cells are slightly less expensive to make but are slightly less efficient in converting light into electricity.

The third important method of making silicon cells was developed in the 1970s. The cells are made of *amorphous* silicon containing a small amount of

(a)

(b)

Figure 2.2   Single-crystal silicon cells in a solar module.
(a)   A close-up view of circular cells showing the pair of series connections between each cell.
(b)   A solar cell module containing thirty-six square cells. Other specifications of this module are peak power 53 W, length 1.29 m (51 in.), width 0.33 m (13 in.), thickness 36 mm (1.4 in.), and weight 5.7 kg (12.6 lb). (Source Siemens Solar Industries.)

Figure 2.3   One polycrystalline silicon cell of 100 × 100 mm (4 × 4 in.) showing the pattern of crystals and network of metal strips for the negative contact. (Source BP Solar.)

hydrogen and formed as a *thin film*. The manufacturing process for thin-film silicon is simpler and cheaper than for the single-crystal or polycrystalline types. Also interconnections between the cells to make a module are formed at the same time as the cells are made (see Figure 2.4).

For cells made from crystalline silicon, the silicon must be carefully prepared as a big crystalline block, which is then cut into slices. For cells made from amorphous silicon, the silicon and other raw materials are coated directly onto a piece of glass as a thin film. Also, instead of the pattern of metal strips for the front electrical contact, a transparent electrical material is coated between the glass and the silicon. Figure 2.4(b) shows thin-film silicon on glass from a solar-powered calculator. The film is divided into five parts to form five separate cells.

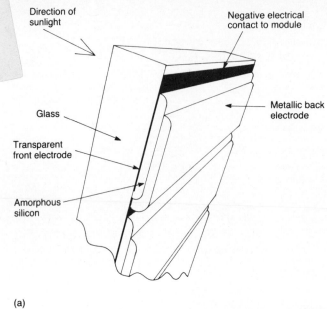

Direction of
sunlight

Negative electrical
contact to module

Metallic back
electrode

Glass

Transparent
front electrode

Amorphous
silicon

(a)

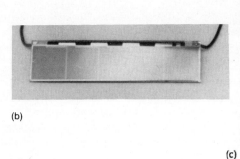

(b)

(c)

Figure 2.4   Thin-film silicon cells in a solar module.
(a)   Drawing of one cell at the end of a thin-film silicon module. The thickness of the
layers on the glass is very exaggerated to show how the electrical connections are
formed between each cell. The back of the module is covered by a plastic layer (not
shown) to protect these layers.
(b)   The strip from a solar-powered calculator which is divided into five areas to form
five separate solar cells.
(c)   A complete module containing twenty-nine cells. Other specifications of this
module are peak power 1.8 W, length 313 mm (12.3 in), width 160 mm (6.3 in),
thickness 22 mm (0.875 in), and weight 0.77 kg (1.7 lb).

Single-crystal and polycrystalline cells have been in use for many years. Experience shows that they are very reliable and most manufacturers provide a ten-year guarantee on the power output.

Solar cells made of thin-film silicon have not been in use for long enough to know whether they will last as well. Nevertheless, thin-film silicon is becoming more established year by year as better modules become available.

Future developments

A lot of research is going on to improve the performance and reduce the manufacturing costs of solar cells. Apart from silicon, other materials that are being investigated are *gallium arsenide* (GaAs), *cadmium sulphide* (CdS), *cadmium telluride* (CdTe) and *copper indium diselenide* ($CuInSe_2$ or CIS). The last material, CIS, is sensitive to the red and infrared parts of the sunlight spectrum that amorphous silicon does not absorb. One proposal for a highly efficient module contains thin-film silicon and CIS behind one another in a *tandem cell structure*.

Modules

Each silicon solar cell produces a little over 0.4 V d.c. in bright sunshine. Higher voltages are produced when several cells are connected in series as in a module. For charging 12 V batteries, solar modules must produce a minimum of about 13 V at the battery terminals. Modules designed for this purpose contain between twenty-eight and forty silicon solar cells each. The thin-film form of silicon produces a slightly higher voltage than the crystalline form, so thin-film modules can have less than twenty-eight cells.

The cells selected to make up one module are carefully matched by the manufacturers to ensure that they have the same output current. This is important since if just one cell gives a low current, the performance of the whole module is affected.

Encapsulation of crystalline silicon cells

Since modules are used outside, the cells must be well protected from the weather, especially moisture in the air. The cells are sealed in a module by a process called *encapsulation*.

Before being encapsulated, the cells of one module must be arranged in series and connected by small metal strips soldered from the back of one cell to the front of the next. The example in Figure 2.2(a) shows circular cells in a module with two strips connecting each cell. The two strips are known as *redundant connections* because the current can still flow when one connection gets damaged.

In the next stage of manufacturing modules, the cells complete with connections are set in a clear plastic called *ethylene vinyl acetate* (EVA). EVA is not affected by continuous exposure to sunlight so it provides a waterproof encapsulation for the cells over the whole life of the module. The cells set in plastic are covered by a sheet of tempered glass which is very hard and protects the front of the cells from mechanical damage. The glass is even tough enough to withstand hailstones.

The plastic at the back of the module is covered by layers of materials such as aluminium foil and Tedlar plastic (Dupont registered trademark) with silicone rubber used to seal the edges. These layers provide a tough and waterproof protection to the back of the module. They are also quite thin so that air flowing over the back of the module can keep the cells cool. For sites by the sea, special modules are available. They have a sheet of glass or metal over the back to give extra protection in the harsh environment.

A strong aluminium frame is attached around the glass to protect the edges and prevent the module from being twisted (see Figures 2.2(b) and 2.4(c)). Holes are drilled in this frame so that the module can be bolted into place at the site. One or two junction boxes are mounted on the back of the module where the positive and negative connections are made.

Encapsulation of thin-film silicon modules

For thin-film silicon, the way of making modules is slightly different. The thin film of silicon and transparent electrical conductor that coats one side of a piece of glass is divided into parallel bands or segments. Each band is a separate solar cell. When the positive contact is put on the back of each cell, it overlaps the transparent contact of the band on one side (see Figure 2.4(a)). In this way, the series connections between the cells are made without the soldering required for crystalline cells (see Figure 2.2(a)). Since thin-film silicon modules are made in one piece, they are described as being *monolithic*.

The final stages are encapsulation of the silicon, fitting a frame around the edge of the glass, and attaching wires or a junction box for the connections (see Figure 2.4(c)).

Bypass diodes

During manufacture of a module, one or two diodes may be included. (A diode is an electronic component that only allows current to flow through it in one direction. Diodes are described in more detail in Chapter 12.) The diodes fitted in modules are known as *bypass diodes* because they protect the module by shunting or bypassing current in certain circumstances.

Bypass diodes are needed when several modules are connected for systems operating at 24 V or higher. At these voltages, problems can occur when a few of the cells in one module are shaded while the output of the whole array has a short circuit. In these circumstances, the bypass diodes prevent the cells in full sunshine from damaging the shaded cells.

It does not matter whether modules have bypass diodes built in or not. In systems operating at 24 V or higher, a bypass diode can easily be fitted across the terminals of a module that does not already have a diode fitted for this purpose.

For the problem of a module being partly shaded, polycrystalline silicon has a slight advantage over single-crystal silicon. A polycrystalline cell is less likely to be damaged when it is shaded while the rest of the module is in full sunshine. Manufacturers write this in a more technical way by saying that polycrystalline silicon cells are 'resistant to hot spot damage under conditions of reverse bias.'

Electrical characteristics of modules

Manufacturers often rate their modules by peak power. For example, the module in Figure 2.2(b) has a peak power of 53 W. However, peak power is not the best way of comparing different types and makes of modules.

What really matters is how quickly a module can charge up a battery. This is decided by the charging current in units of amperes (A) that the module can generate under different conditions. The specifications of a module need to be understood so that the most appropriate type of module can be selected for a particular system. An example of a full specification is given in question 11 at the end of this chapter.

Open circuit voltage and short circuit current

When a module faces the sun, a voltage can be measured between the positive and negative terminals on the back using a voltmeter. No current is flowing because no appliance has been connected yet, so this measurement is called the *open circuit voltage* or V_{OC}.

When an appliance or a rechargeable battery is connected between the two terminals, a current flows from the module. The module now has a voltage less than V_{OC}. By adding more load with another appliance in parallel, more current flows and the voltage gets lower again. For the highest current, the terminals of a module can be connected directly to each other. The voltage is now zero and the current is maximum. By shorting the terminals through an ammeter, the maximum current is measured and is called the *short circuit current* or I_{SC}.

To practise measuring output voltage and current, use the small batteries used in torches and radios: these behave in a similar way to solar modules (apart from not needing the sun to shine on them). It is worth spending some time measuring the voltage and current from some torch batteries by the method shown in Figure 2.5. This is useful to gain familiarity with measurements of V_{OC} and I_{SC}.

Generators of mains voltage behave quite differently since the voltage from

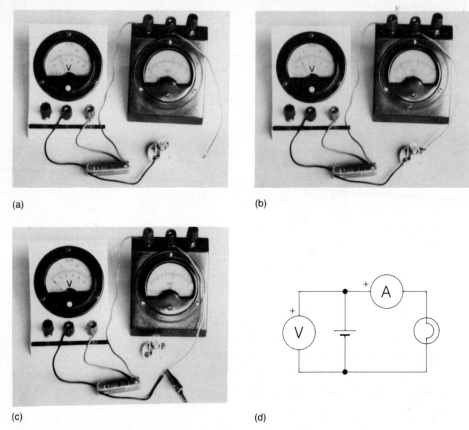

(a)

(b)

(c)

(d)

Figure 2.5   Measuring the *I–V* characteristics of a small battery using: a voltmeter, an ammeter, a bulb from a torch, a clip, and four wires. (For key to electrical symbols, see Table 12.5.)

(a)   Wire from bulb disconnected for measurement of open circuit voltage (V_{OC}).

(b)   Circuit completed with bulb on for measurements at load (V_{AL} and I_{AL}).

(c)   Bulb removed from circuit and wires connected for measurement of short circuit current (I_{SC}).

(d)   Circuit for **(b)**.

a generator should stay the same regardless of whether appliances are switched on or off. Therefore the voltage across an appliance should be the same as the V_{OC} of a generator when there is no load.

In fact the output of a generator should never be shorted intentionally. Fuses or circuit breakers must be fitted in a generator circuit to prevent excessive currents being drawn and damaging the generator. Therefore I_{SC} cannot be measured for a generator without causing damage. On the other hand, no damage at all is done to a solar module when its terminals are shorted together.

I–V curves

When an appliance is connected, the measurements of current against voltage can be plotted on a graph. Figure 2.6(a) shows how one point is put on this sort of graph for a pair of measurements at load (I_{AL} and V_{AL}). By changing the load conditions, new values of current and voltage are measured which can be put on the same graph. Joining the points on the graph together produces a line called an *I–V curve* (see Figure 2.6(b)).

To understand how the *I–V* curve for a solar module is used, start at the bottom right end of the *I–V* curve in Figure 2.6(b). This part of the graph is where the voltage is highest and the current is lowest, as it is when no load is connected to the module. The value of voltage where the *I–V* curve touches the voltage axis is V_{OC}.

As appliances are connected to the module, the current increases from zero which corresponds with moving upwards along the *I–V* curve. Note that the curve is not exactly vertical but slopes to the left. This shows that the voltage gets lower as the current increases. At high currents, the voltage becomes much less and the *I–V* curve bends more to the left. The maximum current is the level where the *I–V* curve stops on the left. The voltage is zero here, so this is I_{SC}.

Factors affecting the electrical characteristics

The current that a solar cell module can generate determines how quickly it can charge up a battery. When connected directly to a 12 V d.c. appliance, the current from a module also determines the maximum power of appliance that can be used. The size of the current depends on seven factors as follows:

1. The amount of sunshine reaching the cells.
2. The temperature of the cells.
3. The number of cells in the module.
4. The area of each cell.
5. The type of silicon.
6. The state of charge of the battery being charged.
7. The effect of system losses, such as from cables and a blocking diode.

The effect that factors 1–5 have on the current can be explained by how each factor changes the shape and position of the *I–V* curve for a module. The current is then found from the *I–V* curve for the voltage required by a load of a battery or appliances. Factors 6 and 7 determine which current on an *I–V* curve is supplied when charging a battery.

Standard modules are designed for charging 12 V lead–acid batteries. These batteries need a minimum charging voltage between their terminals of about 13 V. The required charging voltage rises to about 15 V as a lead–acid battery reaches full charge.

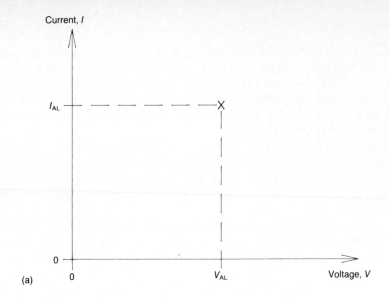

(a)

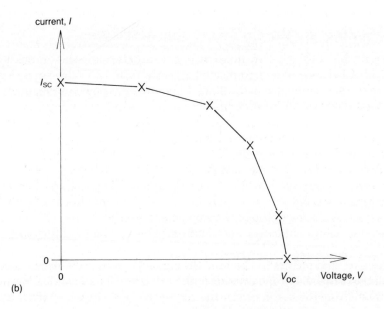

(b)

Figure 2.6   Graphs of output current against output voltage for a solar module.
(a)   One point ($\times$) is put on the graph for one pair of measurements at load (I_{AL} and V_{AL}). The dashed lines show how the position of the point is determined.
(b)   Several points are put on the graph for different load conditions including open circuit and short circuit. The points are joined together to form an I–V curve.

However, the maximum voltage available from a module to charge the battery fully needs to be higher than 15 V because of system losses. There is a drop in voltage between the module and the battery because of the cable and a blocking diode (described later). To compensate for these losses, the maximum voltage available from a module should be about 16 V.

As each factor is explained in the following sections, the *I–V* curves are used to find the current generated at the maximum voltage needed by a lead–acid battery. For the purpose of this explanation, an output voltage of 16 V is used. On the graphs in Figures 2.7–2.11, this voltage is represented by a vertical broken line that passes through 16 V on the voltage axis at the bottom. The height at which an *I–V* curve crosses this line gives the current we are interested in.

Units of irradiance

The amount of sunshine reaching the solar cells at any moment is referred to by many names: *light intensity, light level, solar illumination, solar intensity, solar flux, solar radiation, insolation, irradiation,* and *irradiance*. The last name of irradiance is most common and will be used throughout this book.

The irradiance reaching the ground varies throughout the day with the movement of the sun and the clouds. The total amount of irradiance received over a period of time is a different measurement. Over one day, it is usually called *daily insolation* and this measurement is dealt with in Chapter 8 on sizing systems.

Irradiance is often measured in units of watts per square metre (W/m^2) and milliwatts per square centimetre (mW/cm^2). Note that 'watts' is used here as a measure of the power of the light itself or how bright the light is. As part of the units of irradiance, the watt has nothing to do with electricity or the wattage of light bulbs.

In very clear weather at midday, the irradiance reaching a surface that faces the sun is about 1000 W/m^2. (This is the same as 100 mW/cm^2 because one mW/cm^2 unit of irradiance equals ten W/m^2 units.) An irradiance of 1000 W/m^2 is sometimes called *full sun, one sun*, or *AM1 intensity*.

Air mass standard for testing modules

Modules are tested under a light source of 1000 W/m^2 before leaving the factory as a check of their performance. Since the light is produced artificially, it must be made to appear as real sunlight that has passed through the atmosphere.

Real sunlight has a particular spectrum (different brightness for different visible colours, ultra-violet, and infra-red) when the sun is directly overhead, and this spectrum is called *air mass one* (AM1). When the sun is low in the sky, the spectrum changes and is specified by a different AM number. For testing solar cells and modules, AM1.5 is the standard spectrum for the artificial light and corresponds to the sun being at an angle of 45° above the horizon.

Effect of irradiance

Figure 2.7 shows *I–V* curves for one module at irradiances of 100, 500, and 1000 W/m². As the irradiance increases, the current at 16 V also increases because the *I–V* curves cross the 16 V line at higher positions.

The *I–V* curve at 1000 W/m² is for a module that faces the sun directly. The sun takes up many positions in the sky according to the time of day and the time of year. When the sun is exactly overhead in tropical countries, the module should be horizontal for maximum current. As another example, when the sun is low in the sky at 30° above the horizon, the module should be tilted towards the sun at an angle of 60° from horizontal for maximum current.

However, modules are usually fixed in one position, so they face the sun directly at only a few times. When a module is facing away from the sun, the irradiance actually on the module is less. For example, when the sun is 30° above the horizon and the module is mounted horizontally, the irradiance on the cells is about half the value of 1000 W/m² when the sun is overhead. The effect of this on the current is shown by the 500 W/m² *I–V* curve in Figure 2.7.

Therefore the current from a module fixed in one position varies through the day, even when the weather is clear with no clouds. The charging current rises during the morning, reaches its highest level at midday, and then falls during the afternoon. Most charging of a battery happens over a few hours in the middle of the day.

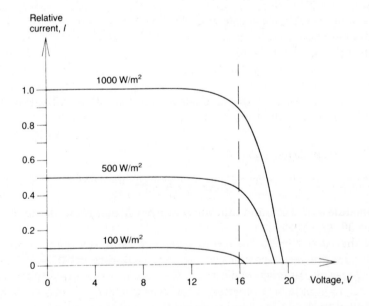

Figure 2.7   The effect that light intensity has on the *I–V* curve for a solar cell module.

To extend the period of charging, the angle of the module can be changed during the day so that it faces the sun more closely for longer. Changing the angle is called *tracking* and is mentioned in Chapter 9.

It is possible to increase the irradiance above 1000 W/m^2 using mirrors or lenses to concentrate sunlight on the cells. However, the irradiance may be uneven over the module which will cause over-heating and damage in cells receiving less light. Also the whole module becomes hotter and extra cooling is then needed. It is not advised to concentrate sunlight on standard modules in any way.

When the sun is covered by clouds, light still reaches the ground and some current is generated by the module. With a thin layer of cloud, the irradiance reaching the module from all parts of the sky might be as much as 300 W/m^2. With thick cloud cover, the irradiance could be reduced to 100 W/m^2 or less. The I–V curve for 100 W/m^2 in Figure 2.7 is very low. This shows that with thick cloud cover, the current at 16 V is almost zero and there is very little charging.

Indoor lighting

Solar modules connected to low-power appliances can be used indoors under artificial light. An example is the solar-powered calculator shown in Figure 1.2(a).

The intensity of visible light reaching a surface indoors is called *illuminance* and is often measured in units of *lux* (see Appendix A for more details). A typical illuminance in an office, for instance, with fluorescent lighting is 200 lux (compare other values in Table A.1). This corresponds to about 2 W/m^2, so is much weaker than direct sunlight.

The response of solar modules is sometimes given in units of *kilolux* (klux). The conversion to W/m^2 units of irradiance is not exact because illuminance is only a measure of visible light and does not include ultraviolet or infrared parts of sunlight. Nevertheless, an approximate conversion is that 100 klux of AM1 light is roughly equal to 1000 W/m^2 or full sun.

Effect of cell temperature

As light shines on the solar cells, they warm up and the electrical output of the module changes. An irradiance of 1000 W/m^2 means the sun is shining directly on the module and it is found that the cells are warmer than the surrounding air by about 30 °C (85 °F).

For the 1000 W/m^2 I–V curve, Figure 2.8 shows the effect of cell temperature. As the temperature rises above 0 °C, V_{OC} falls while I_{SC} gets slightly higher. Even though I_{SC} rises with temperature, the graph shows that the current at 16 V gets less because of the decrease of V_{OC}. Therefore to get the maximum current output, modules should be mounted so that air can circulate around them freely and keep the cells cool.

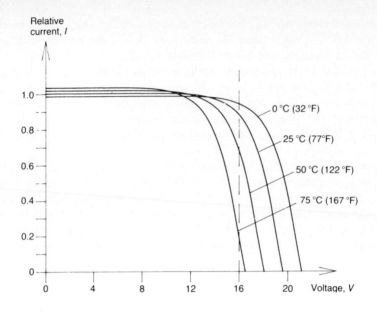

Figure 2.8   The effect that cell temperature has on the *I–V* curve (at 1000 W/m^2) for a solar cell module.

I–V curves are usually shown for cells at a temperature of 25 °C (77 °F). If values from these curves are going to be used in some way, it must be remembered that they only apply where the surrounding air is at a lower temperature.

Effect of the number of cells in a module

The number of cells in a module mainly affects the voltage. Remember that each cell produces a voltage of about 0.4 V. As each cell is added in the series for a module, it increases V_{OC} of the module by about 0.4 V without affecting I_{SC}.

Figure 2.9 shows *I–V* curves at 1000 W/m^2 for various numbers of cells in a module. For thirty cells, the current at a load voltage of 16 V is well below I_{SC}. Modules with thirty-three or more cells supply a current much closer to I_{SC} at 16 V.

There appears to be no advantage in having more than thirty-three cells, especially as each extra cell increases the cost of the module. Modules with more than thirty-three cells are needed, though, for sites in a hot climate. The extra cells compensate for the drop in voltage caused by the cells having to operate at a high temperature.

It also appears from Figure 2.9 that modules with less than thirty-three

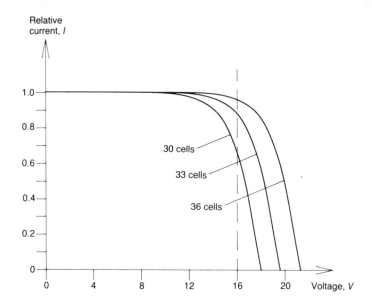

Figure 2.9 The effect that number of cells in a module has on the I–V curve (at 1000 W/m^2 and 25 °C cell temperature) for the whole solar cell module.

cells are not able to charge a 12 V battery to its full charge at the maximum current. However, a low charging current at 16 V is needed when the system does not have a unit to regulate charging. Advice about choosing the best number of cells to have in a module for various situations is given later in this chapter.

Thin-film silicon produces a slightly higher voltage from each cell than crystalline silicon. The minimum number of cells in a module of thin-film silicon used for charging 12 V batteries is twenty-five.

Effect of cell area

The maximum current from a module, I_{SC}, is decided by the size of each cell. At all levels of irradiance, cells with a larger area have a higher I_{SC} than small cells.

Figure 2.10 compares I–V curves at 1000 W/m^2 for two modules with the same number of single-crystal silicon cells. One module has circular cells of 10 cm (4 in) diameter so their area is 78 cm^2. The other module has square cells of 10 × 10 cm (4 × 4 in) so their area is 100 cm^2. The second module generates about 25 per cent more current at 16 V than the first module because its cells are 25 per cent larger. Therefore the size of the cells has a direct effect on the charging current.

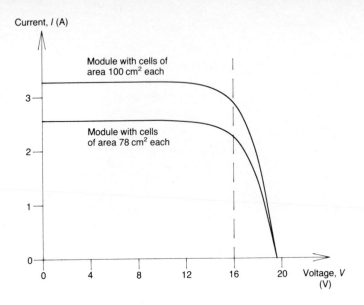

Figure 2.10 Comparison of *I–V* curves (under the same test conditions) for modules containing cells of different area but with the same number of cells.

Effect of type of silicon

The performance of different types of silicon should be compared for cells of the same area. Single-crystal silicon generates the highest current, polycrystalline silicon generates slightly less, and thin-film silicon generates about half the current of single-crystal silicon.

The type of silicon also affects the cost of a module. For the same area of cells, single-crystal silicon is the most expensive and thin-film silicon is the least expensive.

Figures 2.7–2.10 show the effects of various factors on the *I–V* curve for crystalline silicon. For thin-film silicon, the *I–V* curve has a slightly different shape because the silicon is amorphous instead of crystalline. Figure 2.11 compares *I–V* curves for the same size modules made of thin-film and single-crystal silicon.

The curve for thin-film silicon is lower because it generates less current for the same area of module. Also the curve for thin-film silicon slopes more evenly all the way up from V_{OC} to I_{SC}. This means that as the output current increases from zero, the voltage falls steadily. This contrasts with crystalline silicon for which the voltage falls only a little as the output current increases from zero and then falls a lot at currents just below I_{SC}.

Another difference between crystalline and amorphous silicon is in their

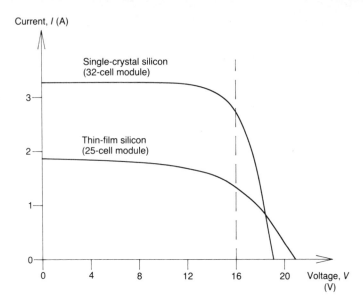

Figure 2.11 Comparison of *I–V* curves (under the same test conditions) for the same size of modules made of thin-film silicon and single-crystal silicon.

response to different colours, or wavelengths, of light. Amorphous silicon is more responsive in the blue sector. One advantage of this is that thin-film cells in solar-powered calculators and small appliances work effectively under the fluorescent light from tube lamps.

Choosing a module

There is a wide range of modules available for small solar electric systems. The differences between them are in the number of cells, the size of each cell, and the type of silicon used. When choosing a module for a solar system, there are five questions to answer:

1. Is a charge regulator going to be used in the system?
2. Is a blocking diode required?
3. Which modules are suitable for the average temperature at the site?
4. How can suitable modules be compared to find which represents best value for money at local prices?
5. How much generating capacity is needed to meet the daily requirement for electricity of the system?

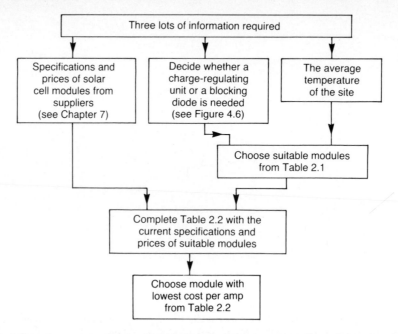

Figure 2.12 Summary of steps for selecting a suitable solar cell module which is the best value for money.

The first four questions are considered in this section, and the way they are related is summarized in Figure 2.12. The last question is to do with the size of a system and is dealt with in Chapter 8.

Regulation of charging

A maximum voltage of 16 V is required from a solar module in order for a 12 V lead–acid battery to be fully charged through a blocking diode. This voltage was used in Figures 2.7–2.11 to illustrate the factors affecting the electrical characteristics of modules. For most of the time, though, a voltage between 12 and 16 V is all that is needed. Furthermore, as soon as full charge is reached, the charging voltage should be reduced to avoid damage to the battery by over-charging.

A good way to charge a lead–acid battery is by starting with a high current at 12 V. As the battery charges up, a higher voltage is needed and less current should be supplied. To reach full charge, 15 V is needed but the charging current should be very low. These requirements of current and voltage are satisfied by a solar module with thirty single-crystal silicon cells (without a blocking diode). Figure 2.13 shows how the electrical output of this module is matched to the needs of charging a 12 V lead–acid battery.

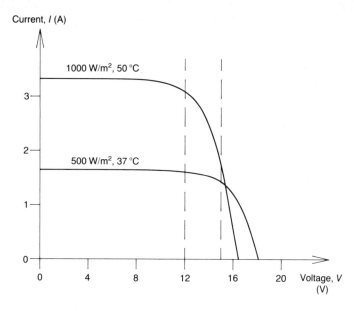

Figure 2.13 *I–V* curves for a module with thirty single-crystal silicon cells that is self-regulating when charging a 12 V lead–acid battery. The values on the two curves are conditions of light intensity and cell temperature for an air temperature of about 20 °C (70 °F).

The *I–V* curves in Figure 2.13 are drawn for the cell temperatures expected in a mild climate with an air temperature of about 20 °C (70 °F). At full sun of 1000 W/m², the cells are heated by the sun so the *I–V* curve for 50 °C is shown in the graph. At a lower irradiance of 500 W/m², the temperature difference between the cells and the surrounding air is less.

The vertical broken line for 12 V crosses both *I–V* curves at high currents. Therefore the thirty-cell module can supply almost its maximum current at each level of irradiance when the battery needs a high charging current. The vertical line for 15 V crosses both *I–V* curves at low currents. Therefore the module automatically supplies a low current when the battery is fully charged.

When modules are called *self-regulating*, it does not mean that they contain some sort of electronic regulating unit inside. All it means is that the electrical characteristics of the module allow it to be directly connected to a battery and a separate regulating unit is not needed. These characteristics are summarized by Figure 2.13.

A disadvantage of self-regulating modules is that the last part of charging is at a very low current and needs many hours of sunshine. Also the battery must be regularly used, especially during sunny weather, to minimize the small amount of over-charging that still occurs.

By using modules with more than thirty-two cells, the maximum charging current is maintained at 16 V and the battery reaches full charge in the shortest time. However, some sort of charge-regulating unit is needed with these modules to limit the current and prevent over-charging. For the choice of method for charge regulation, see Figure 4.6 together with details of charge regulators in Chapter 4.

Blocking diode

Modules allow a small current from the battery to flow back through them at night: this is called *dark current leakage*. The dark current is prevented by a blocking diode.

Most diodes are made of silicon so have a voltage drop of 0.7 V. Two extra cells are needed to compensate for this voltage drop, so a module with thirty-two single-crystal silicon cells is self-regulating with a silicon blocking diode. The Schottky type of silicon diode and germanium diodes both have a voltage drop of only 0.3 V, so a module with thirty-one cells is self-regulating when used with these types.

Note that most charge-regulating units prevent battery discharge through a module at night by a diode or some sort of switch. Therefore a separate blocking diode is not usually required when a charge-regulating unit is used.

Local temperatures

In hot areas where the average temperatures are higher than 20 °C (70 °F), the cells operate at a much higher temperature than 50 °C (125 °F) under full sun. This reduces the voltage of the whole module, as shown in Figure 2.8. To compensate for this drop in voltage, more cells are needed. For average temperatures of 30 °C (85 °F), modules with two extra cells are recommended.

Temperature also affects the charging characteristics of lead–acid batteries. They require about 0.3 V less voltage for each 10 °C (20 °F) increase in temperature. Nevertheless, a module with the two extra cells is still needed to charge them in hot climates. This is because the voltage reduction for the batteries is much smaller than for the modules. Furthermore, the batteries should be stored well out of the hot sun to keep them cool.

Selecting suitable modules for the application

The number of single-crystal silicon cells needed in a module depends on the type of charge regulation to be used and the local temperatures:

☐   Self-regulating modules with thirty to thirty-two cells are good for small solar systems. A separate charge-regulating unit is not needed, which keeps the system simple and low cost.

☐ Modules with thirty-three or thirty-four cells and a charge regulator make better use of the available sunshine to charge batteries in the shortest time.
☐ Extra cells are needed in hot climates and in systems with large system losses to the batteries.

Modules can also be selected according to their open circuit voltage (V_{OC}) which is directly affected by the number of cells. This specification is always given under the *standard test conditions* (STC) of:

☐ 1000 W/m^2 for irradiance.
☐ AM1.5 for type of light.
☐ 25 °C for cell temperature.

The details of how V_{OC} and the number of cells relate to application are summarized in Table 2.1.

For modules made using thin-film silicon, the number of cells is not usually given by the manufacturers although it can be found by counting the number of separate stripes running across the module. Where V_{OC} is given for a thin-film module, it can be used to check the suitability of the module for an application. Table 2.1 has separate columns for crystalline and thin-film silicon. Differences in the *I–V* curves for the two main types of silicon (see Figure 2.11) mean that V_{OC} is higher for thin-film silicon in each application.

Table 2.1 *Selection of a module for various types of systems and climates based on open circuit voltage in volts (V_{oc}) under standard test conditions (STC) or number of cells in the module. (STC: 1000 W/m^2, AM1.5 and 25 °C).*

Application	Local climate			
	Mild (usually below 30 °C (85 °F) at midday)		Hot (usually above 30 °C (85 °F) at midday)	
	Crystalline silicon	Thin-film silicon	Crystalline silicon	Thin-film silicon
self-regulating, no diode	18 V (30 cells)	20 V	19 V (32 cells)	21 V
self-regulating, with a diode[1]	19 V (32 cells)	21 V	20 V (34 cells)	22 V
with a charge regulator	⩾20 V (>32 cells)	⩾22 V	⩾21 V (>34 cells)	⩾23 V

[1]This is for a silicon diode. For Schottky and germanium diodes, the open circuit voltages in the table can be reduced by 0.4 V and one less cell is required.

Standard modules are also available for charging 6 V batteries by self-regulation or with a charge regulator. Since a 6 V battery is half the voltage of a 12 V battery, it requires modules with half the values of V_{OC} given in Table 2.1.

Best value for money

Table 2.1 is used to select a module that is suitable for the application. When this leaves a choice of modules that are all suitable, the one that is best value for money can now be selected. This is not necessarily the cheapest one.

The single specification of a module that shows how quickly the module can charge a battery is the current. The price of each module should be compared to this current in order to choose the module representing best value for money.

The most relevant current to use is at a load voltage of 14 V under STC, although this particular specification is only given by some manufacturers. The following list is of all current specifications under STC. When a choice of currents is given for a module, use the one nearer the top of the list:

1. Current at a load voltage of 14 V or above (I_{AL}).
2. Nominal current at a voltage of 14 V or above (I_N).
3. Current at peak power (I_{PP}).
4. Current at 14 V from an accurate *I–V* curve.
5. Short circuit current (I_{SC}).

Find the local prices for each suitable module and record your answers in a copy of Table 2.2. To complete the last column of your table, divide the price of the module by its current at load (or whichever current specification is given). This number is the *cost per amp* of the module in units of money per amp. It tells you how much each amp of generating capacity costs for each module. The one with the lowest cost per amp is the one of best value for money. Remember that this only applies after selecting modules with the required output voltage.

In comparing the value for money of crystalline and thin-film modules, the total cost for a solar array containing several modules should be considered. Figure 2.11 shows that thin-film modules generate less current than the same size of module with crystalline silicon cells. Therefore a larger area of thin-film modules is required for the same current output. After calculating the total costs of a full solar array, the extra cost of the larger support structure and longer wiring for thin-film modules may affect the choice of module.

In addition to cost, other factors that should be considered are differences between modules in their delivery times and level of technical assistance provided by suppliers.

Table 2.2 *Table for summarizing the details of suitable modules and for comparing their performance and cost. When using the table, cross out the words in the first two lines that do not apply to the system. Suitable modules are selected with the aid of Table 2.1 'Current' is one of the following specifications: I_{AL}, I_N, I_{PP}, I at 14 V from a graph or I_{SC} (see text for details).*

| Type of regulation: | self-reg./self-reg. with a diode/charge reg. | | | | |
| Local climate: | below 30 °C/above 30 °C | | | | |

Details of make and model of each module	Cost for one module			Current (A)	Total cost ÷ current
	Price	Other	Total		

Peak power specification

One specification always given by manufacturers for their modules is *peak power*, *maximum power output*, or W_P under STC. Electrical power is calculated by multiplying voltage and current together. To get the peak power of a module, the current and voltage must both be high and this is at the bend in the *I–V* curve for 1000 W/m^2. Taking the *I–V* curves in Figure 2.11 as examples, the peak power point for both of these curves is where they cross a line drawn up from 14 V.

Since the peak power depends on both the size and number of cells, it is not the best way to compare modules for small systems. For example, a module with thirty-six cells will have a higher peak power than the same type of module with only thirty-three cells. However, unless the high voltage provided by thirty-six cells is needed, this module is no better for the application than the thirty-three cell module of lower peak power but the same current. The peak power specification is more relevant to the design of large solar installations which have sophisticated control systems.

Current specification for sizing calculations

The size and number of modules required for a system depend on both the amount of sunshine available each day and the amount of electricity required by the appliances. These aspects are dealt with later in Chapter 8 on sizing.

One number required for the calculation in Chapter 8 is the actual current generated by a module at 14 V for an irradiance of 1000 W/m^2. If possible, use the *I–V* curve for 1000 W/m^2 at the actual operating temperature expected for the cells which is 30 °C (55 °F) added to the temperature at midday for the site.

☐ *Questions*

1. What are the three types of silicon used to make solar cells and which of them is the cheapest to manufacture?
2. Do solar cells get used up the more they are used?
3. What is the voltage generated by one silicon solar cell when light shines on it, and how does a module generate a higher voltage?
4. What is 'encapsulation' of modules and why is it necessary?
5. What are the meanings of V_{OC} and I_{SC}, and how are they measured for a solar module?
6. Explain clearly how the *I–V* curve for a solar module is used to find the charging current at 16 V.
7. Which one of these conditions does *not* usually increase the charging current from a solar module to a battery?
   (a) More sunshine.
   (b) Higher cell temperature.
   (c) Larger cells.
8. What do the terms 'solar intensity,' 'solar flux,' and 'irradiance' mean when referring to the performance of solar modules?
9. What value of irradiance in units of W/m^2 is used to test solar modules before they leave the factory?
10. Which sort of modules are called 'self-regulating' and what does this mean?
11. The following details are an example of the specifications for a solar module:

Power:	53 W	under standard
Open circuit voltage:	21.8 V	test conditions
Short circuit current:	3.27 A	of 1000 W/m^2, 25 °C
Voltage at load:	17.4 V	cell temperature,
Current at load:	3.05 A	and 1.5 air mass
Number of cells in series:	36	
Cell size:	4.05 in (102.9 mm) square	
Cell type:	single-crystal silicon	

   (a) In deciding whether a charge regulator is needed with this module, which specifications matter?
   (b) Which specification is most appropriate for calculating how quickly this module can charge a battery?

3 | Battery storage of electricity

Batteries are used in solar electric systems to store electricity generated during daylight hours for later use. Rechargeable batteries are required for this purpose: the main ones used in solar electric systems are *lead–acid batteries* and *nickel–cadmium batteries*. These batteries are available in a variety of different types whose suitability for solar systems varies a lot. The choice of which type to use is a matter of balancing a number of factors, because the most suitable types may be unavailable or too expensive.

Figure 3.1 shows the order of sections in this chapter. First it is necessary to introduce a number of terms that describe each aspect of a battery's performance. The requirements of the most suitable battery for a solar system can then be listed. This list of requirements should be kept in mind while reading through the sections which describe the various types of rechargeable batteries in detail.

Most solar electric systems use lead–acid batteries for storage. Although solar systems are very reliable and easy to use, when there is a problem it is usually to do with the lead–acid batteries. The way these batteries are made and work is described here in some detail so that the importance of using the best-quality battery available and of following the maintenance procedures carefully can be appreciated.

One aspect of choosing a battery is cost. A procedure is given for comparing the cost of different types and sizes of battery. The last section lists the advantages and disadvantages for use in a solar system of each type of battery. At the stage of selecting a battery, this section can be referred to first without having to read the whole chapter. Reference is made to the earlier sections of the chapter as required.

Basics of rechargeable batteries

Batteries are familiar to everyone as a convenient source of electricity. When a battery is in a circuit, current flows because of electrochemical changes taking

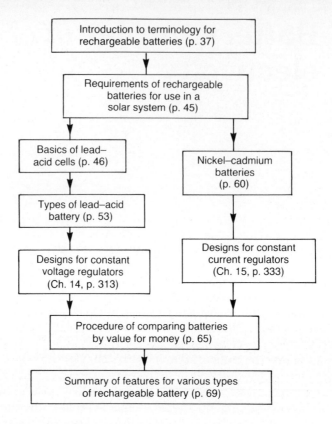

Figure 3.1   Summary of Chapter 3 about rechargeable batteries with cross-references to other chapters (Ch. chapter, p. page references to text).

place inside the battery which gradually discharges. Rechargeable batteries are the type that can be charged up from a d.c. source and reused many times. They are also known as *accumulators* or *storage batteries*.

The simplest operating unit of a battery is called an *electrochemical cell* or just a *cell*. One cell produces a particular voltage depending on the materials it contains. The word 'battery' describes a group of cells connected in series. This is done to achieve a higher voltage than can be obtained from one cell, in the same way that solar cells are connected in series to form a solar module. A battery can also be a single cell (a group of one).

Rechargeable and non-rechargeable batteries

Rechargeable batteries are made up of *secondary cells*. A few examples of these are shown in Figure 3.2. Batteries that can be used only once are made up of

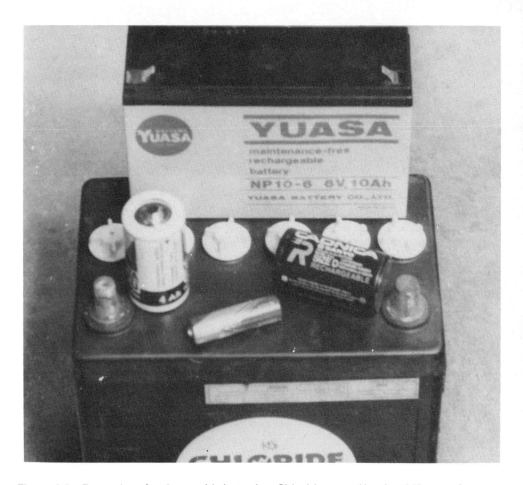

Figure 3.2 Examples of rechargeable batteries: Chloride vented lead–acid battery for SLI (12 V 32 A h 11 kg (24 lb)), Yuasa sealed lead–acid battery (6 V 10 A h 2 kg (4 lb)), and the others are sealed nickel–cadmium cells (1.25 V D-size 1.2 A h at 90 g and 4 A h at 130 g, 1.25 V AA-size 0.5 A h at 20 g).

primary cells. When primary cells become fully discharged, their useful life ends and they are thrown away. Primary cells or use-once batteries are the type most common in electronic wrist-watches, torches, radios, and many other portable appliances. Some examples are shown in Figure 3.3.

It is possible to recharge a button cell by connecting it to one or two D-size cells. This enables the cell to run a wrist-watch for a few more weeks. However, attempting to recharge any primary cells is definitely not recommended. On

Figure 3.3 Examples of batteries made of primary cells. Do not attempt to recharge these batteries, otherwise they might break open and damage the appliance they are in: **1** zinc dry cell (ordinary D-size torch battery); **2** high-power zinc dry cell (contains better-quality manganese dioxide than ordinary dry cell); **3** alkaline manganese dry cell; **4** radio battery (several dry cells in one case); **5** mercury, silver or lithium button cells; **6** air-depolarized zinc battery.

recharging, gases are produced which can break the case, causing chemicals inside to leak out and damage equipment that the cell is in.

Parts of a cell

A cell is a combination of two *electrodes* and a liquid called the *electrolyte*, as shown in Figure 3.4(a). When a cell is discharging or being charged, the chemical reactions that produce electricity are between the *active material* of each electrode and the electrolyte. The electrodes provide structural support for the active material and carry current to the two *terminals* on top.

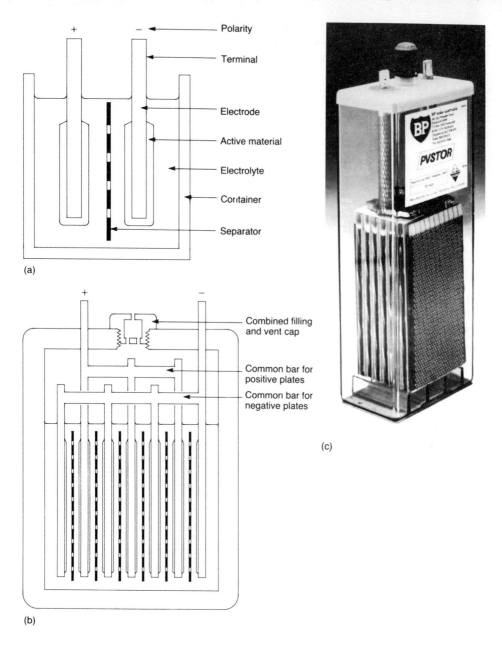

Figure 3.4   The main parts of an electrochemical cell.
(a)   Schematic diagram with the main parts labelled.
(b)   View in section of a cell made up of several parallel plates.
(c)   Lead–acid cell in a glass container with parallel plates. (Source BP Solar.)

The *polarity* of the electrodes refers to which sign of charge they have. It is essential that the positive and negative electrodes do not touch each other, otherwise a short circuit is caused and the cell discharges rapidly. The electrodes are kept apart by the *separator* which is made of a porous insulating material.

During discharge, the active materials are converted from a charged form to a discharged form. When all the active material on either one of the electrodes is converted, the cell is completely discharged or *flat*. Charging is the process of converting the active material from the discharged form back to the charged form.

Capacity

The measure of how much electricity or charge can be stored in a cell is called its *capacity*. The capacity is determined by the amount of active material that may come into contact with the electrolyte. One method of construction that gives a high capacity is to make the electrodes up from several flat pieces called *plates* as shown in Figure 3.4(b).

The plates alternate between positive and negative polarity. Plates of the same polarity are linked by a common bar which serves as a support and provides electrical contact to the terminal. Figure 3.4(c) is an example of a lead–acid cell in a glass container which has parallel plates for the electrodes.

A h units of capacity

Although the *coulomb* (C) is the basic unit of charge in electricity, a more useful unit of charge for the measurement of battery capacity is the *ampere-hour* (A h).

To measure the capacity of a cell, a fixed current is drawn and the number of hours that the cell can supply this current before complete discharge is counted. Multiplying the current by the number of hours gives the capacity in A h. As an example, a cell with a capacity specified as 80 A h can supply 8 A for 10 h, or 4 A for 20 h.

In practice, the measured capacity depends on the discharge current, which is how quickly a cell is used. As the discharge current is increased, the actual capacity obtained is reduced. Therefore capacity is specified for a given *C rate* of discharge current. This is the capacity in A h divided by the discharge time in hours. It can also be written with the number of hours in small digits as a subscript. For example, the capacity of a battery might be specified as 30 A h for a C rate of C/10 or C_{10}. This means that for ten hours it can deliver 3 A (from 30 divided by 10).

State of charge

The *state of charge* at any moment is the amount of charge left that can be used compared to the fully charged capacity. It is measured as a percentage, so 100 per cent is for a fully charged cell, 50 per cent for a cell half discharged and 0 per cent for a completely flat cell.

Cycle depth

The sequence of discharging and then charging back up to the state of charge at the start is called a *cycle*. The *depth* of discharge in one cycle depends on what the cell is being used for and is not always down to 0 per cent state of charge. A *shallow cycle* is when a cell is discharged by only a few per cent before being charged back up. In a *deep cycle*, the depth of discharge is 50 per cent or more.

Cell life

The natural lifetime of a cell is usually defined as when the fully charged capacity is reduced to 80 per cent of its original value when the cell was new. This is a permanent loss of 20 per cent of the capacity because of cycling and age.

On each cycle of a cell, small amounts of active material come off the electrodes and sink to the bottom of the container. Once this material has separated from its electrode, it cannot be used any more so the capacity of the cell is reduced. The number of cycles that can be obtained from a cell before the capacity is reduced to 80 per cent is called the *cycle life*. This number depends on cycle depth, discharge current, and temperature.

In some applications, cells are rarely cycled. An example is a standby battery which is kept on continuous charge until required in an emergency. The capacity is permanently reduced by ageing and this is called the *calendar life* or *standby life* of a cell, and is measured in years. Calendar life depends on temperature and how cells are stored.

Nominal and usable capacity

For some cells, a reasonable cycle or calendar life is only obtained by shallow depths of discharge on each cycle. Since the full capacity is not used, it is referred to as the *nominal capacity* because it is in name only. The amount of capacity that can be used for the required life is called the *usable capacity*.

Over-charging

A cell is fully charged when all the discharged form of the active material on one of the electrodes is converted to the charged form. If charging is continued, a different chemical reaction takes place at whichever electrode is fully charged.

One of the new reactions is decomposition of water that forms part of the electrolyte. This is called *gassing* because bubbles appear on the surface of the electrodes. Water is made up of oxygen and hydrogen as H_2O. During gassing, bubbles of oxygen are formed on the positive electrode and bubbles of hydrogen on the negative electrode.

Slow gassing does not damage a cell. The gentle stirring action of the bubbles is beneficial because it breaks up any *stratification* of the electrolyte (variations in concentration with depth).

As gassing continues, the electrolyte becomes more concentrated and the level of electrolyte falls. Water must be replaced before the level of electrolyte gets too low. A combined filling and vent cap is shown at the top of the container in Figure 3.4(b). It allows gas to escape during gassing and is removed when the level of electrolyte requires topping up. *Sealed batteries* do not have a removable vent cap because the gas from overcharging is absorbed internally.

Another reaction that can happen during over-charging of lead–acid cells is decomposition of the supporting material in the electrodes. This is more serious than gassing because it cannot be reversed and eventually the electrodes fall apart.

Control units

The electrical conditions of charging need to be controlled to prevent damage to a battery. Sometimes the size of a solar module can be matched to a battery so that no damage is caused. A module is called *self-regulating* when used in this way. In other systems, it is necessary to use a control unit to regulate charging.

Control units may also be needed to prevent batteries being discharged too much. This is particularly necessary for lead–acid batteries.

Charging efficiency

Charging efficiency compares the amount of charge used by the loads to the amount of charge needed to recharge the battery back to the original level. An efficiency of 100 per cent means that all the charge going in can be recovered during discharge.

When cycling up to 80 per cent state of charge, the charging efficiency is generally high at 90 per cent or more for most types of battery. On approaching full charge, the charging efficiency decreases because of gassing which wastes charge. A low efficiency means that more solar modules are needed for a given electrical requirement of the appliances.

Self-discharge

All batteries gradually discharge of their own accord when not in use; this is called *self-discharge*. The rate of self-discharge is normally specified by the amount of charge, as a percentage of capacity, that is lost over one month. It is related to how easily the plates gas when over-charging and increases at high operating temperatures.

Voltage characteristics

A cell or battery has a *nominal voltage* (V_{nom}). This means 'in name only' because the actual voltage varies during normal operation. The voltage can be measured in three different states:

1. *Open circuit voltage* (V_{OC}) when no current is flowing through the battery.
2. *Voltage at load* (V_{AL}) when a current is being drawn by appliances and the battery is discharging.
3. *Charging voltage* (V_{CH}) when the battery is being charged up from a solar module, dynamo, or other source of d.c. electricity.

These voltages are not fixed but depend on state of charge, temperature, and size of charging current or current to appliances. Nevertheless, their order of size, starting with the lowest, is V_{AL}, V_{OC}, and V_{CH}.

Requirements for a solar system

The operation of a battery used in a solar system can be summarized by two types of cycling:

1. A shallow cycle each day.
2. Deep cycles over several days or weeks during cloudy weather and winter.

The deep cycles occur when charging during the day is not enough to replace the amount of charge used by the appliances over the whole day. Therefore the state of charge after each daily cycle is reduced slightly and this builds up to a deep cycle over a period of several days. When the weather improves or the days lengthen, there is extra charging and the state of charge after each daily cycle gets higher.

Here is a list of the characteristics required for a battery to perform well in a solar system:

☐ High cycle life for deep cycles.
☐ Low maintenance requirements.
☐ High charging efficiency.
☐ Ability to survive complete discharge.
☐ Low rate of self-discharge.
☐ Reliability.
☐ Minimal change in performance over temperature range of operation.

The next sections describe different types of lead–acid and nickel–cadmium batteries. The performance of these batteries is compared to the list of characteristics above to see how suitable they are for use in a solar system.

Here is a list of other factors which it may be necessary to consider when choosing a battery for a solar system. These factors relate to the setting up of a system:

☐   Availability from suppliers.
☐   Distance, duration, and cost of transport to site.
☐   Cost of usable capacity over one cycle.
☐   Cost of total usable capacity over cycle life.
☐   Maintenance requirements during storage.
☐   Weight.
☐   Availability and cost of control units if required.

These factors may vary a lot between each type of battery and depend on the local circumstances at each site. A procedure is given towards the end of the chapter for comparing the value for money of different batteries. In addition to value for money, the choice of battery involves balancing suitability from the first list of characteristics against the factors in the second list.

Lead–acid cells

The materials used in lead–acid cells are listed in Table 3.1. For cases made of ebonite or hard rubber which is black, all that is seen on the outside of the battery is a pair of terminals and the filling caps (see Figure 3.2). When learning about lead–acid cells, it is helpful to examine a battery in a transparent container made of glass or clear plastic, like the single cell in Figure 3.4(c).

For a fully charged cell, the positive plates are chocolate brown in colour and the negative plates are a silvery grey. As the cell discharges, a layer of lead sulphate is formed on all the plates and they develop the same greyish colour. Although the electrolyte becomes dilute during discharge, there is no change in the appearance of the liquid.

On recharging, the plates return to their original colours. Just before reaching full charge, the positive plates start to gas and small bubbles appear on their surface. If the cell continues to be charged after reaching full charge, bubbles are produced more rapidly and appear on all the plates. For cells in non-transparent containers, gassing can be seen on the surface of the electrolyte by removing the vent cap.

Voltage characteristics

Most lead–acid cells are made in groups of six forming the common 12 V battery found in most vehicles. Other sizes of lead–acid batteries are individual 2 V cells used in laboratories and telephone exchanges, 6 V batteries with three cells for

Table 3.1 *Construction details of lead–acid cells.*

Parts	Materials	
	Charged	Discharged
Active material on positive electrode	Lead dioxide (chocolate brown)	Lead sulphate (grey)
Active material on negative electrode	Lead (silvery grey)	Lead sulphate (grey)
Electrolyte	Sulphuric acid	Acid slightly weaker
Electrode support	Lead	
Container	Hard rubber (ebonite) with bitumen Glass Plastic (polypropylene, polyethylene, or types of styrene such as ABS and SAN)	

motor bikes, 10 V batteries with five cells for standby supplies, and 24 V batteries with twelve cells for trucks.

Voltage characteristics are given in Table 3.2 for individual cells and 12 V batteries. During charging, the voltage can rise to the maximum values given in the table when all the plates are gassing freely. This voltage is also called the *gassing* or *equalization voltage*. Just before it is reached, any differences in state of charge between cells in a battery are equalized because low cells continue to charge while high cells are gassing.

The maximum voltage limit is used in *cyclic applications* where the charging is non-continuous. In solar systems, charging is continuous because the solar modules are permanently connected. Once the maximum is reached, the voltage should be reduced to avoid damaging the plates and excessive loss of water. A lower charging voltage also takes the battery to the fullest charge. At the same time, the solar modules can supply current directly to appliances if needed.

When the modules are running appliances and just keeping the battery fully charged on standby, the battery has no effect on the system voltage and is said to be on *float* in the circuit. With charge control units that produce a constant current, setting the charging current to balance self-discharge is called *trickle charging* or *charge maintenance*.

Table 3.2 *Voltage characteristics of lead–acid cells and batteries.*

Voltage characteristics	Voltages at 20 °C (68 °F) (V)	
	Single cell	Six-cell battery
Nominal	2	12
V_{CH} maximum	2.3–2.5	14.0–15.0
V_{CH} float	2.2–2.3	13.0–14.0
V_{OC} at full charge[1]	2.1–2.2	12.5–13.0
V_{AL} limit for measuring capacity[2]	1.8–1.9	10.8–11.4
Change of voltage characteristics with temperature[3]	−0.05 V per 10 °C rise	−0.33 V per 10 °C rise
	(−0.03 V per 10 °F rise)	(−0.18 V per 10 °F rise)

[1]These voltages apply after leaving disconnected for at least one hour.

[2]Limit set for low-voltage disconnect depends on recommended depth of discharge and load current. See also Table 11.2.

[3]For a fall in temperature, these voltages are added for each 10° fall.

Specific gravity of the electrolyte

During discharge, the electrolyte becomes more dilute as the acid part is used up to form lead sulphate. This affects both the voltage across the terminals (V_{OC} and V_{AL}) and the density of the electrolyte.

The density or heaviness of the electrolyte is also called its *specific gravity* (SG). This compares the weight of electrolyte to the weight of the same volume of water. By this definition, pure water has an SG of 1.000 which is sometimes written with units of grams per cubic centimetre (g/cm^3) or kilograms per litre (kg/l). The SG of pure water is also given as 1000 without the decimal point and this number is sometimes written with kg/m^3 units.

In a fully charged cell, the SG varies from 1200 to 1300 depending on the make and type of battery. When discharged to a cut-off V_{AL} of 10.8 V, the SG falls to about 1100. Discharging further reduces V_{AL} to zero, all the acid part of the electrolyte is used up, and the SG becomes 1000.

Specific gravity is measured using a battery hydrometer (described in Chapter 11) which takes a sample of electrolyte from one cell for measurement.

Sulphation

A particular problem of lead–acid cells is a condition called *sulphating*, *sulphatation*, or *sulphation*. Sulphation reduces the capacity of a cell permanently so all precautions should be taken to prevent it occurring.

Under normal operating conditions, the layer of lead sulphate that is first formed during discharge is very fine grained. This means there are lots of spaces around each small bit of lead sulphate where the electrolyte can still reach the other active materials of lead dioxide and lead. Gradually the fine grains of lead sulphate join together and recrystallize to form much larger grains. This is sulphation and it is a problem because the large grains do not reconvert to lead dioxide and lead during charging.

Sulphation occurs under the following conditions:

☐ Leaving a cell discharged for a long period.
☐ Prolonged under-charging or partial charging.
☐ Continuous operation above 45 °C (110 °F).
☐ Allowing the electrolyte to become strongly concentrated.

When two or more of these conditions occur at the same time, sulphation happens even more quickly.

The first sign of sulphation is when a battery appears to charge up quickly, as indicated by a high charging voltage. However, an SG measurement shows that the state of charge is still low. Maintaining a slow charging current may reverse the damage but usually the capacity is reduced permanently.

The best way to avoid sulphation is to charge the cell regularly so that all the lead sulphate is converted. In deep cycle applications, manufacturers always recommend that the batteries are charged up promptly after each deep discharge. This is not possible in a solar system when the deep discharge results from cloudy weather. It is then necessary for the use of electricity to be drastically reduced over several days or to take the batteries for charging elsewhere.

The rate of sulphation varies between different types of cell depending on the quality of the plates and what the cell is designed for. The active materials contain additives which slow the rate of sulphation but they cannot stop it completely. In places where the average temperature is above about 30 °C (85 °F), a *tropical electrolyte* is used which is a low concentration of acid. The low concentration reduces damage to the grid structure of the positive plates and helps reduce the rate of sulphation.

Construction of plates

The surface area of the active material on a plate needs to be large for good contact with the electrolyte. This is achieved by making it very porous like a sponge. In manufacture, the active material starts as a paste made up of powdered lead, lead oxides, and other ingredients. To convert the paste into active material, plates coated with paste are put into some electrolyte and charged under carefully controlled conditions. This last stage is called *forming* when the porous structure is formed.

On the positive plates, the active material is lead dioxide which changes to lead sulphate during discharge. Lead dioxide is not a strong material and lead sulphate has a lower density so takes up more space. This causes problems for deep cycles because the structure of the plate surface can become broken up as a lot of lead sulphate is formed. When active material becomes separated from the electrode, the capacity of the cell is reduced permanently.

Plates for the positive electrodes of lead–acid cells are manufactured in three different forms:

1. Flat plates.
2. Tubular plates.
3. Planté plates.

The choice of plate type depends on the application and price of the battery.

Flat plates

The method of manufacture is to mould the lead part of one plate as a grid of rectangular holes. These holes are filled with paste which is converted to active material at the forming stage. Plates based on a grid structure are called *flat plates* or *pasted plates*.

Tubular positive plates

Instead of a grid, the positive plates can be made as a series of lead rods which carry the current to the terminal. The active material is packed around each rod and held in place by strong tubes of insulating material (see Figure 3.5). In this type of construction, the positive plates are called *tubular*, *multi-tubed*, *armoured*, or *clad*. The tubes reduce shedding of active material from the electrode so tubular plates are good for deep cycle applications. They are also very resistant to continuous vibration of the battery.

Planté plates

The third type of positive plate consists of solid sheets of lead at 7–12 mm thick with grooved faces to increase the area. The surfaces are coated with paste and formed to produce a coating of porous active material. The thickness of lead acts as a reserve of active material. When active material falls off, the lead that becomes exposed changes to lead dioxide during charging.

These plates are similar to the type used in the very first lead–acid cells. They are called *Planté plates* after the man who made the first rechargeable lead–acid cell.

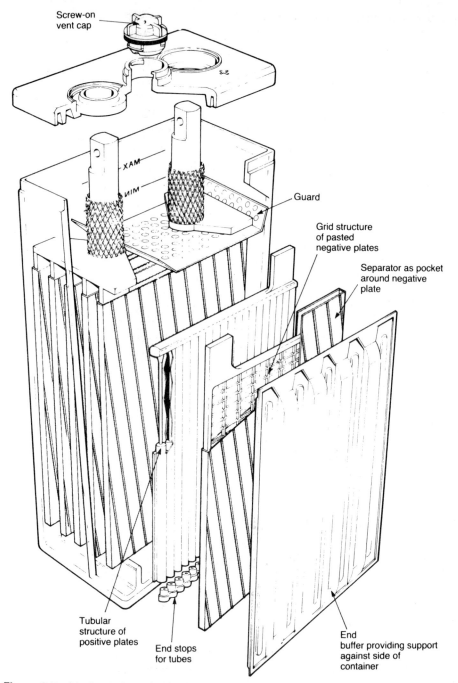

Screw-on
vent cap

MAX

MIN

Guard

Grid structure
of pasted
negative plates

Separator as pocket
around negative
plate

Tubular
structure of
positive plates

End stops
for tubes

End
buffer providing support
against side of
container

Figure 3.5 Method of construction for a lead–acid battery with positive tubular plates.
(Source Chloride Ltd, Industrial Battery Division.)

Lead alloys in positive plates

Pure lead is a soft metal. If it is used for the thin, open mesh grids of pasted plates, they are much too fragile. Antimony and other substances are added to form a lead alloy which is stronger and easier to cast during manufacture than pure lead.

An important advantage of using antimony is that it improves the cycling properties of the cell. This is because it helps bind lead sulphate to the lead support and keeps the active material firm at low states of charge. However, antimony has a bad effect on the cell since it is gradually washed out of the positive grids during operation of the cell. When it reaches the negative plates, it encourages gassing there with the result of low charging efficiency, increased self-discharge, and loss of water from the electrolyte.

Some batteries use modified separators that trap antimony before it reaches the negative plates. Another solution is to use a very small amount of antimony in the lead of the positive plates. Calcium, selenium, tin, arsenic, and silver are alternative alloying materials for strengthening the grid which do not cause extra gassing at the negative plates. However, they do not have the same beneficial effect on the active material of the positive plates for deep cycles.

The chemical abbreviations for some of the materials used in lead–acid batteries are as follows:

lead	Pb
antimony	Sb
calcium	Ca
selenium	Se
tin	Sn
arsenic	As
silver	Ag

Negative plates

Negative plates are always the pasted type using grids of lead alloy that does not contain any antimony. The alloy forming the grids does not require antimony for strengthening because the active material is lead which forms a strong structure with the grid. They are also able to retain their strength as lead sulphate is formed so smaller amounts of active material are shed during deep cycles.

Temperature effects

The characteristic of 12 V lead–acid batteries are given in Table 3.2 for a temperature of 20 °C (68 °F). As the temperature is increased, the full capacity increases. This is clearly an advantage but at the cost of increased rate of self-discharge, reduced cycle life, and faster sulphation in batteries that are not at full charge. Batteries should not be operated continuously above about 40 °C (105 °F), otherwise there is permanent damage to the plates.

A problem with temperatures below 0 °C is that the electrolyte in a discharged battery may freeze solid. The battery cannot operate and permanent damage is caused. Full-strength acid freezes below about −50 °C (−60 °F). As the battery discharges the acid becomes dilute and freezes at a higher temperature. At 20 per cent state of charge, the freezing point is at about −10 °C (15 °F) in a typical battery. Batteries intended for use in very cold climates have a higher concentration of acid which remains liquid at these temperatures.

At a given state of charge, changes in temperature affect measurements of electrolyte SG and voltage. Correction factors to a reference temperature for these measurements are given in Table D.4.

Types of lead–acid battery

Lead–acid batteries are used in many different applications. Each application has its own requirements which decide how the cells of a battery are made.

Types of lead–acid battery that are suitable for use in solar electric systems are sometimes known as *solar* or *PV batteries*. (PV means photovoltaic and is another way of referring to electricity generated by solar cells.) There are two main types of solar lead–acid batteries:

1. Vented with low-antimony positive plates.
2. Maintenance-free with calcium positive plates.

Solar batteries are also available with other alloys, but lead alloys with low antimony and calcium are the most common.

Other types of lead–acid batteries can also be used successfully in solar electric systems. These are often divided into the following groups:

3. *SLI* (starting–lighting–ignition) for vehicles.
4. *Traction* for electrically powered vehicles.
5. *Standby* for emergency and uninterruptible power supplies.
6. *Sealed* for maintenance-free and portable power supplies.

These six groups are now described in detail.

Vented low-antimony solar battery

This battery has the following features which make it suitable for solar systems (an example of a single cell battery with these features is shown in Figure 3.4(c)):

☐ Positive plates made of low-antimony lead alloy at 1 – 3 per cent.

☐ Pasted plates of medium thickness (2.5–3 mm).
☐ Vented cells with filling caps.
☐ Case made of transparent plastic.
☐ Large space or headroom above the plates.
☐ Large mud space at the bottom of the cells.

The use of antimony and medium thick plates gives a high cycle life for deep cycles. Tubular positive plates are also very resilient against deep cycling but are more expensive than pasted positive plates. So the use of pasted positive plates in this battery is a compromise between good resilience to deep cycling and a low cost of construction. The low percentage of antimony means that the effect on gassing and self-discharge is small. The transparent case permits easy inspection of the electrolyte level for each cell, and the headroom means that the time between topping up is long: only once or twice per year.

Loss of water by gassing can be reduced to a very low level by direct recombination of the gases. This is achieved using *catalytic recombination caps* which contain platinum or palladium (see Figure 3.6). When the hydrogen and oxygen gases come into contact with the catalyst, they recombine to form water, which is allowed to drip back into the cell. It is important that the catalyst material does not come into direct contact with acid, otherwise it stops working.

One advantage of vented cells is that the battery can be supplied *dry-charged*. The electrolyte is added at the site when the battery is being installed. This is an important feature if long delays may occur between despatch of the battery from the supplier and installation at the site. For example, delays often occur for imported batteries and transport to remote sites. By supplying the battery dry, there is no possibility of sulphation resulting from self-discharge. Also there is no problem if the battery is turned upside down by mistake. However, dry-charged plates do degrade very slowly so should not be left in storage for longer than really necessary.

The mud space below the plates improves reliability. This is because the

Figure 3.6 Catalytic recombination caps to reduce water loss on a battery of three cells. (Source BP Solar.)

build-up of shed material at the bottom is less likely to touch the lower edge of the plates and cause a short circuit. The transparent case allows the amount of mud or sediment to be inspected. Since it is active material lost from the electrodes, the build-up of sediment at the bottom gives an indication of life remaining in the battery.

With a transparent case, the condition of the plates and separators along their edges can be inspected. Correct performance of a charge regulator can also be checked. There should be uniform gassing from all plates at the equalization voltage and a low level of gassing at the float voltage.

Although the battery is designed for deep cycle operation, it should never be totally discharged and precautions must be taken to prevent this happening. An electronic control unit with low-voltage disconnect feature prevents discharge below a certain V_{AL}. Alternatively, the state of charge can be checked each day with a voltmeter. When the state of charge is low, the number of appliances that can be used must be reduced.

The capacity of a solar battery is usually specified at a discharge rate of C/100. This rate is over a hundred hours which is appropriate for use in a solar system. Batteries of 12 V are most convenient to use. Separate 2 V cells are also available and they have the advantage of a reduced risk of theft since they are less easy to use in vehicles.

Maintenance-free calcium solar battery

The main drawback of the vented low-antimony battery just described is that the small amount of maintenance it requires must be done regularly to avoid permanent damage. This involves checking the level of the electrolyte and topping up with distilled or deionized water when required. For some sites, organization of maintenance can be a problem. Also distilled water is a consumable which can be expensive and difficult to obtain regularly.

Another disadvantage of vented batteries is the *acid mist* produced by gassing. A fine spray of very small drops is formed when bubbles from gassing burst at the surface of the electrolye. These drops are carried through venting holes in the cap and settle on any surfaces nearby. Since the droplets are acid they damage metal parts of the electrical contacts to the terminals.

Low-maintenance solar batteries use a lead alloy with calcium instead of antimony in the positive plates. This makes the rate of gassing so small that the electrolyte rarely requires topping up. The terminals need to be cleaned only every twelve months.

'Non-spill' batteries have a maze-like structure of tubes leading to the venting holes. These tubes prevent liquid slopping out when a battery is moved quickly. However, these batteries should never be turned upside down. Liquid may escape which cannot be replaced because refilling is impossible through the tubes.

There are two disadvantages of low-maintenance batteries for solar systems. One is a low cycle life for deep cycles compared to positive plates with low antimony. The other disadvantage is that they are always supplied ready filled with electrolyte. This adds to the risk of deterioration during the delivery period, and electrolyte can be lost if they are turned over by mistake. Charging is required every few months while in storage to avoid sulphation and this is not always possible during transport.

SLI batteries

The most common type of lead–acid battery is for vehicles where the main job of the battery is to power the electric motor that starts the engine. Two other jobs are to power the lights and the ignition system, so the battery is called *starting–lighting–ignition* (SLI). As soon as the engine is running on fuel, the battery is charged back up by the dynamo or alternator.

To get the starter motor turning, the current drawn in the first second after switching on is very high at 100 A or more. SLI batteries are designed to supply a high discharge current for a short time by having a large surface area of the active material in contact with the electrolyte.

The range of capacity for SLI batteries is 30–100 A h specified at C/10 or C/20 rates of discharge. However, this does not mean that an SLI battery, of, say, 50 A h is intended to supply 5 A regularly for ten hours. Capacity is easier to specify than the ability to supply a high current, so the capacity is simply used as an indication of the maximum current that can be supplied.

SLI batteries are made with pasted plates of 1.5–2.5 mm thick. The plates are thin to minimize weight while still being able to supply a high current and have a high cycle life for shallow cycles of 5–20 per cent in depth. However, thin plates are unsuitable for deep cycle operation. After a few deep cycles, most of the active material is lost from the plates and the capacity is drastically reduced.

Since SLI batteries are made in large numbers, they are easily available and are the least expensive type of lead–acid battery when compared by nominal capacity. They are not recommended for use in solar systems because of the short cycle life for deep cycles. Nevertheless, SLI batteries are used in many developing countries for deep cycle applications, such as powering televisions for homes without mains supply or a generator. This is force of circumstance because better batteries cannot be obtained or are too expensive. Credit may not be available to buy the most cost-effective battery. Figure 3.7 shows a typical charging facility in a small town of a developing country.

Low-quality SLI batteries are made with high antimony levels of 4–8 per cent. This limits the calendar life to one to three years by the increase of self-discharge. Also they require frequent maintenance to keep the electrolyte topped up and the terminals clean.

SLI batteries for trucks and buses are more suitable for solar systems. They are sometimes described as 'heavy duty' because they are designed to withstand

Figure 3.7 Example of a typical charger in a developing country for batteries providing power in remote areas, such as for televisions. (Source Peter Thornley.)

more vibration and deeper cycling than those for cars. They have thicker pasted plates of 2.5–3 mm which are inserted into pocket-shaped separators to increase their resistance to shock and to prevent shedding of active material. SLI batteries with tubular positive plates are even better but are more expensive.

Versions of the maintenance-free calcium solar battery are made for SLI use. Their calendar life is not limited by increase of self-discharge but they still have a short cycle life for deep cycles, as for the low-quality type with antimony.

Traction batteries

Traction batteries provide the motion for electric vehicles. Examples are fork-lift trucks in factories and warehouses, delivery vehicles such as milk floats and golf carts. The service conditions are severe with deep cycles of 80 per cent every day. The capacity is usually specified at C/5 since five hours of use is typical for an eight-hour working day. Cycle life is 1000–1500 deep cycles, which at one deep cycle per day gives a life of three to six years.

The electrodes are either thick pasted plates of 3–6 mm or tubular positive plates with pasted negative plates. The positive plates contain a high level of antimony at 4–8 per cent which is essential for deep cycling performance. Separators absorb some antimony before it can reach the negative plates but self-discharge is still high. This is not a problem in traction applications because the batteries are normally put on charge every night.

Although traction batteries have good cycling characteristics, they are an expensive option for a solar system. Second-hand traction batteries can be good value if their self-discharge is not too high. A procedure for checking the condition of old batteries is given in Appendix D.

Standby batteries

Rechargeable batteries are used as a standby where there is a risk of momentary interruptions or power cuts in the main source of power from the mains or a generator. They are also called *stand-alone* batteries and the application is for *stationary* or *float* service. Examples of equipment requiring standby batteries are found in telecommunications, railway signalling, starter motors for stationary engines, hospital operating theatres, and emergency systems in public buildings for lighting and alarms. Standby batteries also form part of *uninterruptible power supplies* to ensure absolute continuity of supply to computerized control systems.

In float service, the batteries are kept fully charged all the time and are ready to take up the load demand immediately they are required. The most important characteristics of a standby battery are reliability, low rate of self-discharge, and long calendar life of ten years or more. Since the batteries are stationary, characteristics of high weight and poor resistance to vibration are not problems.

Their capacity is usually rated at C/10 or C/3 but they are only deep cycled occasionally when called on to provide emergency power. The positive plates are either Planté plates, tubular plates, or thick pasted plates formed on low, antimony grids.

Although standby batteries generally have a low cycle life for deep cycles, they are suitable for solar systems. Low-antimony stationary batteries with tubular plates are used in many large solar installations because of their reliability. These installations are designed carefully so that the batteries undergo few deep cycles.

For small solar systems, standby batteries may be an expensive option. Second-hand batteries are worth considering after testing their capacity using the procedure in Appendix D. They are often designed to be taken apart so that faulty plates and separators can be repaired or replaced.

Sealed batteries

Lead–acid batteries that are fully sealed are very desirable because there is no risk of contact with the electrolyte and no maintenance is required. Sealed batteries use the *oxygen cycle* to eliminate loss of water under normal operating conditions. The oxygen cycle works in the following way.

The total size of the positive plates is slightly less than the size of the negative plates. The positive plates reach full charge first so the capacity of the cell is said to be 'positively limited'. The importance of this is that only the positive plates gas so only oxygen is produced. This oxygen is allowed to flow through the electrolyte space to the negative plates where it reacts to form lead sulphate and water. Further charging changes this lead sulphate to lead and restores the chemical balance of the cell. The overall result is that oxygen cycles from the positive to the negative plates during over-charging, so is not lost from the cell.

The cycle only works for oxygen. This is why the cell is positively limited to prevent the negative plates from reaching full charge and producing hydrogen which is only absorbed very slowly.

As part of the oxygen cycle, there must be a free flow of oxygen gas from the positive to the negative plates. Routes for passage through the electrolyte are achieved in two ways. One method uses a spongy separator material which is 'starved' of electrolyte so that there are lots of small tunnels for gas to pass through. Examples of this type of cell are made by Yuasa (see Figure 3.2) and the 'Cyclon' brand by Chloride-Gates Energy Ltd in Europe.

In the other method, the electrolyte is prevented from flowing around by making it into a jelly-like consistency, called a 'gel', using silica-based additives. Microcracks in the gelled electrolyte allow gas to pass through. An example of this type of battery is the 'Dryfit' brand by Sonnenschein.

One-way vent valves are always fitted at one end of sealed cells. These remain closed most of the time and only open for safety when the gas pressure increases because of a build-up of hydrogen or excessive over-charging. The valve also prevents oxygen outside from saturating the negative plates.

Sealed cells have a compact structure because the plates are thin and held in close contact with the separators. Active material is prevented from falling off the plates so a mud space is not required at the bottom. Good support of the plates means that the cells can survive a complete discharge more effectively than other types of lead–acid cell. However, they should be recharged as soon as possible to prevent permanent damage developing.

Sealed cells are very suitable for solar systems because they do not require maintenance and are useful for portable appliances. Small 6 V batteries can be charged at constant voltage in a 12 or 24 V solar system using one of the voltage regulator designs in Chapter 14. They must never be charged using car-battery type chargers from mains voltage

The main disadvantages of sealed cells are high cost, short cycle life for deep cycles, and no possibility of being delivered as dry-charged. Although they have a low rate of self-discharge, they can be permanently damaged by sulphation if stored for several months without charging.

Nickel–cadmium cells

The main materials and characteristics of nickel–cadmium cells are given in Tables 3.3 and 3.4. The electrolyte of potassium hydroxide is an alkali, which is harmful like the acid of lead–acid cells. Another difference from lead–acid cells is that nickel–cadmium cells can be deep cycled and left discharged without any bad effects to the plates.

The plates in nickel–cadmium cells are available as two basic types of construction called *pocket plates* and *sintered plates*. Vented nickel–cadmium cells generally have pocket plates while small sealed cells generally have sintered plates.

Vented nickel–cadmium batteries

In most vented batteries, the active material is held on the electrodes in pockets. These are made up as rectangular *pocket plates* which are suspended in the electrolyte, as shown in Figure 3.8.

The pocket plates are made from a low carbon mild steel strip with a large number of small holes of about 0.2 mm diameter. The steel strip is nickel–plated and formed into channels by rollers. One channel is filled with active material while a second channel is placed on top and crimped to close the pocket. The required number of filled strips is then interlocked to form a single rectangular plate. The cut edges are enclosed by steel strips and current collector lugs are attached by spot welding. The plates are rigid and remain flat during cycling of

Table 3.3 *Construction details of nickel–cadmium cells.*

Parts	Materials	
	Charged	Discharged
Active material on positive electrode	Nickel (III) hydroxide	Nickel (II) hydroxide
Active material of negative electrode	Cadmium	Cadmium hydroxide
Electrolyte	Potassium hydroxide alkali	Alkali slightly stronger
Electrode support	Nickel Nickel-plated mild steel	
Container	Nickel-plated steel Polyethylene Polystyrene (translucent)	
Separator	Plastic spacers for vented cells Terylene or polypropylene for sealed cells	

Table 3.4 *Voltage characteristics of nickel–cadmium cells and batteries.*

Voltage characteristics	Voltages at 20 °C (68 °F) (V)	
	Single cell	Ten-cell battery
Nominal	1.25	12
V_{CH} maximum for vented	1.50–1.65	15.0–16.5
V_{CH} float for vented	1.40–1.45	14.0–14.5
I_{CH} for sealed	C/10	C/10
V_{OC} at most states of charge	1.20–1.35	12.0–13.5
V_{AL} limit	0	9[1]

[1]To avoid polarity reversal for the first cell in the battery that becomes fully discharged.

the cell. Therefore the separators need only to be plastic rods or an open mesh that set the spacing between the plates in the container.

Hydrogen and oxygen produced by gassing escape through a vent in the top and the electrolyte must be topped up with distilled water occasionally. The vent is not a simple hole but a one-way valve to prevent carbon dioxide from the air being absorbed in the electrolyte.

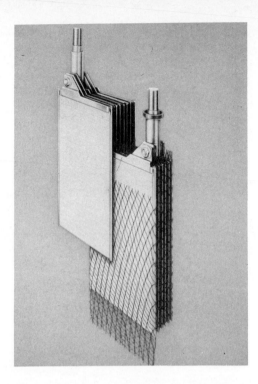

Figure 3.8   Method of construction for a vented nickel–cadmium battery. (Source Varta Batteries AG.)

Sealed nickel–cadmium cells

Sealed nickel–cadmium batteries are available in the same sizes as zinc dry cells (the common non-rechargeable torch batteries). An example is the D-size cell of diameter 32 mm and length 57 mm. Although the voltage of nickel–cadmium cells at 1.25 V is less than the voltage of zinc dry cells at 1.4 V, they can be used in the same appliances.

The similarity in shape and size of these two types of batteries has led to some confusion, with users expecting, or hoping, that primary cells are also rechargeable (compare the cells in Figures 3.2 and 3.3). Do not attempt to recharge any small batteries unless charging conditions are specified on the case.

Most sealed nickel–cadmium cells have *sintered plates*. The starting material for manufacture of the plates is nickel sheets with many holes. Powdered nickel is pressed on and plates are heated above 800 °C (1500 °F). The temperature is not enough to melt the nickel but the particles of powder join together in a process called sintering to form plates that are strong and very porous like a sponge. The spaces in the sintered plates are then filled with the active materials.

In sealed cells, such as the D-size shown in Figure 3.9, there is only one plate of each polarity. The two plates are wound in a spiral to form a compact roll and are isolated from each other by a porous separator. The case of the cell is made of nickel-plated steel which is not affected by the alkaline electrolyte. It is linked to the negative of the cell and is covered with plastic to avoid short circuits between cells connected in series.

By sealing the cells, the electrolyte cannot leak out and requires no topping up. However, the products of gassing must be dealt with, otherwise the cell will explode. The oxygen cycle is used, as for sealed lead–acid cells. This means that the negative plate is larger to make the capacity positively limited. The separator is made of 'fleecy' plastic so that oxygen can pass freely from the positive to the negative plates. On the negative plates, oxygen is absorbed, forming cadmium hydroxide. Further over-charging decomposes the cadmium hydroxide to cadmium and water to complete the cycle.

Sealed cells can be over-charged continuously without any loss of gas, provided the current is not too high. At excessive over-charging currents, oxygen is not absorbed quickly enough and hydrogen is also produced. A safety valve is fitted inside the top of the case which opens when the pressure inside goes above ten atmospheres (150 p.s.i. or $1\,000\,000$ N/m^2). When this operates, some of the electrolyte is released which could damage equipment and also lead to loss of capacity.

Charging nickel–cadmium cells

Sealed cells should only be charged at constant current. Charging from a constant voltage supply is only suitable for vented cells because they have different charging characteristics. This also means that batteries of sealed cells cannot be charged in parallel from the same current supply without a regulator on each series group.

The recommended charging current is usually the capacity number divided by ten hours, a C/10 rate. For example, 1.2 A h cells should be charged at 0.12 A. Fully discharged cells require fourteen to sixteen hours' charging at this rate to reach full charge. The correct current can be set by a suitable size of solar module or with a current regulator (see Chapter 15).

Perhaps surprisingly, the charging efficiency for sealed cells is worse when charging more slowly than the recommended rate of C/10. For currents below about C/40 in some sealed cells, there is no charging at all. Also the cycle life is reduced for regular charging at a low current. This means that it is better to charge sealed cells at constant current from a regulator rather than directly from solar modules which supply a varying current.

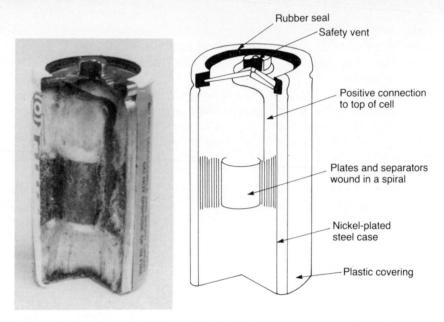

Figure 3.9   A sealed sintered-plate nickel–cadmium battery cut open to show the construction. The battery is D-size with a capacity of 1.2 A h. (In the 4 A h version, the roll of plates fills the full length.)

Temperature effects

Vented batteries can be used over a wide temperature range of -25–$45\,°C$ (-15–$115\,°F$). Standard strength electrolyte freezes below the lower temperature limit but no damage is caused.

In order to obtain the full life of a sealed cell, it is important to keep the cell temperature well below $45\,°C$ ($115\,°F$) at all times, especially during overcharging when heat is produced by the cell. Above $45\,°C$, the separator slowly degrades and eventually the plates touch. This means the cell is shorted internally and cannot be used again. A good precaution is always to leave some charge in a cell. If an internal short begins to develop, charge remaining in the cell will automatically burn it out by supplying a high current just as contact is made.

Another problem with high temperatures is that the high-pressure seal around the top of the casing becomes less effective. The electrolyte slowly dries out, leaving an open circuit between the plates. 'High temperature' sealed cells have a better separator and seal to withstand temperatures up to about $65\,°C$ ($150\,°F$).

The voltage and capacity specifications are usually given for $25\,°C$ ($77\,°F$). At higher or lower temperatures, the voltages are slightly different. There is no significant change in capacity with temperature except below about $-20\,°C$ ($-5\,°F$) when it starts to drop.

Below about $5\,°C$ ($40\,°F$), oxygen absorption is slow so the over-charging current for sealed cells should be less than C/10 to avoid production of hydrogen.

Suitability of nickel-cadmium batteries for solar systems

Nickel–cadmium batteries are ideal for solar electric systems because there are no problems from deep cycles or of being left discharged. Unfortunately, high cost has limited their use in small systems.

When comparing batteries of the same nominal capacity, nickel–cadmium are more expensive than lead–acid. This is mainly because cadmium metal is rare, construction of the plates is complicated, and cadmium is poisonous, so difficult to work with. However, when their costs are compared according to usable capacity over either one cycle, cycle life, or calendar life, nickel–cadmium batteries are cheaper. A procedure for making this cost comparison is given at the end of the chapter.

Sealed cells are useful for portable appliances because they substitute directly for standard dry cells. Since the capacity required for portable appliances is not high, the cells should be more affordable.

One disadvantage of nickel–cadmium batteries compared to lead–acid is that there is no simple means of measuring their state of charge. This is because there is very little variation of the voltage or the specific gravity of the electrolyte during discharge. Therefore no warning can be given of when full discharge is reached, which is inconvenient to users.

One solution is to use a sophisticated control unit which displays charge in A h as calculated automatically from continuous measurements of the charging and load currents. Another solution is to have one reserve battery which is kept at full charge on standby.

Choosing a battery and comparing prices

The first step in choosing a battery is to find out which ones are available. Then their details, specifications, and price should be listed in a copy of Table 3.5. The price should include the cost of delivery to the site and all other incidental costs for each battery.

The choice of battery from this list is done by comparing their cost and relative advantages. How to compare batteries by value for money based on usable capacity and total usable capacity over life is explained next and the last section of this chapter summarizes the advantages and disadvantages of each type of battery for use in a solar electric system.

The voltage supplied by a battery depends on the number and type of cells from which it is made. Batteries should be compared at the same voltage of 12 V.

Table 3.5 *Summarizing details of rechargeable batteries that are available. For the last column of 'Cost for a 12 V battery', use Formula (3.1).*

Number	Make and model	Nominal capacity (A h)[1]	Voltage (V)	Costs for one battery			Cost for a 12 V battery
				Price	Transport and other	Total	
1							
2							
3							
.							
.							
.							

[1]At C/100 or C_{100} (measured for a full discharge over 100 hours).

The nominal capacity is converted using the following formula with the answer put in the last column of Table 3.5:

$$\boxed{\begin{array}{c}\text{Total cost of}\\\text{one battery}\\\text{(local currency)}\end{array}} \times \boxed{\begin{array}{c}12\\(V)\end{array}} \div \boxed{\begin{array}{c}\text{Nominal voltage}\\\text{of one battery}\\(V)\end{array}} = \boxed{\begin{array}{c}\text{Cost for a}\\\text{12 V battery}\\\text{(local currency)}\end{array}} \qquad (3.1)$$

Lead–acid batteries should not be cycled over their full nominal capacity otherwise their cycle life is too short. The usable capacity is calculated as follows:

$$\boxed{\begin{array}{c}\text{Nominal capacity}\\(A\,h)\end{array}} \times \boxed{\begin{array}{c}\text{Usable depth}\\(\%)\end{array}} \div \boxed{\begin{array}{c}100\\(\%)\end{array}} = \boxed{\begin{array}{c}\text{Usable capacity}\\(A\,h)\end{array}} \qquad (3.2)$$

Another useful specification relates to the capacity used over the cycle life of a battery. This is calculated as follows:

$$\boxed{\begin{array}{c}\text{Usable capacity}\\(A\,h)\end{array}} \times \boxed{\begin{array}{c}\text{Cycle life at}\\\text{usable depth}\\\text{(cycles)}\end{array}} = \boxed{\begin{array}{c}\text{Total usable capacity}\\\text{over cycle life}\\(A\,h)\end{array}} \qquad (3.3)$$

These capacity values can be listed in Table 3.6. The procedure for comparing different batteries is summarized in Figure 3.10. Often the full

Table 3.6 *Comparing batteries by value for money of various aspects. Calculations for capacity summarized in Figure 3.10. Where specifications are not given by the supplier, typical values can be used from Table 3.7.*

Number	Nominal capacity (A h)	Cost for a 12 V battery	Usable cycle depth (%)	Cycle life[1] (cycles)	Capacity (A h) Usable	Total usable[2]	Relative value for money One cycle	Cycle life	Life
1									
2									
3									
.									
.									
.									

[1]At usable cycle depth.

[2]Over cycle life.

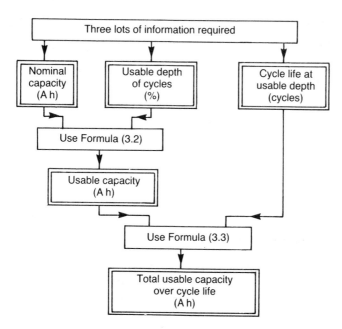

Figure 3.10 Summary of procedure for calculating different types of capacity for a battery:
- □ steps involved
- ▣ results at each stage with units in brackets

Table 3.7 *Specifications for various types of rechargeable batteries that can be used in solar electric systems. Note that these specifications are only given as typical values for the purpose of comparison. When completing Table 3.6, use specifications from individual suppliers where possible.*

Type of battery	Usable depth (%)	Cycle life (cycles)	Calendar life (years)	Self-discharge[1] (capacity % per month)
Lead–acid				
Low antimony (for solar and	50	3000	8	3
stationary use)	80	1200	4	
Antimony-free: calcium	20	1000	5	3
	50	300	5	
pure lead	80		15[2]	3
High antimony: SLI for cars	20		1–3	30
	80	10		
SLI for trucks	50	500	5	10
traction	80	1500	6	7
Sealed: gelled	50	400	8	3
	100[3]	200	8	
starved electrolyte	100[3]	250	8	10
Nickel–cadmium				
Vented (pocket plate)	100	1200–2000	20	3
Sealed (sintered plate)	100	500–1000	4	30

[1]At 20 °C (68 °F).

[2]Only applies when used on standby at float voltage.

[3]Should recharge immediately.

specifications are not given to enable Table 3.6 to be completed. Table 3.7 lists typical specifications of various types of rechargeable batteries. This can be used as a guide to complete the calculation of capacity figures. However, when comparing individual brands of battery, always use the specifications for that brand as provided by the supplier.

For the last columns in Table 3.6, each of the capacity figures is divided by price to give a number which is 'value for money'. The higher the answer, the better the value for money of battery.

There are two approaches to balancing the starting and running costs of a system:

1. To minimize the system cost at the start, aim for high usable capacity. A disadvantage is that the battery may have a short life.
2. To minimize the cost over the life of the battery, aim for a high value of total usable capacity over cycle life.

Summary of battery features

The types of rechargeable battery are listed in this section in the following groups:

1. Lead–acid with low-antimony plates (for solar and stationary use).
2. Lead–acid with calcium plates (for solar, stationary, and SLI use).
3. Lead–acid with Planté plates.
4. Lead–acid with high-antimony plates for
    (a) SLI in cars;
    (b) SLI in trucks;
    (c) traction.
5. Sealed lead–acid.
6. Vented nickel–cadmium.
7. Sealed nickel–cadmium.

Each type of battery has a list of features relevant to use in a solar system with '+' signs for advantages and '−' signs for disadvantages. A summary of performance characteristics is also given in Table 3.7.

For further details about the features and explanations of the technical terms, refer back to previous sections of this chapter or use the index.

Lead–acid batteries with low-antimony lead alloy for the positive plates

−   Poor supply.
−   Medium cost for nominal capacity.
+   High cycle life for deep cycles.
−   Requires a control unit with low-voltage disconnect or a state-of-charge meter.
+   Can be supplied dry-charged.
+   Low consumption of distilled water.
+   Maintenance required only twice each year to top up electrolyte and clean terminals.
+   Reliable.
+   Low rate of self-discharge.

Lead–acid batteries with calcium lead alloy for the positive plates

- − Poor supply (except for SLI type in industrialized countries).
- − Medium cost for nominal capacity.
- + Standby type may be good value if obtained second-hand (after checking capacity).
- − Low cycle life for cycle depth of more than 50 per cent or more than 20 per cent for SLI type).
- − Requires a control unit with low-voltage disconnect or a state-of-charge meter.
- − Cannot be supplied dry-charged so risk of electrolyte spillage and sulphation before installation.
- + No acid spray from the vents.
- + No consumption of distilled water.
- + Maintenance once each year to check terminals.
- + Reliable.
- + Low rate of self-discharge.

Lead–acid with Planté plates

- − Poor supply since specialized use.
- − High cost since designed for very high reliability and long calendar life.
- − Low cycle life for deep cycles.
- − Requires a control unit with low-voltage disconnect or a state-of-charge meter.
- + No acid spray from the vents.
- + No consumption of distilled water.
- + Maintenance required only twice each year to top up electrolyte and clean terminals.
- + Reliable.
- + Low rate of self-discharge.

Lead–acid with high–antimony plates for SLI in cars

- + Good supply since used for cars.
- + Low cost for nominal capacity since made in large numbers and locally available.
- − Short cycle life for cycle depth of more than 20 per cent, so high cost for usable capacity.
- − Requires a control unit with low-voltage disconnect or a state-of-charge meter.
- − Self-discharge increases with age, so high cost for calendar life.
- − Must expect to replace after one to two years of operation.

+ Can be supplied dry-charged.
− A lot of acid spray from the vents.
− High consumption of distilled water.
− Maintenance required every month to top up electrolyte and clean terminals.
− Poor reliability, so do not use in an array of more than two or three batteries.
− High rate of self-discharge, so must be charged up every month by some other means when disconnected from system.

Lead–acid with high-antimony plates for heavy-duty SLI use in trucks

+ Good supply since used for trucks and buses.
+ Low cost for nominal capacity since made in large numbers and locally available.
− Medium cycle life for deep cycles, so cost may be high for usable capacity.
− Requires a control unit with low-voltage disconnect or a state-of-charge meter.
− Self-discharge increases with age, so high cost for calendar life.
+ Can be supplied dry-charged.
− A lot of acid spray from the vents.
− High consumption of distilled water.
− Maintenance required every month to top up electrolyte and clean terminals.
+ More reliable than SLI batteries for cars.
− High rate of self-discharge, so must be charged up every month by some other means when disconnected from system.

Lead–acid with high-antimony plates for traction

− Poor supply since specialized use.
− High cost since designed for regular deep cycles, rapid charging, and vibration while in use.
+ May be good value if obtained second-hand (after checking capacity and self-discharge).
+ High cycle life for deep cycles.
− Requires a control unit with low-voltage disconnect or a state-of-charge meter.
− A lot of acid spray from the vents.
− High consumption of distilled water.
− Maintenance required every month to top up electrolyte and clean terminals.
+ Reliable.

–   High rate of self-discharge, so must be charged up every month by some other means when disconnected from system.

Sealed lead–acid batteries

–   Poor supply.
–   High cost.
–   Requires a charge regulator.
–   Requires a control unit with low-voltage disconnect or a state-of-charge meter.
+   High cycle life for deep cycles.
–   Cannot be supplied dry-charged so risk of sulphation before installation.
+   Portable and can be used with mobile appliances such as a cassette player.
+   Small capacity batteries can be charged up as a service to neighbours who do not have their own solar system.
+   No acid spray from the vents.
+   No consumption of distilled water.
+   No maintenance required.
+   Reliable.
–   Medium rate of self-discharge, so must be charged up every month by some other means when disconnected from system.

Vented nickel–cadmium batteries

–   Poor supply.
–   High cost.
+   No control unit needed to restrict depth of discharge.
+   High cycle life for deep cycles.
+   Can be left discharged so delays in delivery not a problem.
+   Can be charged in parallel.
–   No simple method of measuring state of charge.
+   Low consumption of distilled water.
+   Maintenance required only twice each year to top up electrolyte and clean terminals.
+   Reliable.
+   Low rate of self-discharge.

Sealed nickel–cadmium batteries

–   Poor supply.
–   High cost.
–   Only available in small capacities up to 4 A h.
–   Requires charge regulator or self-regulating modules, and charging is inefficient at low charging currents.

- Cannot be charged in parallel without own series regulator.
+ No control unit needed to restrict depth of discharge.
+ High cycle life for deep cycles.
+ Portable and available in sizes to fit mobile appliances such as torches and radios.
+ Can be charged up as a service to neighbours who do not have their own solar system.
+ No acid spray from the vents.
+ No consumption of distilled water.
+ No maintenance required.
+ Reliable.
- High rate of self-discharge.

☐ Questions

1. Explain the difference between primary and secondary cells and give examples of each type.

2. What is wrong with attempting to recharge a mercury button cell?

3. Name the main parts of one cell in a rechargeable battery.

4. What is the difference between nominal and usable capacity of a rechargeable battery?

5. What does the 'cycle life' of a battery mean?

6. List the main characteristics required of a solar battery.

7. Why are deep cycles bad for some types of lead–acid batteries?

8. Why is antimony used in some types of lead–acid batteries and what problems does it cause?

9. What causes the level of electrolyte to go down in vented batteries and which liquid should be used for topping up?

10. There are three types of charging that involve either an equalization voltage, a float voltage, or a trickle current.
    (a) Explain the differences between them.
    (b) Which type of charging causes the most gassing?

11. What is 'sulphation' of lead–acid batteries? Name two precautions that should be taken to prevent it.

12. Describe two ways of finding the state of charge of a lead–acid battery with vented cells.

13. What do the abbreviations A h, SLI, V_{AL} and V_{CH} stand for?

14. How many nickel–cadmium cells are required to make a nominal 12 V battery?

15. Under what condition of charging can sealed nickel–cadmium cells be continuously over-charged without causing them any damage?

16. Why are nickel–cadmium cells more suitable for solar systems than lead–acid cells?

17. List four reasons why solar batteries are more suitable than car batteries for a solar system.

18. A battery has a nominal capacity of 90 A h and a cycle life of 1200 for a cycle depth of 60 per cent. Calculate the following:
    (a) The usable capacity over one cycle.
    (b) The total usable capacity over the cycle life.

4 Control units

For a solar electric system with rechargeable batteries, protection is required against the following problems:

- ☐ Risk of cable damage and fire from short circuits.
- ☐ Over-discharge of lead–acid batteries.
- ☐ Excessive charging of batteries.

A control unit is used to provide this protection. Other functions are to indicate performance of the whole system and to provide switching for separate circuits.

The order of sections about control units is summarized in Figure 4.1. The first section deals with safety aspects. Users and electricians are perhaps more familiar with mains voltage a.c. than low-voltage d.c. so the safety requirements for solar electricity are compared to the practice in mains electricity. The two sections that follow cover protection of batteries and the last section gives some examples.

When deciding which control unit to use, it is important to bear in mind a number of different aspects. These are cost, reliability of operation and ease of operation for the users. A number of high quality control units are available commercially. However they may be difficult and expensive to obtain, especially when imported. Details of cheaper substitutes are also given in this chapter.

Safety requirements

Safety is an important concern when dealing with any electrical system. The first concern in mains wiring is to avoid giving people electric shocks. For solar systems operating at 12 or 24 V, there is no danger of electrocution because these voltages are low.

Another concern in mains wiring is to avoid starting a fire from a short

75

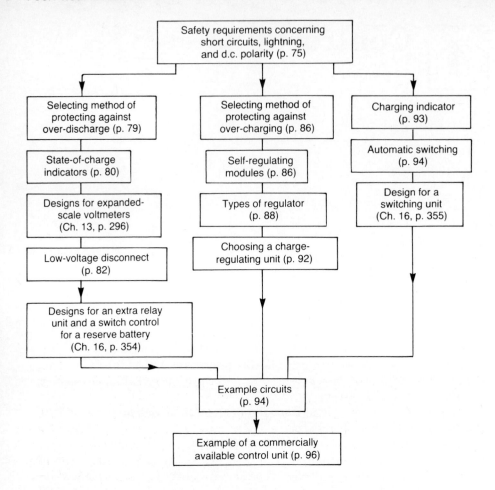

Figure 4.1 Summary of Chapter 4 about control units with cross-references to other chapters (Ch. chapter, p. page references to text).

circuit. This is equally important in solar electrics. Lead–acid batteries are able to supply hundreds of amps into a short circuit. The effect of this is over-heating of the cables, perhaps leading to the insulation catching fire.

Short circuit protection

The most essential part in a control system is a fuse fitted near the battery. This is required to protect the wiring and thus avoid the risk of fire.

The simplest way to fit a fuse is by using an in-line type, as used in vehicles, which does not need to be mounted on a wall (see Figure 4.2(b)). The connections between the module, battery, fuse, and appliances are shown in Figure 4.2(a). A

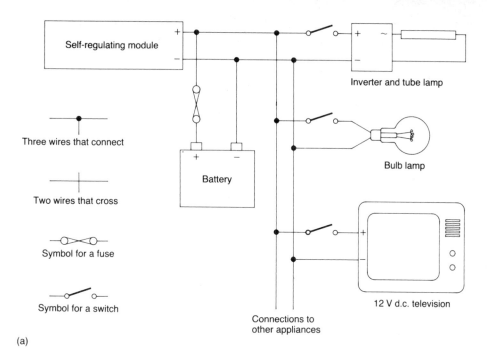

Self-regulating module

Three wires that connect

Two wires that cross

Symbol for a fuse

Symbol for a switch

Inverter and tube lamp

Battery

Bulb lamp

12 V d.c. television

Connections to
other appliances

(a)

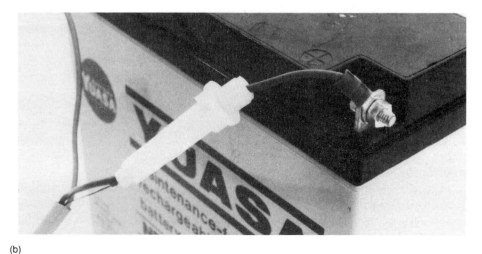

(b)

Figure 4.2 The minimum requirement for control in a solar electric system with
battery storage is a fuse connected close to one of the battery terminals.
(a) Full circuit for connecting module, battery, fuse, and appliances.
(b) Example of an in-line-type fuse, as used in vehicles.

15 A fuse is sufficient for one battery. If a control unit is used, a fuse may be included in it but this is not always the case (see the example in Figure 4.12).

A *miniature circuit-breaker* (MCB) can be used in place of a fuse. This is an automatic switch which opens when the current exceeds a certain value. The protection it provides against excess currents is said to be 'close' because it opens in a shorter time than a fuse of the same rating takes to melt. Resetting an MCB is easier and quicker than replacing a fuse but MCBs are an expensive option.

Residual current circuit-breakers are recommended in mains systems that are earthed to provide better protection for users. They work by breaking the circuit when a short circuit to earth causes a difference in the current between the two conductors. However, they do not protect against excessive currents flowing in the two conductors so are of no use in low-voltage solar systems.

Protecting appliances and modules

Some appliances might require their own protection against an internal short circuit. If a fuse holder is not provided in the appliance, a fuse can be fitted in a fusible plug (see Figure 9.7) or by an in-line fuse in the cable (see Figure 4.2(b)). Note that fuses introduce an additional voltage drop in the distribution system. Extra fuses should only be used for individual appliances if there is a high risk of a short circuit. An example is apparatus used by pupils in a school science laboratory.

A blocking diode (mentioned later in this chapter) provides extra safety for modules. If a short circuit develops in a module, the diode prevents the battery supplying a high current and causing more damage.

Protection against lightning

Lightning strikes can cause damage in solar electric systems. The strike itself is unlikely to hit the module support structure directly, especially if there are tall buildings and trees nearby. However, a close strike induces high voltages in the wiring which can destroy the electronic circuits in control units and inverters for tube lamps.

Circuits should be protected against current surges caused by indirect lightning strikes by using a *metal oxide varistor* (MOV). This is an essential feature for control units used at sites which are known for frequent lightning.

Live conductor

Some precautions against the risk of electrocution in mains systems are to fit single-pole switches and fuses in the live conductor connecting each appliance. When the switch is open or the fuse has blown, the wiring in an appliance is at the voltage of the neutral, which is not dangerous. The need for earthing is to blow a fuse when a fault makes the metal container or other exposed metal parts become live.

'Live' as an electrical term means a high voltage relative to the earth on which people stand. In a.c., the live conductor rapidly changes back and forth between positive and negative as the current alternates. In d.c., the two conductors are called positive and negative. At the low voltage of most solar systems (below 50 V), there is no danger to a person who touches either conductor, so neither the positive nor the negative conductors can be called live.

High voltages are possible during installation if several batteries or modules are connected in series by mistake. Once a system is operating correctly at 24 V or below, there is no risk of electrocution. For systems designed for a voltage higher than 24 V, full precautions against electrocution should be taken, as for mains voltage.

Cables, switches, and other fittings for mains systems are often used for solar systems. When using these parts, the usual practice is to connect the positive conductor to terminals marked 'L' using wires with red or brown insulation. Following the practice in mains wiring, single-pole switches and fuses are put in the positive conductor. Also, negative wires are joined together in the same way that the neutrals are all connected at the neutral bar of a mains fuse box. The negative can even be connected to an earth at one point but this is not essential unless a power inverter is used.

Electricians wiring a solar system sometimes use the word 'live,' 'line,' or 'phase' in place of 'positive' but this terminology is not recommended. The terminals of modules, batteries, and d.c. appliances are always marked with '+' and '−' signs, not 'L'. Parts from auto-spares' suppliers, such as car radios, can be used in solar systems. They are sometimes marked as being for use with either negative- or positive-earthed wiring systems which can cause confusion for electricians using the word 'live'.

Importance of correct polarity

Even though neither the positive nor the negative is as dangerous as a high-voltage live conductor, *polarity* of wiring should always be correct when wiring a solar system. This means that the positive is connected to red insulated wires, the negative is connected to terminals marked 'N,' and so on.

If the polarity is reversed (positive and negative connected the wrong way around), some d.c. appliances will not work, others will be damaged, and the solar modules will not charge the batteries.

Protecting against over-discharge of lead–acid batteries

Most batteries used in small- and medium-size solar systems are the lead–acid type because of availability and reasonable cost. To obtain the best life from them, it is essential to avoid over-discharge. An indicator for state of charge informs users when the batteries are low and should not be used any further. A

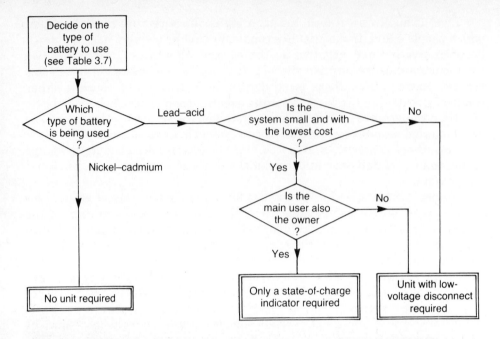

Figure 4.3 Summary of steps for selecting a method of protecting batteries from over-discharge:
☐ input of information
◇ decisions
▣ recommendations

more reliable approach requiring less involvement by the users is to use a control unit which automatically disconnects the appliances.

Over-discharge is not a problem for nickel–cadmium batteries which can be totally discharged and left discharged with no ill effects. If nickel–cadmium cells are available, they should be seriously considered as an alternative to lead–acid batteries because of their reliability. Although they are more expensive, all their charge is available for use which offsets part of the high cost (see Chapter 8 on sizing battery capacity).

The choice of solutions to over-discharge of batteries is summarized in Figure 4.3.

State of charge indicators for lead–acid batteries

The most convenient way to monitor the state of charge of a lead–acid battery is by measuring the battery voltage accurately. (This is also the only way for sealed

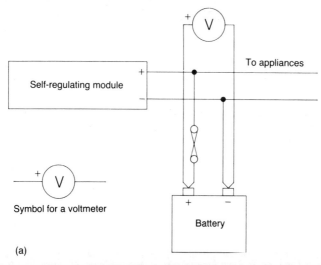

(a)

(b)

Figure 4.4 Monitoring the state of charge of lead–acid batteries by measuring voltage.
(a) Circuit for connecting a voltmeter. Separate wires connect to the battery terminals to avoid the voltage drop along the main current-carrying wires.
(b) Examples of state-of-charge meters: **1** four-figure digital voltmeter; **2** control unit with three charge indicator LEDs showing battery states of 'FULL,' 'OK,' or 'LOW'; **3** expanded-scale voltmeter.

batteries.) A general circuit for connecting a meter is shown in Figure 4.4(a) and three different instruments for indicating battery voltage are shown in Figure 4.4(b).

The digital voltmeter with a four-digit display measures to an accuracy of 0.01 V and reading the measurement is straightforward. Some control units have a light that comes on to show when the voltage is low. The example shown in the figure has three lights indicating three conditions of the battery. An expanded-scale voltmeter is accurate over the voltages of interest around 12 V.

Of the three types shown, the expanded-scale voltmeter can be made from locally available parts without much difficulty, and full details are given in Chapter 13. By painting a coloured band over the left end of the scale, the meter looks like a fuel gauge with the needle clearly indicating whether the state of charge is OK or low.

The main connections to the battery carry the charging current during the day and the appliance current at night. When the current flowing in either direction is high, or where the wires are more than 2 m (6 ft) long, there is a small voltage drop along them. Since this voltage would affect the measurement of battery voltage, the expanded-scale voltmeter has its own wires connected directly to the line of batteries. On a control unit, these wires are connected to terminals marked *battery sense* because they are only for sensing a voltage, not for carrying high currents.

Low-voltage disconnect

In a home system, the owner can appreciate that over-discharging the battery will result in having to replace it within two years rather than after three or more years. Therefore the owner as the main user will pay careful attention to the voltmeter indicating the state of charge. When the state of charge becomes very low, appliances are switched off to avoid damaging the battery.

A more reliable method of protecting against over-discharge is to use a control unit which automatically disconnects the appliances when the state of charge is too low. This feature is known as a *low-voltage disconnect* since it works by disconnecting the appliance circuits when a low state of charge makes the battery voltage low. A control unit with this feature is particularly recommended for small institutions where the users are not really involved in the day-to-day operation of the solar system.

There are two parts to a low-voltage disconnect mechanism, as shown in Figure 4.5. One part is a small electronic circuit which measures or 'senses' the voltage across the wires from the battery. The other part is an electrically operated switch called a *relay* (see Chapter 12 for full details about relays). When the battery voltage falls below a certain level, the voltage-sensing circuit activates the relay to disconnect the appliance circuits.

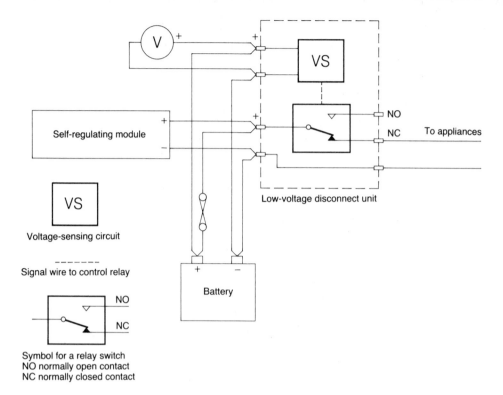

Figure 4.5 Circuit for connecting a control unit with low-voltage disconnect. A voltmeter is included to indicate the state of charge. Where the wiring between the battery and the control unit is less than 2 m (6 ft) long, separate wires are not needed to connect the VS terminals directly to the battery terminals.

Voltage setting of disconnect

The disconnect voltage is usually set at 11.5 V for deep cycle and solar batteries. A higher voltage should be used for other types of lead–acid battery and recommended values are listed in Table 11.2. On some units, the disconnect voltage can be adjusted when the unit is installed. After setting the disconnect voltage correctly, the place where the adjustment is done should be sealed over in some way to prevent unqualified people readjusting it out of curiosity.

It should be noted that the voltage of a lead–acid battery is not an exact measure of the state of charge but varies under the following conditions. At one state of charge, the voltage becomes less when a current is drawn, when the temperature rises, and immediately after the cells are topped up. Therefore disconnection will occur over a range of states of charge depending on the current to the appliances, temperature, and condition of the battery. Also, poor connections to the battery terminals will give a low reading, perhaps causing unnecessary disconnection. It is recommended that the specific gravity of the electrolyte in vented cells is measured occasionally as a double-check of the state of charge.

Voltage compensation for current and temperature

In some units with a low-voltage disconnect feature, there is compensation for the variations in the battery voltage caused by appliance current. When the current is high, disconnection takes place at a lower voltage which corresponds to the same state of charge of the battery. However, this compensation is not very accurate because the drop in voltage of a battery is not related to appliance current in a simple way. Also the compensation factor should be adjusted according to the type and capacity of battery being used, but this adjustment is not available.

In conditions where the variation in battery temperature is 10 °C (18 °F) or more, a controller with the feature of temperature compensation in the voltage-sensing circuit should be used. A temperature sensor is either built into the back of the control unit itself or connected to the control unit by a pair of wires so that the sensor can be attached to the side of the battery. The action of the sensor adjusts the voltage settings for disconnection. The changes required are given in Table 3.2 for lead–acid cells and batteries.

Current rating of switch contacts

When selecting a low-voltage disconnect unit, the current rating of the switch contacts must be higher than the total appliance current that is expected. Allowance should be included for the surge currents as motors start. If extra appliances are added, it is not necessary to get another complete unit. Only another relay is needed and the coil for this new relay is run like one of the appliances from the existing relay. A circuit for adding another relay is given in Chapter 16.

Types of reconnect

Once disconnection has happened, reconnection of the appliance circuits takes place under different conditions which vary with the type of control unit.

Disconnection happens when the battery needs charging, so some units reconnect when the battery voltage reaches about 13.5 V. This will be the following day as soon as the module is supplying a charging current. A more extreme measure is for the unit to reconnect at 15 V. This corresponds to the battery reaching full charge, so it could take several days before power is available again.

These voltage settings for reconnection could be very inconvenient to users in systems that provide lighting, for instance. An arrangement that avoids the sudden loss of all power is for the relay to disconnect only the less important appliances. The circuits for a few essential appliances, such as security lighting, are wired to bypass the relay so that they remain on for the rest of the evening. To use this arrangement, it is necessary for the electrical requirement of the essential appliances to be much less than the total electrical requirement.

Other types of units offer manual reconnection. Reconnection is possible with these units after switching off some of the appliances. This is because a reduced appliance current does not lower the battery voltage by so much, so the battery voltage will be above the disconnect level. The end result of using manual reconnection is much the same as dividing the circuits into essential and non-essential, with the essential ones bypassing the relay.

Manual override of disconnect

On some units, there is a switch for overriding the low-voltage disconnect feature. The problem with having such a switch is that some users are tempted to leave the switch in the override position all the time. Used in this way, there is little point in having a disconnect feature which is automatic. An expanded-scale voltmeter is a cheaper alternative which also requires users to act responsibly in reducing the number of appliances in use when the battery is at a low state of charge.

Generator or reserve battery

Manufacturers of control units suggest that instead of disconnecting appliances, the relay can automatically start a small generator which charges the battery (using the 'normally open' connection shown in Figure 4.5). This is obviously the ideal solution for protecting the battery. However, it is only feasible in applications where the solar system is used for reducing fuel cost rather than completely replacing a generator.

The relay could automatically connect a reserve battery that is kept on standby at full charge. If the switch-over to the reserve battery is automatic, there is no motivation for users to deal with the situation or even realize that the switch has happened. To overcome this problem while keeping the convenience of a reserve battery, a unit with a key-operated switch is described in Chapter 16. By using a key, control of whether the reserve battery is switched in is restricted to responsible users at an installation.

State of relay coil for connection

There are two ways that the relay coil is operated in control units with low-voltage disconnect. One way is that the appliances are connected to the normally closed (NC) contacts so that disconnection involves energizing (supplying a current to) the coil to open these contacts. Although the appliances are disconnected, the coil is now acting as a small load and drawing current, as much as 0.1 A for some relays.

The other way is to have the appliance circuits on the normally open (NO) contacts so that the relay must be energized all the time to keep the appliances connected. The coil current is a continuous small drain on the battery, but this way has the advantage of being fail-safe. This is because the connections to the relay coil must be correct initially for appliances to be on, and any failure in the coil supply will leave the appliances off rather than on. Also when the battery is low, causing the appliances to be disconnected, there is no waste of charge through the relay coil.

It is possible to avoid the current drain in either condition by using a *latching relay*. This only requires current when switching from one state to the other. However, no commercially supplied units appear to use a latching relay for the disconnect feature.

Regulating the charging voltage

Charging of rechargeable batteries needs to be regulated in some way to avoid damage to the batteries. Methods of providing regulation are summarized in Figure 4.6.

Self-regulating modules

The simplest type of control is possible with solar cell modules that are self-regulating for lead–acid batteries. Refer to Table 2.1 for a list of modules that are self-regulating under various conditions. The module is directly connected to a lead–acid battery through a fuse, as shown in Figures 4.2, 4.4, and 4.5. When the battery reaches full charge, the charging current is automatically reduced to a trickle.

To ensure that the over-charging trickle current does not damage the battery, the minimum battery capacity is recommended as 40 A h for each amp of current capacity (under STC). For example, a 22 W module with thirty cells has a current at load of 1.65 A under STC. Therefore the minimum capacity of battery with which it can be used is 66 A h (from 40 multiplied by 1.65).

Dark current leakage

A point to note about direct connection of a battery to a module is that current can leak back through the module at night. For a module with a current output specification under STC of 1 A, the leakage or dark current is about 0.015 A. The

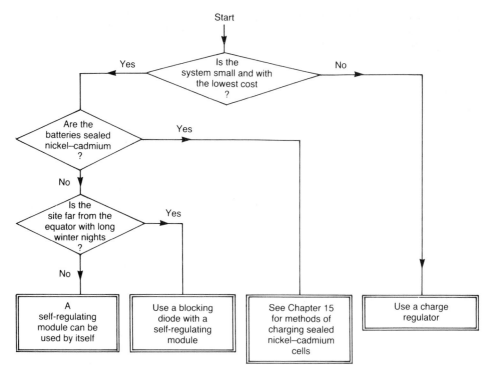

Figure 4.6 Summary of steps for selecting a method to regulate battery charging:
◇ decisions
▢ recommendations

total loss of electricity by dark current leakage through a number of modules with other current specifications can be calculated from the following formula:

$$
\boxed{\begin{array}{c}\text{Number of}\\\text{modules}\\\text{in array}\end{array}} \times \boxed{\begin{array}{c}\text{Current output}\\\text{of each module}\\\text{under STC}\\\text{(A)}\end{array}} \times \boxed{\left(\dfrac{0.18}{\dfrac{\text{VA}}{\text{A}}}\right)} \times \boxed{\begin{array}{c}\text{Length of}\\\text{night}\\\text{(hours)}\end{array}} = \boxed{\begin{array}{c}\text{Total loss of}\\\text{electricity}\\\text{by dark current}\\\text{(W h per day)}\end{array}} \quad \textbf{(4.1)}
$$

The answer is in units of W h per day so that it can be directly compared to the requirement for electricity by the appliances, as calculated in Chapter 8 (see Table 8.3).

Using the 22 W module as an example again, the loss of electricity can be calculated for twelve hours of darkness using this formula:

$$1 \times 1.65 \times 0.18 \times 12 = 3.6 \text{ W h per day at 12 V}$$

A typical amount of electricity generated from a 22 W module over one day is 80 W h per day at 12 V. Therefore the loss of charge at night is about 4 per cent of the amount generated during the day. This amount of loss is not too high. However, the dark current loss may be unacceptable during winter for countries away from the equator. Days are shorter so less charge is generated, and nights are longer so more charge is lost.

To prevent this leakage, the dark current can be blocked from flowing by a diode which is called a *blocking diode* when used this way (see Figure 4.7(a)). To compensate for the voltage drop across a silicon diode when a charging current is flowing, two extra cells are required in the module. For a Schottky or germanium diode, only one extra cell is required, although they should be used only with 12 V systems. (This is because they do not have a high enough breakdown voltage in reverse bias for use in systems operating at 24 V or higher.) Suitable modules are listed in Table 2.1.

Some modules already have a blocking diode in their junction box which simplifies the connections. However, the diode in the box may be a bypass one which serves a different purpose. The identity of the diode should be checked with the instructions that come with the module to see whether a separate blocking diode is needed.

Diodes can also be used to convert a module with more cells than are needed for self-regulation into a self-regulating module. This may be necessary as a temporary solution when a regulator is not yet available. It involves using more than one blocking diode to cancel the voltage from the additional cells. Figure 4.7(b) shows the arrangement for a module of thirty-six cells used as a self-regulating module of thirty cells.

Charge regulators

Two disadvantages of self-regulating modules are that the batteries are not charged as quickly as possible and the charging current is low in cloudy weather. Modules with more cells produce a higher voltage. This gives them the advantage that they have sufficient voltage to supply their maximum current at all states of charge of the batteries.

On approaching full charge, the voltage at the battery terminals rises. If it is allowed to go above about 15 V, gassing becomes excessive. In batteries with vented cells, this results in damage to the plates, loss of water from the electrolyte, and acid spray or mist leaving the vents. In sealed cells, excessive gassing causes a build-up of gas pressure and over-heating. Also appliances used during charging may be damaged by a voltage higher than 15 V. To limit the voltage, there is a variety of charge regulators available for use with solar modules.

For nickel–cadmium cells, the vented type can be charged in the same way as for lead–acid batteries. Different voltage settings are required in the regulator, so check with the supplier first. The charging of sealed cells is different

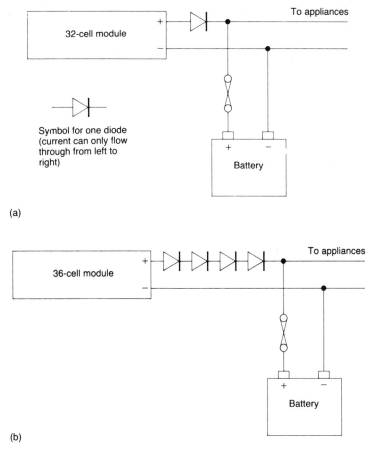

Figure 4.7 Preventing dark current leakage of electricity when a self-regulating module is directly connected to a battery.
(a) One blocking diode.
(b) Use of four blocking diodes to convert a module with thirty-six cells to one with thirty-two cells that is self-regulating with just one blocking diode. This system could be used while waiting for a regulating control unit to be delivered or repaired.

because they are limited to a maximum charging current. Methods of charging these cells are given in Chapter 15.

Over-voltage shunt for charge regulation

An over-voltage shunt is a regulator that prevents the battery voltage going above 15 V. The regulating part contains a high-power transistor as a shunt which means that the transistor is connected in parallel with the battery, as shown in Figure 4.8. (Transistors are described in detail in Chapter 12.)

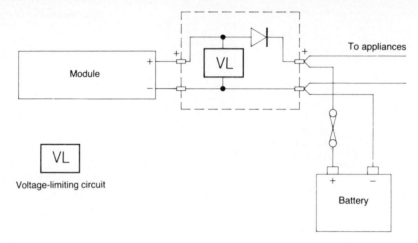

Figure 4.8   Charge regulation using an over-voltage shunt to limit the battery voltage. When the voltage across the battery reaches a certain value, usually set at 15 V, the voltage-limiting circuit shunts sufficient current to prevent the voltage going any higher.

While the battery voltage is below 15 V, the shunt transistor is off and all the current from the module goes to charging the battery. When the voltage reaches 15 V, the regulator starts to shunt just enough current in parallel to the battery to stop the voltage going any higher. Shunt regulators produce a lot of heat so should be mounted where air can flow over them freely to avoid over-heating.

One disadvantage of this type of regulation is that maintaining 15 V still causes some unnecessary gassing. Also lead–acid batteries only reach their fullest charge when the final stage of charging involves reducing or pulsing the current on and off repeatedly.

Pulsing regulators

Two types of pulsing regulator are shown in Figure 4.9. Both have small electronic circuits for monitoring the voltage of the battery, like the one for the low-voltage disconnect in Figure 4.5. This circuit controls a switch for turning the charging current on and off.

One type of pulsing regulator uses a shunt transistor as a solid-state switch before the blocking diode (see Figure 4.9(a)). When the battery voltage reaches 15 V, the shunt switch is closed, shorting the module output completely so there is no charging current to the battery. This does not damage the module at all and the blocking diode prevents the battery losing any charge. While the module output is shorted, the battery voltage slowly falls. On reaching about 13 V, the shunt switch is opened allowing the voltage of the module to rise so that a charging current can flow through the diode again. When the switch goes on and

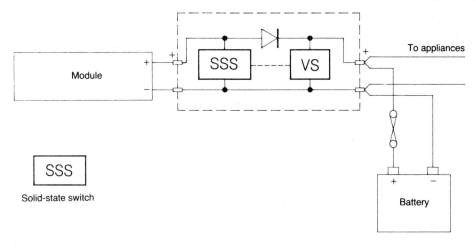

(a)

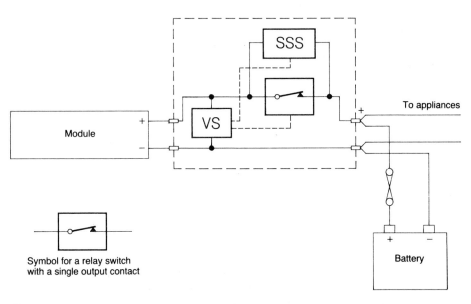

(b)

Figure 4.9 Two types of pulsing regulator.
(a) When the battery voltage reaches about 15 V, the shunt switch is closed by the VS circuit to stop charging.
(b) When the battery voltage reaches about 15 V, the series switches of a relay and a solid state switch are opened by the VS (voltage-sensing) circuit to stop charging.

off repeatedly, the battery is approaching full charge and current is going to the battery only in short pulses.

Unlike the over-voltage shunt, the solid-state switch produces only a small amount of heat. Even though the full module current is going through the switch while shorting the module, the voltage drop across the switch is only about 1 V.

Another type of pulsing regulator has a relay switch in series with the battery which is opened when the battery voltage reaches 15 V (Figure 4.9(b)). Since the measuring circuit is now disconnected from the battery, it cannot tell when the battery voltage has fallen to 13 V. To overcome this problem, the measuring circuit is designed to wait for about fifteen minutes after opening the switch. Then the switch is closed and remains closed until the voltage reaches 15 V again. The switch is also opened occasionally to measure the voltage of the module alone. When the module voltage is low, it is night-time and the switch is left open until the voltage rises, showing that the new day has started.

The control unit shown in Figure 4.9(b) has a solid-state switch in parallel with the relay switch. The solid-state switch is opened just after the relay is opened and closed just before the relay is closed. This reduces the voltage across the relay contacts at the times when they open or close to prevent sparking. Sparking damages the surface of the contacts so the life of the relay is extended by stopping such sparking.

One advantage of a regulator with a series relay is that a blocking diode is not required. Compared to a system with a diode, a cheaper module with two cells less can be used.

Dual-voltage regulators

Two-step or dual-voltage regulators control charging in two stages. As shown in Figure 4.10, there is a relay switch connecting the module directly to the battery. When the battery voltage reaches 15 V, the voltage-sensing circuit opens the switch. The battery is now maintained at a float voltage of about 13.5 V by a series regulator so that a low-charging current flows. Compared to the parallel arrangement in Figure 4.8, the voltage drop across a series regulator is small so less heat is produced.

Unlike the pulsing regulators, the relay switch in a dual-voltage regulator stays open for the rest of the day. This gives the option of using 'surplus' current from the module to charge a reserve battery or to run a non-essential appliance such as a cooling fan. Surplus current is diverted through the relay contact that is closed when the battery is on float charge.

Choosing a regulator

In comparing these regulators, the ones without a relay are preferred for reliability. The mechanism and switch contacts of a relay are more likely to fail than the transistor of a solid-state switch which has no moving parts. On the

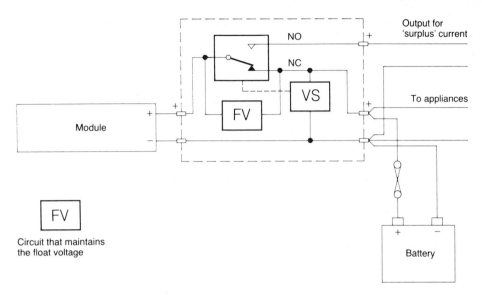

Figure 4.10 Two-step or dual-voltage regulator. The relay is switched by the VS (voltage-sensing) circuit putting the battery on float charge when the battery voltage reaches about 15 V. The normally open (NO) connection of the relay can be used to charge a reserve battery or run a cooling fan.

other hand, a relay avoids the need for a blocking diode with its voltage drop so a cheaper module with two cells less can be used.

Pulsing and dual-voltage regulators result in higher battery charging and longer battery life than the over-voltage shunt type. However, the decision on which to use is most likely to be determined by availability and price.

Regulators all have a limit on the current they can handle. When using an array of modules, the maximum possible current from the modules should not exceed the current rating of the regulator. (For shunt regulators, the short circuit current specifications apply.) If the maximum output of the array is too high, a regulator with a higher rating should be used. Alternatively the array can be subdivided with a separate regulator for each group of modules.

Try to use a regulator that is protected against reverse polarity of its connections and current surges caused by lightning.

Other features on control units

Charging indicator

It is helpful and reassuring to have some indication that the module is charging the battery during the day.

A quick and simple way to check is by touching the blocking diode (if it is accessible) which will feel hot when carrying a current. Controllers with a built-in blocking diode have a red light-emitting diode (a description of light-emitting diodes (LEDs) is given in Chapter 12) which goes on when the blocking diode is conducting. Pulsed and dual-voltage charge regulators also have a red LED to indicate when they are in charge mode. On an expanded-scale voltmeter, a voltage of 12.5 V and above shows charging.

For more information about charging conditions, an ammeter can be fitted in series between the module and the battery. This is worth while in a large solar system where there are technical staff who can use the ammeter reading to check the charging performance. Likewise an ammeter is useful on the appliance side, particularly when deciding how to ration the charge in cloudy weather.

Automatic switching

If use of the lighting circuits is to be automated, they can be switched on automatically at dusk. This is done by an electronic circuit which uses the modules as a light meter, and is activated when the voltage of the modules falls below about 10 V. To turn the circuits off automatically at the end of the evening, an electronic clock or a timing circuit is needed. A few controllers are available with this feature.

Example circuits and control unit

Simple system

A simple control system is shown in Figure 4.11(a) which fulfils the requirements for safe and efficient operation of a solar electric system.

The simple approach to its design is recommended for several reasons. The simpler a control system, the easier it is to understand, so minimizing confusion and the risk of mistakes during installation. The expanded-scale voltmeter and control unit can both be made from commonly available materials (see Chapters 13 and 16). This reduces dependence on parts that cannot be repaired locally or replaced quickly when problems occur. It also keeps the costs down.

The extra control unit divides the appliances into separate circuits, with each circuit having its own switch and fuse. By using separate fuses, a short circuit only blows the fuse for one appliance circuit and the other circuits remain operational.

The separate switching of circuits helps in efficient use of the stored charge. For example, the socket circuit can be left on all the time, while the lighting circuit is only on during the evening when lighting is needed. The main switch for the lighting circuit is left off at other times. This avoids wasting charge if

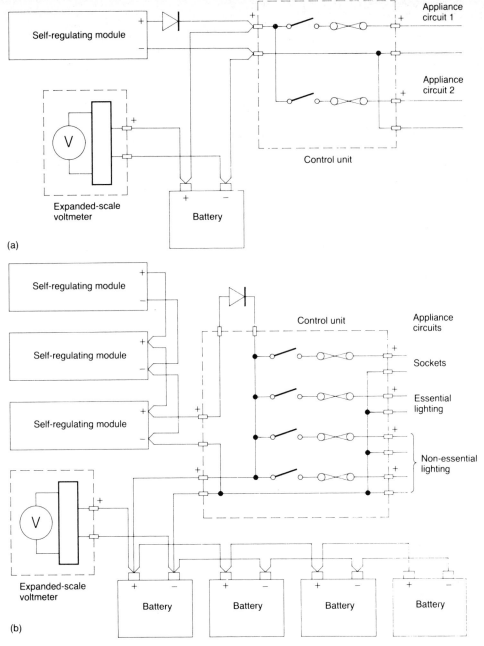

Figure 4.11 Examples of simple control systems using a blocking diode and modules that are self-regulating. The appliances are divided between separate circuits. (A design for this type of control unit is given in Chapter 16.)

(a) System suitable for a home with one module, one battery, and two fused circuits for the appliances.

(b) System suitable for a medium-size system in an institution such as a school or hospital.

(a)

Figure 4.12   Example of a commercially available control unit. The specification is charge regulation for a maximum of 12 A and low-voltage disconnect for a maximum of 10 A. It features: protection against lightning damage using a metal oxide varistor; an LED to indicate charging; a pulsing type of charge regulator; a blocking diode; a low-voltage disconnect.
(a)   Front view of unit mounted on a wall.

individual light switches are turned on by mistake during the day or left on over-night.

The simple system of Figure 4.11(a) can be extended to a larger system with more than one module and battery as shown in Figure 4.11(b). Parallel connections are made between the three modules (forming an 'array') and in the group of four batteries. The appliances are divided between four circuits with separate switches and fuses for each circuit.

In institutions, the essential and non-essential appliances can be put on separate circuits so that during cloudy weather when the batteries are low, non-essential appliances can be left off or switched on for only a short time.

Commercially available control unit

Figure 4.12 shows an example of a controller that combines several features into one unit. It has lightning protection, a charging LED, charge regulation, a blocking diode, and low-voltage disconnect. The circuit itself is fully encapsulated for protection from moisture and mechanical damage.

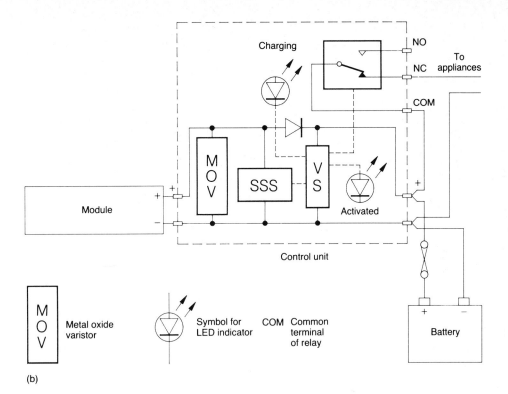

(b)

Figure 4.12
(b) Schematic circuit showing the principle of operation and external connections. (**SSS** solid-state switch.)

One feature not included in this particular unit, though, is a fuse. This has to be fitted separately in the connection to the battery (see Figure 4.2).

☐ *Questions*

1. Why are control units required in solar electric systems?

2. What does 'reverse polarity' mean and why might it be a problem?

3. What is a 'blocking diode' and what is it used for?

4. Describe three instruments that can be used in a control system for showing the user when a lead–acid battery is at a low state of charge.

5. What sort of control system would you choose in a small solar system for a home to keep the cost down?

6. How could the system in your answer to Question 5 be improved to protect the battery from deep discharges where the users have little understanding of electricity?

7. Under what circumstances are battery-sense wires recommended?

8. In which systems is a charge regulator needed?

9. What is the difference between a relay and a solid-state switch, and which is the most reliable?

10. What is the most important part required in a control system to ensure safe operation?

5 | Distribution at low voltage

Cables distribute electricity from the modules and batteries to each of the appliances in a solar electric system. There is a drop in voltage along all cables carrying a current because the wires in a cable have a small resistance. In a solar system, this voltage drop must be kept below a certain limit otherwise the appliances will not work properly.

In the design of the distribution system, the size of each cable is chosen according to the acceptable voltage drop. The cable cost is also important and the cables used should only be as large as required for a low voltage drop in order to keep the total cost down. Larger cables are an unnecessary expense.

Most of this chapter is about selection of cables, and the various sections are summarized in Figure 5.1. In medium- and large-size systems, the cost of cables can often be reduced by operating at a higher voltage of 24 V d.c. Then for each circuit within a system, the recommended size of cable can be found using tables. For cable sizes outside the range of the tables, a more general formula method is also given.

The same cables available for mains systems can be used for solar electricity. Much thicker cables are generally needed, though, because of the higher currents and lower acceptable voltage drop.

Cable sizes

Table 5.1 lists the standard sizes of cables that are usually available and a few examples are shown in Figure 5.2.

Some of the smaller sizes are a single wire while most sizes are available as *stranded* with seven wires. Stranded cable can be bent during installation but is intended to be fixed in one position as permanent wiring. No earth wires are needed so the cable ordered should be 'twin-flat without earth'. If three-core cable must be used, the earth wire can be connected as one of the negative conductors.

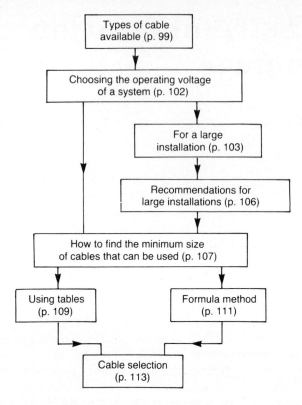

Figure 5.1   Summary of Chapter 5 about selecting the size of cables for the distribution system (p. page references to text).

Flexible cord or *flex* connects an appliance or lamp to the fixed wiring of a circuit at an outlet point. The conductors in flex consist of many fine strands of wire twisted together which allows the whole cable to be flexible.

The size of cable is given by the total cross-sectional area of all the strands in each conductor. The standard units for this are square millimetres (mm^2), while American wire gauge (AWG) is still used on equipment from the United States (see Table 5.1).

Current rating of cables

The third column of Table 5.1 gives the maximum current that each size of cable can carry without becoming too hot. The main fuse must not be more than this rating since the fuse should blow well before the insulation on the cable melts.

Books on electrical installation work (see Appendix F) give full details on how these current ratings can be corrected for other factors. These factors are

Table 5.1 *Standard sizes of cables.*

Cable size		Current rating (A)
Cross-sectional area (mm²)	Wire gauge (AWG or SWG)[1]	
1.0	18	10
1.5	16	15
2.5	14	20
4.0	12	30
6.0	10	35
10.0	8	50
16.0	6	70
25.0	4	90

[1]AWG stands for American wire gauge and SWG stands for standard wire gauge.

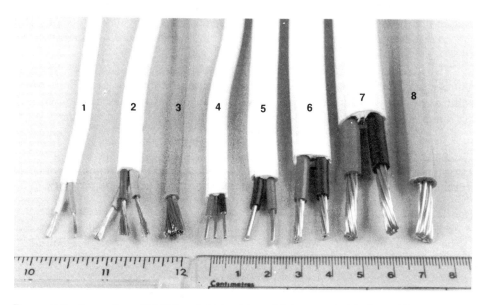

Figure 5.2 Examples of PVC-insulated cables which are suitable for solar electric installations. Cable sizes: **1** 0.5 mm²; **2** 1.25 mm²; **3** 6 mm²; **4** 1.0 mm²; **5** 2.5 mm²; **6** 6 mm²; **7** 10 mm²; **8** 16 mm². 1–3 are flexible cord or 'flex', 4–8 are cables which should be fixed in position when installed.

the temperature of the surroundings, current protection by fuse (coarse) or miniature circuit breaker (close), type of insulation, number of cables bundled together, and routeing through conduit or clipped to an open surface. However, for solar installations, the cables are normally used well below their current rating so these corrections are unlikely to be necessary.

Choice of operating voltage

Compared to mains systems, thicker cables are required for distribution at low voltage because currents are higher and the voltage drop along the cable must be lower. This is best explained by an example.

Suppose a circuit is required for six 40 W lamps and the cable length from the supply to the last lamp is 25 m. The minimum size of cable can be chosen to give a certain voltage drop when all the lamps are on. In this example, a voltage drop of 10 per cent is used and Table 5.2 lists the details for four operating voltages. The mains voltages are 240 and 110 V, while 24 and 12 V are common in solar systems. As the operating voltage decreases down the table, the current gets larger and the acceptable voltage drop gets less. The effect of both these changes is that very thick cables are needed when operating at a low voltage.

Most small solar systems operate at 12 V. For medium- and large-size systems, the total cable cost is much higher because of higher currents and longer distances. The cable cost can be reduced by operating at 24 V because the cables can be quarter the size compared to those required when operating at 12 V.

The standard operating voltage of 12 V originates from the batteries used for cars, so it is interesting to compare lorries and buses to cars. Since these vehicles are larger than cars, the starter motor and other electrical appliances are more powerful and further from the battery. To avoid using very thick

Table 5.2 *Example to show the dependence of cable size on system voltage for the same power requirement. In this example, the cable serves six 40 W lamps with 25 m from the supply to the last lamp. The maximum acceptable voltage drop along the cable is taken as 10 per cent.*

System voltage (V)	Current for six 40 W lamps (A)	Values of 10% voltage drop along cable (V)	Minimum size of cable required (mm²)
240	1.0	24	0.04
110	2.2	11	0.2
24	10	2.4	4
12	20	1.2	17

cables, these vehicles operate at 24 V d.c. The supply is either from two 12 V batteries connected in series or from a single 24 V battery containing twelve lead-acid cells. All the motors and bulbs are made for operation at 24 V and the dynamo charges at this voltage.

Large solar systems operate at 24 V for the same reasons. Bulbs and other appliances from large vehicles are a good source of parts for systems operating at 24 V.

Options for large installations

When planning the distribution part of a large installation, there are three options that should be considered:

1. Use a centralized configuration operating at 12 V d.c.
2. Use a centralized configuration operating at 24 V d.c.
3. Divide the installation into several small independent systems, each operating at 12 V d.c.

Cost comparison

The first stage of choosing between these three options is to calculate the total cost of cables for each option. The procedure for doing this is summarized in Figure 5.3 and uses Table 5.3.

Since the cable cost depends so much on cable length, it is important to site the batteries near the centre of the installation. This minimizes the total length of all the cables leading to each place.

Comparing the two centralized configurations, the total cost of cables for 24 V operation should be ⅓–¼ of the cost for 12 V operation. This is because quarter the amount of conductor is needed at double the voltage (compare cable sizes for 12 V and 24 V in Table 5.2).

The next stage is to add the cost of the other parts of the solar system to the total cost of the cables. Chapter 7 gives suggestions for a variety of suppliers. Note that appliances and control units may have different prices for the versions that operate at 12 or 24 V.

Comparing the centralized configurations operating at different voltages, differences between the total costs are due to the following reasons.

☐ Appliances and control units for 24 V are made in smaller quantities than the 12 V versions so are more expensive. This also means they are less likely to be held in stock by suppliers.
☐ The lower currents at 24 V mean that control units and switches with low current ratings can be used which may reduce their cost.
☐ Some d.c. appliances, such as televisions, are only available for 12 V. These need a voltage adaptor for use in a 24 V system.

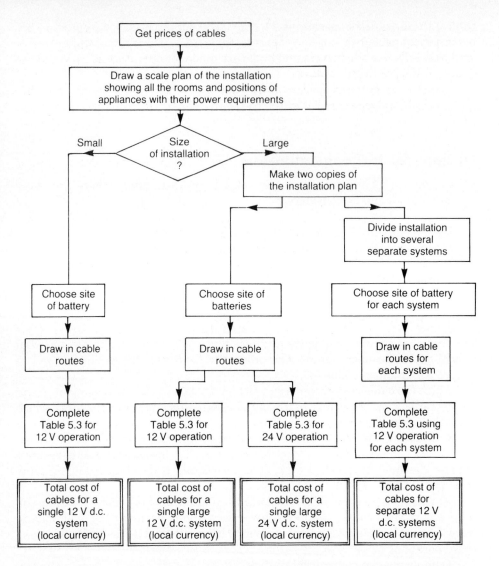

Figure 5.3 Procedure for comparing the cable cost of different options for a medium-size installation that is spread out. The options are operating at either 12 or 24 V and for arranging the installation as either several separate systems or a single centralized system:

☐ steps involved
◇ decision
◫ results at the end with units in brackets

Table 5.3 *Table for calculating the total cost of cables required in a system. 'Maximum current' values are calculated using Formula (5.2). See Figures 5.4 and 5.5 for methods of finding the 'Minimum cable size'. 'Cable requirements' are for sizes of cable that are commonly available and easy to handle for installation.*

Name or type of circuit	Appliances		Length of cable to last appliance in circuit (m)	Minimum cable size (mm^2)	Cable requirements (m)		
	Total power (W)	Maximum current (A)	Horizontal + Vertical = Total		$2.5\,mm^2$	$4\,mm^2$	$6\,mm^2$

Total requirement for each size of cable (m):

Unit price for each size of cable:

Cost for each size of cable:

Total cost of cables:

Comparing the centralized configurations to the configuration of small independent systems, differences between the total costs are due to the following reasons:

☐ For a centralized system, only one or two control units and module supports are needed. Separate systems, on the other hand, each need their own control unit and module support stand.
☐ In separate systems, there is over-capacity because the requirements for each separate system must be met by a whole number of modules and batteries.
☐ Separate systems use shorter lengths and smaller sizes of cables.

Advantages of one centralized system

The approach of separate systems may turn out to have the lowest total cost. However, centralized systems have a number of advantages:

1. Only one secure place is needed for the batteries and control unit.
2. Maintenance of the batteries and modules is easier, quicker, and perhaps more likely to be done properly with them all in one place.
3. During cloudy weather, the charge stored in all the batteries can be conserved by switching on fewer circuits.
4. The generating and storage capacity of the system can be increased gradually by adding extra modules and batteries one by one over a few years. As the capacity increases, more appliances can be used and left on for longer during cloudy weather.
5. A faulty battery can be removed from a centralized system with only a small reduction in the total storage capacity. One small system is put out of action completely when its battery is removed.

It is important that reliable batteries are used in the battery bank of a large system. Ordinary car batteries, for instance, should not be used. They are unreliable for deep cycle operation and a short in one battery will discharge the whole battery bank.

Recommendations for large installations

For large installations, centralized solar systems have important advantages over separate small systems. A centralized system is easier to maintain and makes better use of module and battery capacities. The cost of the system can be spread out over a few years by starting at a medium size and expanding gradually. However, it is essential to use good-quality batteries. These are necessary to minimize the risk of a fault in one battery affecting all the others.

If appliances and control units for 24 V are difficult to get, a centralized system should be operated at 12 V. Since this might be the most expensive approach, the position of the batteries must be chosen carefully to minimize the total length and cost of the cables.

If the buildings in an installation are widely spaced, a single centralized solar system may not be practical and small separate systems should be considered.

Higher voltages

By operating the system at 48 V, even smaller cables can be used over long distances to reduce the cable costs. However, 48 V appliances and control units are even less common than 24 V versions.

Also the total number of modules and batteries must each be a multiple of four. For example, if six modules are estimated to be sufficient for a system, eight modules must be bought in order to have two groups of four for charging at 48 V. The cost of the extra pair of modules may cancel out the gains in reduced cable costs of the higher voltage.

Selecting the minimum size of cables

The simplest way to select the correct size of cables is to use tables of maximum cable length which are given later in this section. For values not given in the tables, a formula method has to be used.

Both methods of selecting cable size require some value for the voltage drop along the cable. This is described first.

Voltage drop

To ensure that the appliances operate properly, the drop in voltage between the supply and any point in an installation should not exceed a certain percentage of the supply voltage.

For the wiring of mains systems, many countries have regulation values for the maximum voltage drop. As an example, regulations by the IEE (Institute of Electrical Engineering in the United Kingdom) state that the voltage drop should not exceed 2.5 per cent of the nominal voltage when the conductors are carrying the full load current. The 2.5 per cent limit is 6.0 V in a mains voltage of 240 V.

For solar systems, the voltage drop is not set by any statutory regulations but depends on the operating range of the battery supply and the appliances. Considering the variation in voltage of the supply, lead–acid batteries with a nominal voltage of 12 V actually supply between 11.5 and 12.5 V depending on their state of charge and how much current is being drawn. The upper limit rises to 15 V when they are being charged during the day.

Fluorescent tube lamps with a good quality inverter (inverters are described in Chapter 6) can operate with a variation in voltage of 10–15 V. Bulbs with filaments do not stop shining at low voltages. However, a 12 V bulb receiving less than 10 V is very dim so the same minimum of 10 V applies.

The maximum acceptable voltage drop along a cable is the difference between the minimum supply voltage and minimum voltage that appliances need. Using the values just given for a battery and the inverter of a fluorescent tube lamp, the maximum acceptable voltage drop is 1.5 V (from 11.5 minus 10.0 V). This is 12.5 per cent of the nominal 12 V system voltage.

In 24 V systems, the operating range of good-quality inverters is 20–30 V. Pairs of batteries are connected in series to provide a nominal 24 V supply and their voltage range is 23–30 V, double the range of one battery. Therefore the

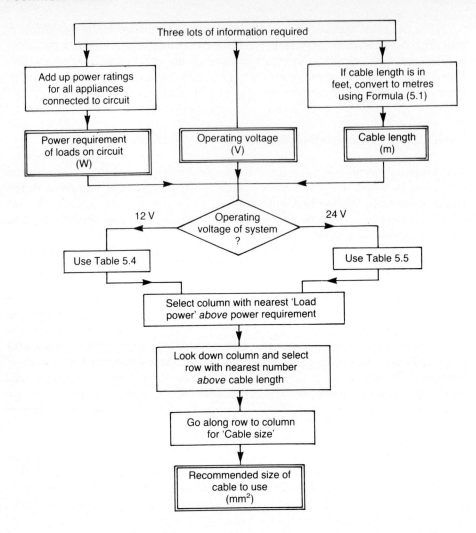

Figure 5.4 Summary of steps for selecting the smallest size of cable required for one circuit using Tables 5.4 and 5.5:

☐ steps involved
◇ decision
▣ results at each stage with units in brackets

maximum acceptable voltage drop is 23 minus 20 V which is 3 V. This is 12.5 per cent of the nominal 24 V operating voltage, the same percentage as for 12 V.

The operating range of low-cost inverters and some other appliances may not go as low as 10 V (or 20 V for the 24 V systems). Furthermore, a low voltage can shorten the life of some inverters. In order to ensure high reliability and effective operation of all appliances, the procedures that follow for selecting cables are for a smaller percentage of voltage drop. The value used is 5 per cent which corresponds to 0.6 V for 12 V systems and 1.2 V for 24 V systems.

Tables method of selecting minimum cable size

Tables 5.4 and 5.5 show maximum cable length for all standard sizes of cable and various powers of appliances connected to the cable. The procedure for using the tables is summarized in Figure 5.4.

The first step is to calculate the maximum power that the cable will carry when all the appliances connected to it are switched on. To do this, the power rating (wattage) of each appliance connected to the cable is added up.

The second step is to measure the length of the route for the cable from the battery to the last appliance in the circuit. (The tables and calculations are for route length and include the voltage drop from both positive and negative wires in the cables.) Values in the tables are based on cable length in units of metres. If a length is measured in feet, it should be converted to metres as follows before using the tables:

$$\boxed{\text{Length (ft)}} \times \boxed{0.305} = \boxed{\boxed{\text{Length (m)}}} \tag{5.1}$$

Table 5.4 *Maximum cable length for an operating voltage of 12 V and a maximum voltage drop along the cable of 0.6 V. See Figure 5.4 for instructions on how to use the table.*

Cable size (mm²)		Maximum cable length (m) for various load requirements						
	Load power (W):	24	36	48	60	72	96	120
	Current at 12 V (A):	2	3	4	5	6	8	10
1.5		12	8	7	5	5	4	3
2.5		20	13	10	8	7	6	5
4.0		31	21	16	13	11	8	7
6.0		46	31	23	19	16	12	10
10.0		76	51	38	31	26	20	16

Table 5.5 *Maximum cable length for an operating voltage of 24 V and a maximum voltage drop along the cable of 1.2 V. See Figure 5.4 for instructions on how to use the table.*

Cable size (mm^2)	Maximum cable length (m) for various load requirements						
Load power (W):	48	72	96	120	144	192	240
Current at 24 V (A):	2	3	4	5	6	8	10
1.5	23	16	12	10	8	7	5
2.5	38	26	20	16	13	10	8
4.0	61	41	31	25	21	16	13
6.0	91	61	46	37	31	23	19
10.0	151	101	76	61	51	38	31

Table 5.4 is for a voltage drop of 0.6 V, the maximum acceptable drop in a 12 V system. The top line of the table is the total load power when all the loads in that circuit are switched on. Table 5.5 is for 24 V systems where the maximum voltage drop is 1.2 V.

Example 5.1

Calculating the smallest size of cable that can be used for a 30 m route to six 18 W lamps and one 8 W lamp. The system voltage is 24 V.

First the total power is added up:

$6 \times 18 + 1 \times 8 = 116$ W

Table 5.5 for a 1.2 V drop is used because the system is operating at 24 V.

The total power of the lamps is 116 W so the nearest power above this along the top line of the table is 120 W. Looking down the column for 120 W, the maximum cable lengths at the top for cable sizes of 1.5 mm^2, 2.5 mm^2 and 4 mm^2 are less than the required length of 30 m. Further down this column, the maximum cable length for 6 mm^2 is 37 m which is longer than 30 m. Therefore 6 mm^2 is suitable.

The range of values in Tables 5.4 and 5.5 is for load currents up to 10 A, cable sizes up to 10 mm^2, and a maximum voltage drop of 5 per cent in the supply voltage. For higher currents, thicker cables, or a different voltage drop, the smallest cable size for a circuit must be calculated from the formula method.

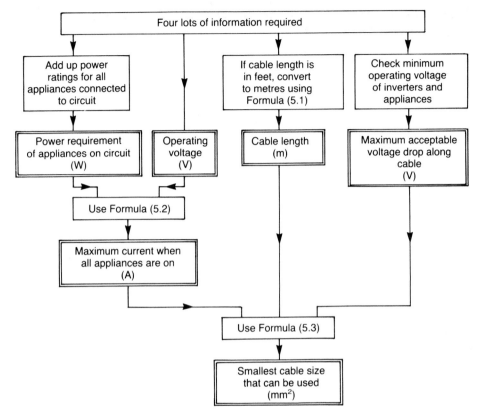

Figure 5.5   Summary of steps for calculating the smallest size of cable required for one circuit using Formulas (5.2) and (5.3). These formulas are used when current or size of cable fall outside the ranges of Tables 5.4 and 5.5 or when a different voltage drop is required:

☐   steps involved
▣   results at each stage with units in brackets

Formula method of selecting minimum cable size

The full procedure for the formula method is summarized in Figure 5.5. The total power of appliances connected to the cable is calculated as before. Using the operating voltage of the system, this value is then converted to a maximum current as follows:

$$\boxed{\text{Total power (W)}} \div \boxed{\text{Operating voltage (V)}} = \boxed{\text{Maximum current (A)}} \qquad \textbf{(5.2)}$$

Next the length of cable from the battery to the last appliance in the circuit is measured, as for the tables method. The formula given here requires the cable length to be in units of metres. If it is measured in feet, it should be converted to metres using Formula (5.1).

Using this length together with the maximum current and the voltage drop, the smallest size of copper cable that can be used is calculated from the following formula:

$$\boxed{\begin{array}{c}\text{Maximum}\\\text{current}\\\text{(A)}\end{array}} \times \boxed{\begin{array}{c}\text{Cable}\\\text{length}\\\text{(m)}\end{array}} \times \boxed{\left(\dfrac{0.04}{\dfrac{\text{V mm}^2}{\text{A m}}}\right)} \div \boxed{\begin{array}{c}\text{Maximum}\\\text{acceptable}\\\text{voltage drop}\\\text{(V)}\end{array}} = \boxed{\begin{array}{c}\text{Smallest}\\\text{cable}\\\text{size}\\\text{(mm}^2)\end{array}} \qquad (5.3)$$

From the list of standard cable sizes in Table 5.1, the standard size just larger than the answer from the formula is the one that is suitable.

Example 5.2

Take the same circuit as described in Example 5.1 but use the formula method to find the smallest size of cable that can be used.

From Example 5.1, the total power requirement is 116 W. The maximum current is found from Formula (5.2) using this power and the system voltage of 24 V:

$$116 \div 24 = 4.8 \text{ A}$$

The cable length is 30m and the maximum acceptable voltage drop in a 24 V system is 1.2 V. Using these values in Formula (5.3), the smallest size of cable that can be used is:

$$4.8 \times 30 \times 0.04 \div 1.2 = 4.8 \text{ mm}^2$$

The nearest standard cable size above this answer in Table 5.1 is 6 mm². This is the smallest size that can be used, in agreement with Example 5.1.

Three-core cable

In some situations, the only cable available may be three-core. By using two wires for the negative conductor, there is a small reduction in the minimum size of cable that can be used. As long as the three wires are all the same size, Formula (5.3) can be used to calculate the smallest cable size with 0.04 replaced by 0.03.

Example 5.3

Take the same circuit as described in Example 5.1 but for a three-core cable with equal-size wires. Two wires are used for the negative and one for the positive. Apply the formula method to find the smallest size of cable that can be used.

The cable length is 30 m, maximum acceptable voltage drop in a 24 V system is 1.2 V, and the maximum current is 4.8 A from Example 5.2. These values are used in Formula (5.3) together with 0.04 replaced by 0.03 because the wire is three-core:

$$4.8 \times 30 \times 0.03 \div 1.2 = 3.6 \text{ mm}^2$$

The nearest standard cable size above this answer in Table 5.2 is 4 mm^2. This is the smallest size that can be used and is one size smaller than for a two-core cable.

Accuracy of tables and formula

Where several appliances are connected along the length of a cable, the selection of minimum cable size from Tables 5.4 and 5.5 or by Formula (5.3) both give an over-estimate for the size required. This is because the total length of cable is used assuming that the appliances are all connected at the end with the total current flowing for the entire length. In reality, the current actually decreases in steps along the cable after the junction to each appliance.

Nevertheless this over-estimate should not be taken as a reason for using a smaller and therefore cheaper cable. The over-estimate just ensures that there is less likely to be a problem when all the loads are switched on. It also compensates for the small voltage drops at all the T-off joints along the cable to each appliance.

Cable selection

Home system

For solar systems operating at 12 V in homes, the cable lengths are usually less than 30 m and there are a small number of appliances. Throughout the installation 2.5 mm^2 cable can be used without any problems. Referring to Table 5.4, it can be seen that this size is OK for loads totalling 36 W at 13 m (43 ft) or loads totalling 72 W at 7 m (23 ft).

House already wired according to mains wiring regulations

A house may already be wired for mains in anticipation of getting a generator or being connected to the mains supply. In most cases, the existing wires can be used for a solar system.

For 240 V mains, typical sizes of cables used in a house are 1.5 mm^2 for each lighting circuit, 2.5 mm^2 in a ring circuit for socket outlet points, and 4.0 mm^2 for a medium-size electric cooker. The 1.5 mm^2 cable for lighting can be used for solar electricity as long as the lamps are of low-power and the battery is inside the house so that the distance to each lamp is short. If there is any doubt about using 1.5 mm^2 cable, the lengths can be measured and compared to the maximum lengths in Table 5.4.

If mains voltage is also available, perhaps from a generator, it *cannot* share the same wires as used for the solar system. Mains voltage requires an earth system, proper covering of all live parts, and appliances that work at the mains voltage. Mains and solar systems should be treated totally separately with warning signs next to switches, sockets, and other fittings stating clearly to which system they are connected.

Cable from solar modules to batteries

The cable carrying the charging current from the solar modules to the batteries must also be selected according to voltage drop. By keeping the voltage drop to less than about 1 V, the maximum charging current is obtained at all levels of irradiance. Figure 5.6 summarizes the steps involved in checking the voltage drop along whichever size of cable is chosen.

For one module, the short circuit current under STC should be used for the maximum current in the formula. When there is an array of modules with a single cable leading to the batteries, the short circuit current of each module is combined using the following formula:

$$\boxed{\begin{array}{c}\text{Short circuit}\\\text{current of}\\\text{one module}\\\text{(A)}\end{array}} \times \boxed{\begin{array}{c}\text{Number of}\\\text{modules}\\\text{sharing}\\\text{cable}\end{array}} \times \boxed{\begin{array}{c}12\\\text{(V)}\end{array}} \div \boxed{\begin{array}{c}\text{System}\\\text{voltage}\\\text{(V)}\end{array}} = \boxed{\boxed{\begin{array}{c}\text{Maximum current}\\\text{along cable}\\\text{(A)}\end{array}}} \qquad \textbf{(5.4)}$$

The drop in voltage is calculated as follows:

$$\boxed{\begin{array}{c}\text{Maximum}\\\text{current}\\\text{(A)}\end{array}} \times \boxed{\begin{array}{c}\text{Cable}\\\text{length}\\\text{(m)}\end{array}} \times \boxed{\left(\dfrac{0.04}{\dfrac{\text{V mm}^2}{\text{A m}}}\right)} \div \boxed{\begin{array}{c}\text{Cable}\\\text{size}\\\text{(mm}^2)\end{array}} = \boxed{\boxed{\begin{array}{c}\text{Voltage drop}\\\text{along cable}\\\text{(V)}\end{array}}} \qquad \textbf{(5.5)}$$

Three-core cable can be used with two wires for the negative conductor and one for the positive conductor. As long as the three wires are all the same size, Formula (5.5) can be used to check the voltage drop with 0.04 replaced by 0.03.

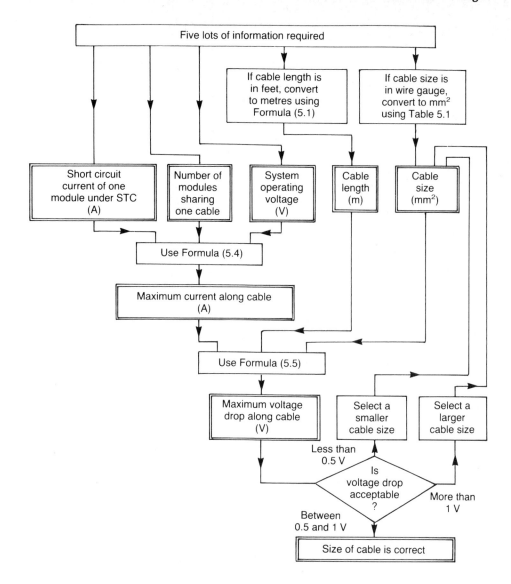

Figure 5.6 Summary of steps involved in checking the size of cable connecting the modules to the batteries:
☐ steps involved
☐ results at each stage with units in brackets
◇ decision

Example 5.4

In an array of four modules, each module has a short circuit current under STC of 2.2 A and the modules are connected together in parallel for 12 V operation. The array is connected to the batteries by a twelve-gauge cable, length 55 ft. Is this size of cable large enough?

The short circuit current of each module is used to find the maximum current from the array which is:

$$2.2 \times 4 \times 12 \div 12 = 8.8 \text{ A}$$

Since the cable length is in units of feet, it must be converted to metres using Formula (5.1):

$$55 \times 0.305 = 16.8 \text{ m}$$

Twelve-gauge corresponds to a cable size of 4 mm² from Table 5.1. Using these values in Formula (5.5), the voltage drop is:

$$8.8 \times 16.8 \times 0.04 \div 4 = 1.48 \text{ V}$$

This is more than 1 V so it is better to use a thicker cable. Repeating Formula (5.4) for a 6 mm² cable, the voltage drop is:

$$8.8 \times 16.8 \times 0.04 \div 6 = 0.99 \text{ V}$$

This voltage drop is more acceptable, so a 6 mm² cable (ten-gauge) should be used in place of the 4 mm² size.

☐ *Questions*

1.   Name the three factors that affect the minimum size of cable that can be used in each part of an installation.

2.   List the advantages and disadvantages of operating a large solar installation at 24 V instead of 12 V.

3.   For a large solar installation, explain why one centralized system is easier to maintain and gives better performance than several separate systems.

4.   Why is a figure of 0.6 V used for the maximum voltage drop along cables in a system operated at 12 V?

5.   A group of three outside latrines are each illuminated by 20 W 12 V bulbs. The length of cable from the batteries to these latrines is 15 m.
   (a) Calculate the maximum current carried by the cable.
   (b) What is the smallest standard size of cable that can be used?

6.   An array of six solar modules are connected in series in pairs to charge a 24 V system. The short circuit current of each series pair is 3.2 A and the three pairs are connected by separate cables to the batteries that are 18 m away. Find the smallest standard size of cable that can be used to keep the voltage drop along each cable below 1 V.

6 Electrical appliances, inverters, and lighting

A wide range of appliances can be run on solar electricity. Two factors which decide whether an appliance is suitable are its operating voltage and power rating. In small- to medium-sized systems, most appliances are rated at much less than 100 W. Power ratings determine the amount of electricity that is required and this aspect is dealt with in Chapter 8 on sizing.

The areas covered by this chapter are summarized in Figure 6.1. For appliances that operate at a lower voltage than the system voltage, a number of solutions are available. Appliances requiring a higher voltage usually operate on a.c. and can be supplied through a *power inverter*. Lighting is an important application of solar electricity, so a section is devoted to types of lamp and their use. A few details are given at the end about water pumps and refrigerators which are usually run by themselves in self-contained systems.

Voltage requirement of appliances

When the operating voltage of an appliance is the same as the system voltage of 12 V d.c. or 24 V d.c., the appliance can be connected directly to the system. When the operating voltage is higher or lower than the system voltage, another method is required, such as an inverter or a low-voltage adaptor. The steps involved in selecting how to connect an appliance according to its voltage are summarized in Figure 6.2.

Some appliances can be connected directly to a system operating at 12 V d.c. Examples of appliances which are available at a 12 V d.c. rating are as follows:

- ☐ Filament bulb.
- ☐ Fluorescent tube with its own inverter.
- ☐ Black and white television.
- ☐ Appliances from cars, e.g. clock, fan, radio/cassette player.
- ☐ SW radio transmitter and receiver.

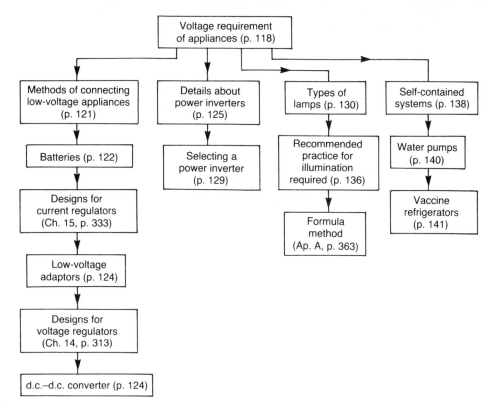

Figure 6.1 Summary of Chapter 6 with cross-references to other chapters and an appendix (Ch. chapter, Ap. appendix, p. page references to text).

- ☐ Control unit for electric fencing.
- ☐ Small water pump.
- ☐ Refrigerator.

Battery-powered appliances use low-voltage d.c. but they usually require less than 12 V. The voltage needs to be stepped down in some way so that these appliances can be connected to the system. Here are some examples of small, battery-powered appliances:

- ☐ Torch.
- ☐ Radio.
- ☐ Cassette player.
- ☐ Calculator.
- ☐ Small personal computer (PC).
- ☐ Electric clock.

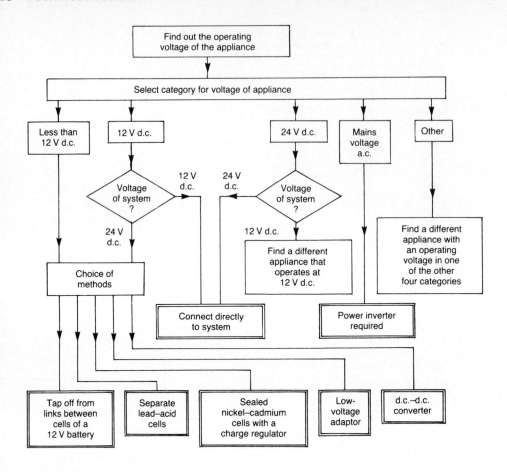

Figure 6.2 Summary of different methods for running an appliance in a solar electric system. Each method is selected according to the operating voltages of the appliance and the system voltage.
☐ steps involved
◇ decisions
▣ methods

☐ Small lamps, e.g. in microscopes.
☐ Small electric motors, e.g. in a cordless drill.

There is another group of appliances that have power low enough to be used economically in a solar system. However, they are only available in versions that run at mains voltage a.c. To use them in a solar system, a power inverter is needed to convert low-voltage d.c. to mains voltage a.c. Examples of low-power appliances needing high-voltage a.c. are as follows:

☐ Record and CD (compact disc) players.
☐ Colour television.
☐ Video cassette recorder (VCR).
☐ Slide and film projectors.
☐ Electric typewriter.
☐ Calculating machine with a printer.
☐ Personal computer with a printer.
☐ Electric drill.
☐ Electric soldering iron.
☐ Slow cooker.
☐ Microwave oven.

Power inverters are expensive. They are also inefficient so more solar modules and batteries are needed to compensate for loss of power in the inverter. To keep costs down, it is best to look for appliances that work at low-voltage d.c. before resorting to the purchase of an inverter and operating at mains voltage. Lighting should always be run directly from the system at low-voltage d.c.

In large solar systems, the operating voltage may be higher than 12 V. This restricts the range of appliances that can be connected directly and 12 V appliances will need their own voltage adaptor. Appliances that are available at a 24 V d.c. rating are as follows:

☐ Filament bulb.
☐ Fluorescent tube with its own inverter.
☐ Appliances from large vehicles (buses and lorries) such as fan motors.

Water pumping is an important application. Large water pumps are usually run in a separate system with their own array of modules and a special control unit.

Running low-voltage appliances

Small battery-powered appliances usually require a voltage below 12 V d.c. To run them in a solar system, the voltage must be stepped down in some way from the system voltage of 12 V or 24 V. Here is a list of methods of reducing the d.c. voltage in a solar system:

☐ Tapping off from the links connecting cells in a 12 V battery.
☐ Dividing a 12 V battery into separate cells.
☐ Using sealed nickel–cadmium cells.

Table 6.1 *Details of five methods for running low-voltage appliances in a solar electric system. The type of appliance is identified by the number of dry cells that it normally uses which are listed in the left column.*

Number of dry cells normally used in low-voltage appliance	Details of methods supplying low voltage for appliance			
	Tap off from links between cells of a 12 V lead–acid battery counting from the negative	Number of substitute cells required		Output voltage from low-voltage adaptor or d.c.–d.c. converter (V)
		Lead–acid	Nickel–cadmium[1]	
2	Between cells 2 and 3	2	2	3
3	Between cells 2 and 3	2	4	4.5
4	Between cells 3 and 4	3	5	6
5	Between cells 4 and 5	4	6	7.5
6	Between cells 5 and 6	5	7	9
8	Positive terminal	6	10	12

[1]Some sealed nickel–cadmium cells can be obtained which are the same size as dry cells and fit the battery compartment of the appliance. In this case, the same number of these cells as dry cells can be used since most battery-powered appliances can operate at the lower voltage.

☐   Using a low-voltage adaptor.
☐   Using a d.c.-d.c. converter.

A transformer is not included in the list because transformers can only work for a.c.

Each method of stepping down voltage is described here in detail and their specifications are summarized in Table 6.1.

Low-voltage tapping from a battery of cells

A 12 V lead–acid battery is made up of six 2 V cells. By making a connection to the metal link between the cells, voltages can be tapped off at 2, 4, 6, 8, and 10 V.

On some 12 V batteries, the links are across the top and easy to connect by drilling a hole and using a self-tapping screw to make the connection. In other batteries, the links may be just below the top surface. It may be possible to reach these links by breaking through the top with a screw. However, this should be attempted only by battery dealers or others who are familiar with lead–acid batteries. The connections should be covered with grease to prevent corrosion from acid mist.

Low-voltage tap offs should not be made to sealed lead-acid batteries, such as the Yuasa one shown in Figure 3.2. Any damage to the case or break in the seal will shorten the life of the battery because the electrolyte inside will dry out.

Taking a low-voltage tap off from a large battery is a good solution in a home system where there is often just one appliance requiring a low voltage. This may be a radio/cassette player requiring 6 or 9 V.

A problem to beware of when a battery has a tap off point is that the cells gradually become unbalanced as they are discharged by different amounts. The cells between the tapping point and the positive terminal which are not used by the low-voltage appliance are frequently over-charged. This means they will need to be topped up with distilled water more often than the others. In addition, care is required to prevent over-discharge of the cells between the negative and the tapping point which are used by the low-voltage appliance.

Larger systems have a circuit permanently wired in for power outlet points. This circuit should be run at the system voltage to avoid confusion and complications. Therefore a different method from tapping into a battery is needed to run low-voltage appliances in large systems.

Separate cells

An alternative to tapping off between the cells of a 12 V battery is to use lower-voltage batteries or separate cells. They are connected together in series for charging from the main 12 V battery and then separated to provide the lower voltages. Examples of combinations are two 6 V motorcycle batteries, six individual lead–acid cells, and ten vented nickel–cadmium cells. It is important that the 6 V batteries or individual cells that are connected for charging have the same A h capacity to ensure even charging in series.

Use of separate cells is suitable for specialized applications, such as a school laboratory where the 2 V cells are used for experiments. The laboratory technician has the responsibility of keeping the cells regularly charged and in good condition.

Sealed nickel–cadmium cells

Sealed nickel-cadmium cells are a good way to run low-voltage appliances. They do not require maintenance and can fit into the battery compartment of battery-powered appliances. Although the voltage of a nickel–cadmium cell is 0.25 V less than for a new dry cell, appliances usually tolerate the lower operating voltage, so can be run with the same number of cells.

One feature of nickel–cadmium cells is that their voltage remains almost constant while they are discharging. In comparison, the voltage of dry cells gradually drops towards the end of their life, as shown by a torch becoming dimmer or a radio becoming quieter. This means that there is less warning of when nickel–cadmium cells are near to running flat. Possible solutions to the lack of warning include charging the cells regularly when the appliance is not in use, or having a second set of cells ready charged.

The problem in using these cells is how to charge them since the charging units sold for them work only from the a.c. mains. A regulator is required to maintain the constant charging current that the cells require from a 12 V supply. A d.c.-powered current regulator is not difficult to build, though, and instructions are given in Chapter 15.

Low-voltage adaptor

A voltage adaptor is an electronic unit that steps down the voltage. It does this by 'losing' the extra voltage as heat.

Voltage adaptors are sold for use in cars and are designed to plug into the cigarette lighter socket. The output wire usually has a multi-way plug on the end (plug 6 in Figure 9.7) to suit a wide range of d.c. input sockets. The adaptor has one switch to select the output voltage according to the number of batteries used by the appliance (see Table 6.1). Another switch sets the polarity of the connections on the plug.

When using the adaptor in a solar system, connections need to be made to the contacts on the side of the plug. This is done by opening up the plastic box and connecting a cable to the spring contacts. The side contact is negative and the end one is positive.

Voltage adaptors are not difficult to make and a number of circuits are described in Chapter 14. They range from a very simple circuit using a few diodes to circuits with a fully adjustable and stable output voltage.

D.c.–d.c. converters

A d.c.–d.c. converter is an electronic unit which can step a d.c. voltage down or up. Examples are shown in Figure 6.3. They are more complicated than a voltage adaptor and work by a method called *pulse width modulation*. The input to a d.c.–d.c. converter is switched on and off very quickly. The relative length of on and off times is adjusted so that after smoothing the required d.c. output voltage is obtained.

A good application for a d.c.–d.c. converter is in systems operating at 24 V where the converter can reduce the voltage down to 12 V for a number of appliances. D.c.–d.c. converters are more expensive and less common than voltage adaptors but they have the advantage of a higher power efficiency. A typical power efficiency is 85 per cent while a voltage adaptor doing the same job of halving the voltage can be no better than 50 per cent efficient.

Figure 6.3   Examples of d.c.–d.c. converters for reducing or increasing a d.c. voltage.

Power inverters

A power inverter or *transverter* is used in a solar electric system to convert low-voltage d.c. to mains voltage a.c. This is needed when using appliances that only work from a mains voltage a.c. supply.

A power inverter may seem to be the best solution of running all the appliances at mains voltage but it has several disadvantages. Good-quality power inverters are expensive and difficult to obtain in many countries. Also they make the solar system more complicated by adding another unit that can fail and be difficult to repair.

Therefore it is strongly recommended that an attempt is first made to find a supply of low-voltage d.c. appliances. If these appliances turn out not to be available, then resort to using mains voltage appliances with a power inverter.

Another use for a power inverter is in a large system covering a wide area. The size of long-distance cables is reduced by operating at a high voltage. Bearing in mind the disadvantages of using a power inverter, there must be a large reduction in the cost from using small cables at high voltage to make this approach worth while.

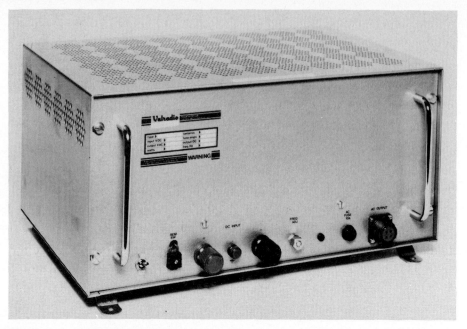

Figure 6.4   Example of a solid-state power inverter. From a 24 V d.c. input, this inverter provides 240 V sinusoidal a.c. output with a rating of 100 W. The weight of the unit is 37.3 kg (17 lb). (Source Valradio Power Ltd.)

Types of inverter

There are basically two ways that an inverter can operate. In the solid-state electronic type, transistors switch the d.c. input on and off many times per second. The current is now changing so it can be transformed to other voltages by a transformer. The output from the transformer is a.c. An example of a solid-state power inverter is shown in Figure 6.4.

The older type of inverter is mechanical instead of solid-state. It is called a *rotary inverter* or *motor generator* and consists of a d.c. motor and an a.c. dynamo connected directly in one unit. The motor runs at low-voltage d.c. and drives the dynamo. The output from the dynamo is high-voltage a.c. Rotary inverters are lighter than solid-state inverters for the same power output but the moving parts require regular maintenance. They are also less efficient.

Waveform of a.c. output

In mains a.c., the current change is *sinusoidal*. This means that whenever the current alternates direction, it decreases gradually to zero current and increases gradually up to the full negative current. As the current varies with time, it follows a sine curve and so is sinusoidal (see Figure 6.5(a)).

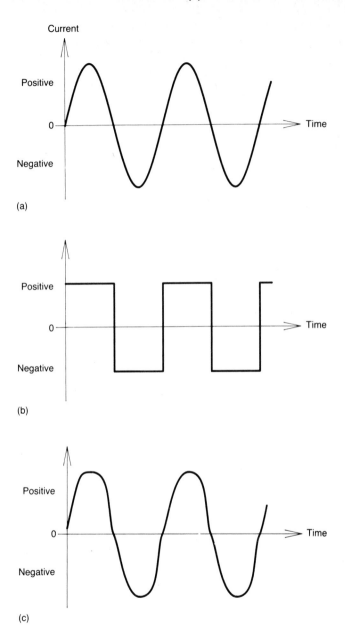

Figure 6.5 Waveforms of a.c. (alternating current).
(a) Sinusoidal wave.
(b) Square wave.
(c) Modified sine wave.

The a.c. output from a rotary inverter is a pure sine wave so it is just like mains a.c. In contrast, the simplest way for a solid-state electronic inverter to work is by switching the d.c. on and off. This produces a square wave type of a.c. at the output (see Figure 6.5(b)).

Lamps and heaters work equally well on sinusoidal and square wave a.c. This is not so for most appliances containing electronics such as televisions and computers. There is a rapid change in voltage as the current alternates, which can damage these appliances. Motors can be powered by square wave a.c. but are less efficient than with sinusoidal a.c.

More expensive electronic inverters produce a modified or *quasi* sine wave output (see Figure 6.5(c)). They work by switching the d.c. input using pulse width modulation, as for d.c.–d.c. converters. A modified or pure sine wave output is required for most appliances that contain electronic circuits.

Frequency of a.c. output

The frequency of a.c. is given by how many times it alternates every second. It is measured in units of *hertz* (Hz) which is short for cycles per second.

There are two systems of mains frequency around the world which are 50 and 60 Hz. Appliances are marked with the frequency they should be run at. When ordering a power inverter, the frequency must be checked to make sure it will suit the appliances.

Cassette and record players that are run directly from mains voltage a.c. use the frequency of the a.c. to feed the tape or turn the record at the correct speed. For proper control of the speed in these appliances, the variation in a.c. frequency should be less then 1 per cent, and some inverters feature accurate control of the frequency for this purpose. This feature is called *internal crystal control* using a *crystal-controlled oscillator*.

Efficiency of inverters

Some electrical power is used by an inverter itself so more power must be put in than is available as high-voltage a.c. Therefore the efficiency is always less than 100 per cent and varies a lot between different makes and types of power inverter. Efficiencies are in the range 50–90 per cent with square wave power inverters being the best value for money.

The efficiency of many power inverters tends to be lower when they are operating well below their maximum rated power. For the best operating efficiency, choose a power rating that is just a little higher than the total power required by the appliances.

Inverters have a standby consumption of electricity when the appliances are switched off. Therefore a good feature to include in a power inverter is automatic switching off when appliances are not in use. This avoids wasting electricity while the inverter is on standby.

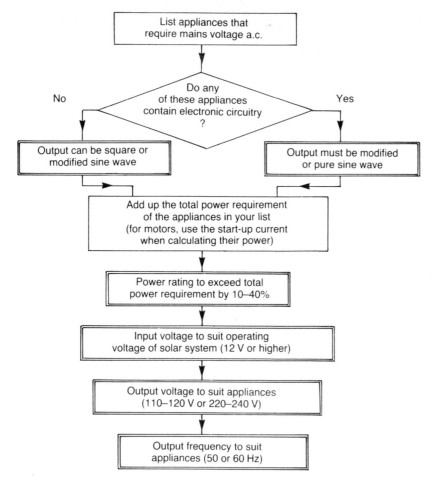

Figure 6.6　Procedure for preparing the specifications of a power inverter for a solar electric system:
☐　steps involved
◇　decisions
▣　specifications of power inverter

Choosing a power inverter

A procedure to follow when listing the specifications of a power inverter is summarized in Figure 6.6. Check that the power inverter has the following features which are essential to prevent damage:

☐　Protection against overload, reversed input polarity, and short circuit of output.
☐　Thermal cut-out (to switch inverter off if it over-heats).

Here are a number of optional features which are often worth including.

☐ Automatic cut-out or automatic load demand switch (for when appliances are not being used continuously).
☐ Low-voltage cut-out or disconnect (to prevent excessive discharge of lead–acid batteries by the inverter).
☐ Video synchronization (to minimize interference of pictures when supplying a television).
☐ Noise filter (to reduce interference for radios used nearby).
☐ Internal frequency control (for correct speed of tape recorders and record players).

Power inverters are used in a variety of applications. Some of the features required for other applications are unnecessary in a solar electric system so can be avoided to reduce the cost. Here are some unnecessary features:

☐ Battery charger (unless occasionally charging from a generator).
☐ *Uninterruptible power supply* (UPS) or *standby power supply* (SPS) control system which automatically switches to battery supply when a mains power supply fails.
☐ *Dynamic* type for supply from an alternator or dynamo. (A *static* power inverter is the correct type for battery supplies.)

Lamps

Lighting is probably the main use of electricity in small solar systems and is of great benefit to users. Lamps are low-power, inexpensive, and commonly available for operation at 12 V d.c. For effective operation, it is important that lamps are carefully chosen for the task required. A common mistake by users is to connect extra lamps and then discover that the batteries run down because of over-loading.

Specifications of lamps

The total amount of light that comes out of a lamp is measured in units of *lumens* (lm) and is called *luminous flux*. Another name for this quantity is *spherical luminous intensity* measured in units of *candlepower*. The lumen unit is used in this chapter so specifications given in candlepower should be converted using this formula:

$$\boxed{\begin{array}{c}\text{Spherical luminous}\\\text{intensity}\\\text{(candlepower)}\end{array}} \times \boxed{12.6} = \boxed{\boxed{\begin{array}{c}\text{Luminous}\\\text{flux}\\\text{(lm)}\end{array}}} \qquad \textbf{(6.1)}$$

Table 6.2 *Details of four types of lamp used in solar electric systems.*

Shape	Parts	Method of operation	Efficacy (lm/W)	Average life (hours)
Bulb	Coil in an inert gas	Incandescence of a filament	8–15	1000
Bulb	Coil in halogen gas	Incandescence of a filament	30	2000
Tube	Mercury vapour and a phosphor	Gas discharge and fluorescence of a phosphor	50–75	4000
Tube	Sodium vapour (SOX)	Gas discharge	120	4000

Lamp manufacturers sometimes provide the luminous flux specification of their products to show how much light is produced. Usually, though, only the rating in watts and operating voltage are marked on the lamp itself.

The *luminous efficacy* of a lamp shows how much light is given out compared to the amount of electricity used. It is measured in units of lm/W (lumens per watt). The efficacy and other details of various types of lamp used in solar systems are summarized in Table 6.2. Examples of some lamps are shown in Figure 6.7.

Filament bulbs

The type of electric lamp familiar to most people is a simple filament bulb or *general lighting service* (GLS) bulb. A tungsten filament inside a glass bulb is heated by electricity flowing through it. Light is given off when the filament reaches a high temperature and this is called *incandescence*. Most of the electricity goes to producing heat and only a small proportion to producing light, so bulbs have a low efficacy.

To make bulbs more effective, the filaments in some of them are wound in a double coil, called *coiled-coil*. This is done by first winding the tungsten wire in a coil and then winding this coiled wire in a bigger coil. The first coiling is very small but it can be seen by careful inspection of a bulb which has clear glass. The bulb is filled with an inert gas, usually nitrogen, or evacuated of all gas.

Halogen bulbs

A different type of bulb called *tungsten halogen*, *quartz halogen*, or just *halogen* has an efficacy of about 30 lm/W. This means that twice as much light is given off by a halogen bulb compared to an ordinary tungsten filament bulb of the same power rating (see Table 6.2).

The improvement in efficacy is achieved by running the tungsten filament

Figure 6.7   Examples of lamps: **1** sealed-beam filament headlight with plug;
2 fluorescent tube; **3** side-light bulb with socket from an old car; **4** mains-type bulb;
5 quartz halogen bulb.

at a higher temperature than in an ordinary bulb. This causes tungsten to evaporate rapidly from the filament. To prevent tungsten condensing on the inside of the glass, the gas inside the bulb includes a small amount of a special gas. This gas is a halogen (iodine or bromine) and it prevents tungsten vapour from reaching the bulb by reacting with it. When gas containing tungsten drifts near the filament, the high temperature makes the halogen gas deposit tungsten back on the filament. This process is called the 'halogen regenerative cycle'.

To prevent any deposits forming on the bulb, the temperature on the inside of the glass must be higher than about 200 °C (390 °F). Halogen bulbs are small (see Figure 6.7) so that they heat up to above about 400 °C (750 °F), much hotter than for ordinary bulbs. Also the gas inside the bulb reaches a higher pressure than for ordinary tungsten bulbs.

The bulb of a halogen lamp must withstand high operating temperatures and pressures, so is made of strengthened glass or quartz. The surface of the glass must not be touched by fingers, otherwise a greasy mark is left which damages the glass when the bulb is operated. This is because more heat is absorbed at the mark, causing a hot spot. A warning on the bulb box gives instructions on holding the bulb by the metal parts only. If the glass parts are touched by accident, they can be cleaned with methylated spirit or alcohol.

Besides being bright, the filament of a halogen bulb is compact so it is easily focused by a curved reflector to make a parallel beam. These features mean that halogen bulbs are often used for headlights on vehicles and in projectors for slides and cine film.

Fittings for bulbs

The most common fitting for bulbs is a bayonet socket. (Two pins on the side of the bulb engage in J-shaped grooves in the socket and the bulb is put in with a push followed by a small twist.) For mains voltage, there are two metal contacts on the bottom of the bulb (see bulb 4 in Figure 6.7). These two contacts press against two sprung pins at the bottom of the socket. Double pin sockets of this sort are readily available for wall mounting, a lamp stand or hanging on a flexible cable. However, bulbs that operate at 12 or 24 V are not generally available. Solar equipment suppliers may stock them but at a higher price than mains voltage bulbs of the same power.

A cheaper and local source of low-voltage bulbs is an auto-spares shop. Bulbs for vehicles have only one contact at the bottom (see bulb 3 in Figure 6.7) while the other connection is through the metal side of the base. New sockets may not be available from auto-spares shops but second-hand sockets can be obtained at low cost from scrap vehicles. Side lights at the front and indicators are best. Avoid using double filament bulbs for the combined brake and side lights at the back. The second filament is unnecessary and the socket has odd grooves that do not accept single filament bulbs.

Two other vehicle bulbs are shown in Figure 6.7. These are a sealed beam headlight and a halogen bulb. Electrical contact to these is made by a crimp connector on the end of a wire that is pushed onto a blade on the bulb. For the headlight shown, the crimp connectors fit in a plug. The type of quartz halogen bulb shown is from a headlight and has only one blade for a crimp connection. On the vehicle, it is mounted through a hole in the back of the headlight reflector and held in place by a spring. The second connection to the bulb is through the metal base to the frame of the vehicle rather than another wire.

Second-hand sockets from scrap vehicles must be adapted for use in a solar system. This may make installation more complicated than when using the double pin sockets for mains. However, using these sockets ensures a cheap and convenient supply of the bulbs both for the person who is installing the system and the user when bulbs need replacing.

Fluorescent tubes

Fluorescent tube lamps have an efficacy of about 60 lm/W which is four times better than an ordinary filament bulb. Therefore a 10 W tube gives off about the same amount of light as a 40 W bulb or a 20 W tungsten halogen bulb.

A fluorescent tube works in a completely different way from an incandescent bulb. The tube contains a small amount of gas and pairs of contacts at each end which connect to electrodes inside. Part of each electrode is a filament made of tungsten with a coating of *electron-emitting* material (see Figure 6.8).

When a high voltage is applied to the ends of a tube, continuous sparking is generated between the electrodes which is known as a *gas discharge* or an *arc*. Fluorescent tube lamps contain mercury and the discharge in mercury gas produces ultraviolet (UV) light. Ultraviolet is invisible so it is converted to visible light by white powder coated on the inside of the tube which is a phosphor.

The whiteness and brightness of visible light from the tube depend on the type of phosphor used. For the highest efficacy, tubes marked 'white' and 'warm white' should be used. Like filament bulbs, they are poor at rendering the proper colour of objects. Phosphors with names such as 'natural', 'cool white', and 'daylight' show objects in their true colour, just like in real daylight, but their efficacy is lower.

As tubes get older, the ends become black inside because of tungsten from the filament. Failure of a tube is not necessarily because the filament breaks. More often the electron-emitting coating on the electrodes is gradually lost and eventually the arc is unable to strike. When a tube in this condition is switched on, the ends have a strong yellow glow but the gas discharge does not start.

Inverters for fluorescent tubes

A fluorescent tube needs a voltage higher than 100 V to work. Small solar systems operate at 12 or 24 V so each tube has its own inverter.

To strike the arc and get the discharge started in the gas when the tube is switched on, two things must happen. The electrodes must be heated up by a

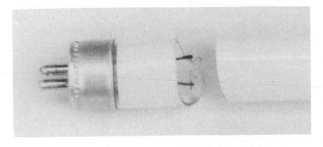

Figure 6.8   End of a fluorescent tube broken open to show the filament inside.

current and an extra high voltage must be applied. Electricians familiar with mains systems know that a *starter* and a *ballast* (containing a choke coil and a power factor capacitor) are needed for each tube that operates at mains voltage a.c. The starter heats the electrodes and the choke in the ballast helps to generate the high voltage. Once the tube is running, the gas discharge keeps the filaments hot.

The inverters made for fluorescent tubes are designed to start the tube as well as generating the required operating voltage. Therefore there is no need for a starter or ballast for tube lamps in a solar system. Inverters for tube lamps are sometimes referred to as 'ballasts' but this is incorrect. The tubes themselves are the same as for mains operation.

The inverters that are supplied with a tube fitting are intended only for this use and should not be used to run any other appliance. Their efficiency is higher than many power inverters because they run at a much higher frequency than mains a.c. of about 10 kHz (10 000 cycles per second). At such a high frequency, light from the tube does not flicker at all but interference may be caused to radio reception, especially on AM wavebands.

Choice of inverters

Good-quality inverters for tube lamps are expensive. They make the cost of the whole tube fitting about ten times more expensive than a simple bulb and socket. Lower-cost inverters are available but they prove more expensive in the long run because they are easily damaged and cannot be repaired.

To help in identifying the quality of an inverter for tube lamps, two inverters are shown in Figure 6.9(a) connected to tubes. When comparing inverters of the same power rating, the better-quality ones are generally bigger, heavier, and more expensive. Also they have two wires going to each end of the tube.

Poor-quality inverters tend to fail under any of the following conditions:

☐ Wrong polarity of the supply wires when installed.
☐ The power is switched on when the tube is broken or when no tube is fitted.
☐ Supply voltage goes too low or too high.

With poor-quality inverters, tubes should be replaced before they fail and damage the inverter. Blackening at the ends of the tube indicates that it is reaching the end of its life.

Sodium tubes

Another type of tube lamp that can be used in solar systems has an even higher efficacy than fluorescent tubes. It is the *low-pressure sodium* or *SOX* tube. It produces yellow light and is used only outside for general illumination, such as street lighting.

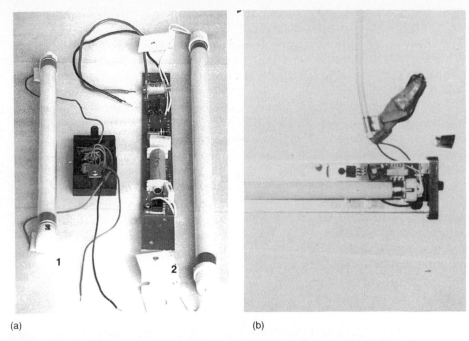

(a)   (b)

Figure 6.9   Examples of inverters for running tube lamps from low-voltage d.c.
(a)   1 low-cost 6 W inverter; 2 high-cost 8 W inverter with double wires to each end of the tube.
(b)   Low-cost unit mounted in the lamp fitting.

An SOX tube contains neon gas and some sodium. Just after switching on, there is a discharge in the neon giving a weak red glow. This is needed to heat up the sodium and turn it into gas. After a short time, a discharge builds up in sodium gas producing a characteristic yellow light.

When used in a solar system, each tube has its own inverter for stepping up the voltage and starting the discharge. Inverters for sodium lamps are not yet in wide use so they should only be considered when planning a solar system for a reasonably large installation.

Recommended practice for lighting levels

Guidance on the lowest power of lamps that can be used in different parts of a solar system is given in Table 6.3.

Compared to lighting powers for systems supplied by the mains or a generator, the minimum lamp powers recommended in Table 6.3 for solar systems are low. However, the level of lighting provided by these lamp powers is acceptable to most users of solar electric systems. In the living areas, the level of

Table 6.3 *Minimum power of lighting recommended for use in four sorts of places.*

Place	Height of lamp (m)	Maximum floor area	Type of lamp and minimum power that can be used
Living-room	2.5 (8 ft)	4 × 5 m (13 × 16 ft)	One 8 W fluorescent tube lamp[1]
Classroom	3.0 (10 ft)	8 × 10 m (26 × 32 ft)	Two 15 W fluorescent tube lamps[1]
Toilet	2.5 (8 ft)	2 × 2 m (6 × 6 ft)	One 8 W filament bulb lamp[2]
Outside	4.5 (15 ft)	30 × 30 m (100 × 100 ft)	Two 8 W fluorescent tube lamps in one sealed fitting (see Figure 6.10(a))

[1]Recommendation assumes that the walls are painted white and that the lamp has a reflector on top or the ceiling is also white.

[2]Not to be left on continuously all evening but used for only short periods as required.

lighting from 8 W tube lamps is adequate for reading, talking, and eating. It is certainly better than the illumination provided by paraffin (kerosene) pressure lamps that may be the only alternative to solar lighting. Figure 6.10(a) shows a double tube fitting on a high pole. This provides about the same illumination for areas outside as a full moon on a clear night.

When using such low-power lamps, it is important that most of the light from each lamp reaches the area where it is needed. The best way to ensure this is by painting the walls and ceiling white. Also, light-coloured curtains should be put over the windows to keep light in the room. Where the ceiling is high or dark-coloured, a reflector should be fixed above the lamp to reflect all the light downwards. A reflector made of a polished sheet of stainless steel is shown over a tube lamp in Figure 6.10(b). Reflectors can also be made from polished aluminium or chrome-plated steel.

For large rooms with low ceilings, it is better to increase the number of lamps rather than use one lamp of higher power. An example is a larger living-room than in Table 6.3 of area 8 × 5 m (26 × 16 ft) with a ceiling height of 2.5 m (8 ft). Two 8 W tube lamps should be fixed in each half rather than one 15 W tube lamp in the middle. Tube lamps of 15 W are suitable for classrooms, though, because classrooms usually have a higher ceiling than living-rooms.

When brighter illumination is needed over a small area for detailed work, the lamp should be brought closer to the work. Bringing a low-power lamp closer is better than increasing the power of a lamp fixed to the ceiling and using more electricity.

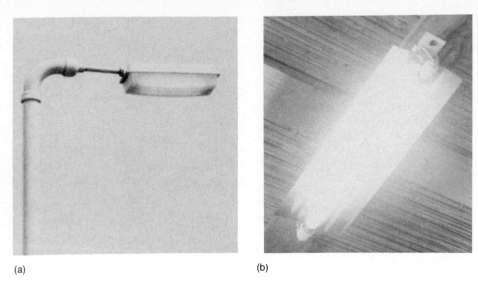

(a)   (b)

Figure 6.10   Examples of special fittings for tube lamps.
(a)   Lamp housing mounted on a pole for use outside. This size of housing takes two
8 W tubes together with their inverters.
(b)   Stainless steel reflector fitted above a tube lamp to reflect light away from the
ceiling and towards the floor.

Formula method for lighting levels

For conditions not covered by Table 6.3, the amount of lighting required can be calculated from formulas. Full details about this method are given in Appendix A.

Self-contained systems

Water pumps and refrigerators can be used together with other appliances in a system. However, it is usually better to run them from their own array of modules as a self-contained system (see Figure 6.11).

Figure 6.11   Examples of appliances that are usually supplied as complete packages.
(a)   Water pump as a surface-mounted unit. The capacity is about 12 m³ (3000 gal) per
day with a solar array of peak power 160 W at 25 °C receiving daily insolation of six
peak-hours per day. This capacity is for water drawn up from a maximum depth below
pump level of 4.5 m (15 ft) and pumped to 5 m (16 ft) above pump level. (Source
Chronar Ltd.)
(b)   Vaccine refrigerator with 60 l (2 ft³) capacity for vaccine on the left and capacity for
making 2.7 kg (6 lb) of ice per day on the right. The daily electrical requirement is about
250 W h for a room temperature of 32 °C (90 °F). (Source FNMA.)

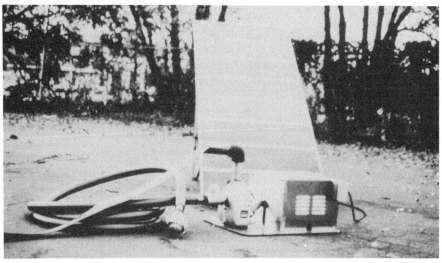

(a)

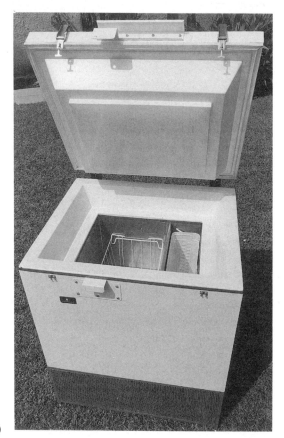

(b)

Water pumps

A pump with a small 12 V d.c. motor can be connected straight into a solar system for pumping water. For large pumps though, it is better to do without batteries and run the pump directly from its own array of modules as a self-contained system. If water is required when power is not available from the array, it can be stored in a tank above ground and distributed by gravity. This is simpler and less expensive than using batteries to store electricity.

In self-contained systems, the pump is usually a centrifugal or turbine type which is designed to cope with a varying power supply. The output of water varies with the irradiance reaching the modules. Two systems that are becoming well established are described here briefly. For more details, refer to other books and suppliers (see Appendices F and G).

For shallow wells and surface sources of water, the motor and pump are combined in a single unit that can float on the water source. The motor is d.c.-powered for direct connection to the array of modules. By using electronic commutation, the motor is brushless for reliability and low maintenance. A medium-size system can pump about 100 m^3 (21 000 gallons) per day through a head of 4 m (13 ft). This capacity requires six to twelve modules depending on the local climate. The system shown in Figure 6.11(a) has the motor and pump unit out of the water.

In systems intended for deep wells, the combined motor and pump are submerged in the water at the bottom of the well. The motor is an a.c. induction type powered by an inverter. The inverter is specially designed to start the motor and has a variable frequency of a.c. for matching array output to the motor load. Since the inverters are matched to the pump, they usually achieve an efficiency better than 90 per cent. A medium-size system can pump about 20 m^3 (5000 gallons) per day through a head of 30 m. This capacity requires fourteen to twenty-eight modules depending on the local climate.

For larger installations, a jack pump may be more appropriate (see Figure 1.2(c)).

Solar-powered water pumps are good for providing a regular and reliable supply of water for a remote village. For irrigating crops, the cost of a solar pumping system should be analyzed more critically. The cost should clearly be less than the value of extra crops over a few years which are directly gained through irrigation.

When comparing the cost of solar-powered to diesel-powered pumps, solar pumps are often found to be cheaper for a flow of less than 50 m^3 per day through a head of less than 20 m (although this varies with local conditions, such as daily sunshine levels and cost of fuel). In other applications where solar pumping is more expensive, the extra cost may be compensated for by higher reliability and lack of running costs compared to diesel.

Refrigerators for vaccine storage

The power requirement of refrigerators is difficult to estimate reliably. It depends on a number of factors, such as the surrounding temperature, how much is put inside, and the number of times the door is opened.

A major application of solar-powered refrigerators is keeping vaccine cold, as part of the 'cold chain' from manufacture in a factory to immunization in the field. Vaccine refrigerators are required to maintain vaccine between 0 and 8 °C (32 and 46 °F) at all times. In addition, there is normally a requirement for a separate freezer compartment to freeze ice packs which are used for transporting vaccines in cold boxes.

Solar-powered refrigerators operate on the same principle as normal compression refrigerators. Low-voltage d.c. motors are used for the compressor, and these are connected directly to the batteries. They should be run as self-contained systems. No other appliances are connected to avoid the risk of draining the batteries and not leaving sufficient charge to keep the contents cold.

Sizes available range from 10 to 200 litres (0.35–7 ft^3) for vaccine storage and ice production rates of up to 5 kg (11 lb) per day. The electricity requirement for storing 100 litres of vaccine is 300–500 W h per day for a surrounding temperature of 32 °C (90 °F). Solar refrigerators have high levels of insulation to minimize gain of heat through their walls. Nevertheless their consumption of electricity is very dependent on the surrounding temperature. In some models, the electrical requirement just given doubles when the temperature rises to 43 °C (110 °F).

☐ *Questions*

1. Name two factors that determine whether an appliance can be used in a small solar electric system.

2. Why should low-voltage d.c. appliances be recommended in preference to mains-voltage a.c. appliances that require a power inverter?

3. Name two types of power inverter and describe briefly the way they operate.

4. One size of portable radio uses four dry cells. Describe two methods for running this radio in a 12 V solar system.

5. Which type of lamp used in solar systems has the highest efficacy (in lm/W) and why is this a good feature?

6. What are the differences between GLS and halogen light bulbs?

7. Why should rooms with solar-powered lighting be painted white?

Part Two

Planning, installation, and operation

7 Sources of information and basic costing

This chapter is about getting started on a solar electric system and finding out what is available. There are several steps to go through which are summarized in Figure 7.1.

The people who are interested in small solar electric systems and are reading this guide can be divided into two groups. One group comprises potential users who are considering a solar system for a place where they live or work. The other group comprises electricians who want to install solar systems and hopefully get an income from this work.

For both groups, the first three steps in Figure 7.1 are the same. After visiting a system, the steps that follow depend on which group of people you are in.

This chapter goes through each of these steps in detail.

Visiting a solar electric system

This book contains details about many aspects of solar electric systems. However, just reading this book is not a substitute for actually seeing a solar system yourself.

Finding out where some working solar systems are may be difficult. Here are some suggestions for sources of information:

☐ Manufacturers of solar equipment (addresses listed in Appendix G) who can suggest the nearest supplier.
☐ Advertisements in newpapers and magazines for solar equipment.
☐ Government bodies such as the ministry or department concerned with energy.
☐ Aid agencies and other NGOs (non-government organizations) involved with development. The WHO (World Health Organization) publishes 'product information sheets' in English, French, and Spanish about solar-powered refrigerators for vaccine storage. (See Appendix F).

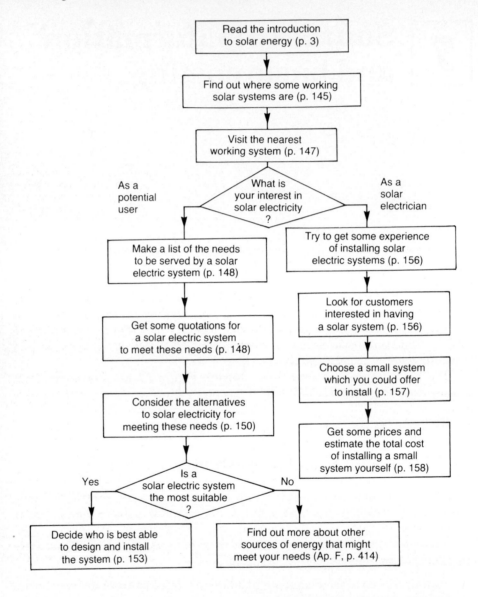

Figure 7.1   Summary of steps involved in finding out about solar electric systems (Ap. appendix, p. page references to text):

☐   steps involved
◇   decisions

Suppliers of solar equipment may have set up a simple system in their office or showroom. This system is used to demonstrate how lamps and other appliances are powered by a solar module. However, to get a better impression of a proper system, ask for a list of some working systems. Although visiting one of these systems may be time-consuming and expensive, the knowledge gained is much more valuable than just seeing a demonstration in a showroom.

When visiting a working system, try to meet the people there who were most involved with getting the system installed. Take along a ruler to measure some dimensions, and a notebook. If a camera is available to you, taking photographs is a good way to record how the modules are supported, the type of control unit, and other details. Also take this book. It may help to answer questions on the visit.

Here is a list of questions to put to the people involved with the system:

1. Details of system:
    (a) How many solar modules?
    (b) What type of modules (make, model, overall dimensions, number of cells, dimensions of each cell)?
    (c) Where are the modules mounted (roof, pole, ground in an enclosure)?
    (d) Which way are the modules tilted (angle of tilt from horizontal and whether towards north, south, or another direction)?
    (e) How many batteries?
    (f) What type of batteries (make, model, overall dimensions)?
    (g) Type of control units (make, model)? (Take a photograph of the front or make a list of the labels next to each of the lights and buttons.)
    (h) How many and what type of appliances (make, model, wattage)?
    (i) How is the whole system arranged? (Draw rough sketch showing the relative positions of each part.)

2. Installation:
    (a) Who designed it (name, address, telephone number)?
    (b) Who installed it (name, address, telephone number)?
    (c) Who supplied the parts (names, addresses, telephone numbers)?
    (d) How long did it take for the equipment to be delivered?
    (e) How long did it take to be installed before it was working properly?
    (f) Were there any major problems during installation (e.g. wrong or damaged parts supplied)?

3. Reliability:
    (a) How long has it been working?
    (b) Do all the appliances work?
    (c) Does it work as originally planned?
    (d) Is it easy to operate?
    (e) Have any parts broken down yet?

(f) Who does the repair of broken parts?

(g) How well does it work during cloudy periods (number of appliances that cannot be used when cloudy)?

4. Costs:

(a) What was the total cost at the start (parts, delivery, installation)?

(b) Are there any running costs (e.g. battery water, replacement light bulbs, extra watchman)?

(c) If it breaks down, how much are the repair charges (parts, labour)?

5. Comparison to your own site:

(a) Are the weather conditions similar (sunshine, temperature, wind, rainfall)?

(b) Are the sites similar (flat or hilly, rural or urban, security problems, vandalism, animals roaming around)?

(c) How do the needs compare (number of users, type of appliances)?

6. Opinions:

(a) Does it live up to their expectations?

(b) Do they have any ideas for improving their system (e.g. different arrangement of parts, more solar modules, more controls)?

(c) What do they recommend for your site and your needs?

Some of the questions may seem too detailed at this stage but it is good to get these details now. They will become useful later when learning more about each part of a system.

After visiting a system, the question to ask yourself is whether you now think that solar electricity can serve your own needs.

Defining needs and getting a quotation

Energy is needed for many activities, such as cooking, getting water, lighting, space heating, water heating, transport, and running appliances. Having seen a real system, potential users should be in a good position to know for themselves whether solar electricity can meet some of their own needs.

For example, solar electricity is good for lighting and running a cassette player, but is not suitable for cooking or space heating because too many solar modules are needed. A solar system is simple to operate and does not require regular supplies of fuel. On the other hand, the full power needed to run all the appliances may not be available from the system after a number of days of very cloudy weather.

To get some idea of how much a system might cost, write to suppliers of solar equipment and ask for quotations. Describe the sort of application, which could be one of the following:

- ☐ Home.
- ☐ School.
- ☐ Community centre.
- ☐ Health centre.
- ☐ Hospital.
- ☐ Mosque.
- ☐ Church.
- ☐ Workshop.
- ☐ Office.
- ☐ Shop.
- ☐ Bar.
- ☐ Farm.

Include in your letter to the suppliers a list of the appliances of interest. Here are some examples:

- ☐ Lighting (number and use of areas needing light).
- ☐ Low-voltage d.c. appliances, e.g. television, cassette player.
- ☐ Refrigerator (volume needed and type of items to cool).
- ☐ Water pump (pumping rate needed and height between source of water and outlet from pump).
- ☐ Electric fencing unit (length needed and type of animals to contain).
- ☐ Air-circulating fan.
- ☐ High-voltage fly killer.
- ☐ Mains voltage a.c. appliances, e.g. electric typewriter.

Also include some details about the site:

- ☐ Type of location (flat or hilly, rural or in a small town).
- ☐ Size of buildings (number and use of the rooms).
- ☐ Draw a plan with a rough scale or some dimensions and show the direction of north.
- ☐ Whether the buildings are already wired or not.
- ☐ Roughly the amount of money that can be afforded for a system.

There may be grants or loans available for installing a solar system. When writing to suppliers of solar equipment, ask about organizations that assist with financing solar systems. The suppliers may know which groups are favoured for receiving grants, e.g. schools, hospitals, and small industries.

Considering alternatives to solar electricity

There are alternative ways of meeting your needs. Here is a list of alternative energy sources that may also be worth considering:

☐ Connection to the mains utility supply (electricity grid).
☐ Diesel- or petrol-powered generator.
☐ Wind generator or wind pump.
☐ Micro-hydro generator on a river.
☐ Hybrid system of solar electricity with a diesel, wind, or hydro generator.
☐ Regular charging of batteries by taking them to the nearest charging point.
☐ Paraffin (kerosene) for lighting, cooking, or refrigeration.
☐ Bottle gas (LPG) for cooking or refrigeration.
☐ Solar heating.
☐ Biogas pit producing methane for cooking.
☐ Efficient stove for wood or charcoal.
☐ Animal power.
☐ Human power, e.g. hand pump, pedal power.

Further information on some of these energy sources can be obtained from the books listed in Appendix F.

Cost comparison

One way to compare solar electricity to the alternatives listed above is by how much they cost. A simple method of doing the comparison is to estimate the total cost of each energy source over, say, ten years or the lifetime of the equipment, whichever is shorter. The costing is done by dividing it into three parts:

1. *Starting cost* – the amount of money spent to buy, transport and install the system.

2. *Annual running costs* – the amount of money spent on operating and repairing the system each year.

3. *Investment costs* – the total amount of interest that must be paid during use of the system on loans taken out at the start.

Solar water pumping: A handbook (Kenna and Gillett, 1985; see Appendix F) has a detailed procedure for comparing costs of solar electric water pumps and alternatives for a variety of situations.

Comparison of solar cell modules to generators

People are much more familiar with generators than solar electricity. Their first choice when considering a source of electricity is usually a diesel- or petrol-powered generator. The advantages and disadvantages of solar cell modules and generators are compared here.

Generators generally have an electrical output from about 1 kW upwards. This high output is needed to power equipment with large motors but can also power a large number of lamps. In a system with a generator, the lamps are often left on all the time that the generator is running. This is because turning off lamps hardly reduces the consumption of fuel. Also for a three-phase generator dynamo, the lamps may need to be left on to keep the phases in balance.

A typical size of solar cell module is 35 W_P. At first sight, solar electricity is much more expensive because perhaps thirty solar modules are needed to match the output of a 1 kW generator. However, if the main use of a generator is for lighting, most homes and institutions can manage quite well with less powerful lamps and fewer of them. Furthermore, not all the lamps need to be on at the same time.

With this approach to lighting, the total power required is reduced well below 1 kW and only a few modules are needed. In this way, the cost of solar electricity with efficient lighting is not very different from the cost of a small generator.

Advantages of solar electricity

Once the loads are minimized, a solar electric system has many advantages to offer compared to generators:

☐ No running costs of buying or transporting fuel.
☐ No dependence on regular supplies of fuel. For many countries that are in or close to the tropics, the amount of sunshine available each day is high for most months of the year.
☐ Solar cells have no moving parts so the system is less likely to break down than the engine or dynamo in a generator. Also a medium-size solar electric system can usually continue to work when one part fails, such as one module in the array or one battery in the storage system.
☐ Installation and maintenance are straightforward, requiring no special expertise or tools.
☐ A solar electric system can be gradually enlarged in small steps. When a generator is found to be too small, it must be completely replaced by a larger one.
☐ The low voltage produced by solar modules is safer than mains voltage and the system does not have to fulfil strict electrical regulations. This keeps down the cost of fittings and the wiring is simpler without an earth.
☐ By storing solar electricity in rechargeable batteries, power is available all the time. A generator has to be started up fully even when only one lamp is needed and this is very wasteful of fuel.
☐ Solar cells work silently and have no exhaust pollution.

Most countries have to import oil to meet their needs for paraffin (kerosene), petrol, and diesel. This uses valuable foreign currency, especially when the price of oil rises. Many governments are encouraging the use of solar modules in place of generators to reduce the country's dependence on imported oil.

Disadvantages of solar electricity

There are some disadvantages of solar electricity compared to generators:

☐ Solar modules are not economical for high-power (high-wattage) appliances, such as heaters and large motors.
☐ The supply of spare parts and expertise for solar systems is not so well established yet, although this situation is changing rapidly for many countries.
☐ The low-voltage d.c. produced by solar modules is less versatile because many appliances can run only from a.c. mains voltage.
☐ Since the source of energy is sunlight, there is less electricity generated during cloudy weather.

Problem of cloudy weather

The last disadvantage to do with the weather can make users become disillusioned with solar electricity. This may happen even though their solar system is serving them better than a generator could.

This attitude may develop because the 'fuel' for a solar system is sunshine which is free and becomes taken for granted. With a generator, the fuel must be bought, transported, and put into the fuel tank. When there is no fuel, users do not blame the generator itself for this problem.

With a solar system, the users only have to switch appliances on and off. Meanwhile the solar modules are outside all the time 'harvesting' sunshine. Users may forget that there must be enough sunshine each week to keep the batteries charged up. When there is not enough sunshine and the batteries get too low to power the loads, the first reaction of most users is to blame the solar system rather than the weather.

Solar electric systems can be designed according to the local climate so that they always provide enough electricity. This approach to design is very important for critical installations which must always work, such as communication repeater stations and navigation lamps. The solar systems serving these installations have lots of modules and batteries to make sure there is always electricity in even the cloudiest weather. The installation may even have a back-up generator that is automatically switched on when the batteries are too low.

In homes and small institutions, designing for the worst weather conditions makes the system expensive. Also it is not really necessary in these applications for all the appliances to operate at all times. There are some appliances that can be used less or switched off completely when the batteries get low during cloudy weather.

Importance of proper design

It is important that small solar systems are designed properly so that all the loads can be used for most months of a year. This is called *sizing* and is dealt with in Chapter 8. However, there will always come a time of unusual weather conditions when there are a lot of clouds. The control unit in the system should warn users in some way that the batteries are getting low so that the users can decide which appliances not to use. An alternative method of preventing damage to lead–acid batteries is to have an automatic disconnect in the control unit (more details on this in Chapter 4).

The plans and installation

Here are some points to consider when choosing the person or organization who will plan and install the system:

1. How much is their quotation for the parts?
2. Which parts are imported from another country?
3. How much is their labour charge for doing the installation?
4. What are their delivery and installation times?
5. How many solar electric systems have they already installed?
6. Do their past customers recommend them? (Check references.)
7. How far is their office from your site?
8. Do they provide free service and replacement of parts after installation (period of guarantee)?
9. How much do they charge for coming to do repairs (after the guarantee period)?
10. Are they specialists in solar electricity or are they mostly involved in some other field of technology?

Try to involve a local electrician in as much of the work as possible. Local electricians are in the best position to provide a good service during the years of operation of the system.

Systems supplied as a complete package

A system can be bought as a complete package which contains all the required parts. An example of a low-cost complete package for a home system is shown in Figure 7.2.

Figure 7.2   Example of a low-cost complete solar system for lighting a house.
Specifications:
☐   solar module with single crystal silicon cells (12 W_P);
☐   control unit containing a sealed lead-acid battery (12 V, 8 A h), charge
     regulator, low-voltage disconnect, individual switches for lamps and a low-
     voltage adaptor for a radio;
☐   tungsten halogen bulbs (5 W) with own reflectors;
☐   cables with plugs;
☐   cable clips and spare bulbs.
For better reliability during cloudy periods, the battery in the control unit should be
replaced by a separate battery with a capacity of 30–50 A h. (Source Helios
Technology SpA.)

Buying a system as a complete package has several advantages:

1.   A single supplier so only one order and delivery are required.
2.   The package is a complete set of parts so there are no unexpected costs.
3.   The parts are designed or selected specifically for solar systems and have a
     guarantee for this use.
4.   All parts are compatible with each other for ease of installation and efficient
     operation.
5.   If installation is offered, the supplier then takes full responsibility for
     ensuring that the system works properly.

Self-contained systems should always be bought as a complete package. Examples of appliances used in self-contained systems are water pumps and refrigerators for vaccine storage (see Figure 6.11). Suppliers of these systems have extensive records of meteorological data for most parts of the world. This enables them to size each part of the system properly since they know the electrical requirements of the appliance.

Reducing costs

A complete package may be an expensive approach for systems with a variety of appliances and that contain mostly imported parts. A cheaper system can be assembled by comparing prices of parts from different solar equipment suppliers and other sources, such as auto-spares shops.

Using parts that are commonly available or made locally is recommended. For example, 12 V bulbs for cars are much easier and cheaper to replace than 12 V bulbs that fit only mains-type sockets which are less common. A battery meter can be made by a local electrician according to one of the designs in Chapter 13. Compared to an imported control unit, the locally made meter is quicker to supply, cheaper, less complicated, and easier to have repaired.

It is important at this stage to consider the costs of having repairs done and getting replacement parts once the system is operating. Local fund-raising to start a system is more productive than collecting money later to pay the running costs. Grants and loans may be restricted to capital items (the starting costs) with no contribution to running costs.

Level of involvement of users

The parts of a solar system are very reliable and easy to use but, as for any equipment, the system can go wrong when not cared for. The continuing success of a system depends to a large extent on how interested the users are in it.

Potential users could stop reading this book here and simply place an order for a solar system with a supplier. However, it is not recommended to pass all responsibility for planning and installation of the system to an outsider.

A good way of generating and maintaining interest is to get involved at some level in the design since the basics of solar electricity are not very complicated or difficult. Here is a list of some of the benefits to be gained from learning more about solar electricity:

1. Understand exactly what is being offered by suppliers of solar equipment.
2. Keep costs down by investigating local sources of supply.
3. Appreciate how the system can be run effectively.
4. Have the knowledge and ability to do the maintenance tasks properly.
5. Sort out minor problems immediately without the cost and delay of waiting for a visit by an electrician.

Advice for electricians

Gaining experience

If you are an electrician wanting to get involved in installing solar systems, you should first visit a working solar system (see earlier section of this chapter). Your next concern should be to gain experience of installing a system, but this may be difficult to do. Here are some suggestions:

1. When contacting suppliers of solar equipment, ask about training courses and offer to help with any installation work that they have.
2. Offer to act as an agent in your area for a supplier of solar equipment. Ask the supplier to give you the price for a complete home system. The supplier should also send you datasheets about the home system and printed enquiry forms. If you manage to find a customer, the supplier should involve you in the installation work under supervision.
3. Many existing solar systems develop minor problems. When visiting a system which has some problems, investigate the problem as much as you can and offer to follow it up yourself with the original supplier of the equipment. If the solution looks simple, try to sort out the problem yourself.
4. Try to make a voltage adaptor according to one of the designs in Chapter 14. The voltage adaptor can be sold to someone who wants to run a cassette player (needing less than 12 V d.c.) from a car battery. Making this circuit builds confidence in the techniques of low voltages. It also provides an income and possibly a future customer for a solar system.
5. If you have some funds already, buy a small solar module and gain experience with it. It can then be used as a demonstration system to attract customers.

Looking for customers

The best possibilities for finding potential customers are in areas without grid electricity. Here are some suggestions for types of people in these areas who may be interested:

1. People that work in a town and come home to their family living in a rural area. In the town, these people are used to the comforts of electric lighting and a television. They would like these comforts at their rural home. Also a town job means they are more likely to be able to afford a small solar system.
2. People who use a car battery to run a television or cassette player. When the battery becomes flat, they carry the battery to the nearest charging point. To get a solar system, all they need is a solar module and module support because they already have a 12 V d.c. appliance and a battery.

3. Institutions such as boarding schools and hospitals that use paraffin lamps at night.
4. Shops and bars that stay open at night. If the owners expect to do more business with better illumination, they can calculate how quickly the system will pay for itself by the extra income.

'Selling solar'

Just as you visited a working solar electric system at the start, your potential customers will also want to see a working system. Make sure that you know where all the nearest systems are and that they are indeed working satisfactorily.

After installing your first system, it is now a demonstration system to attract more customers. When called to solve a problem in a system you have installed, try to sort out the problem quickly. For getting future customers, remember that it is very important to keep your past customers satisfied by providing a good service.

Some people think that solar electricity 'does not work very well' because it has a lower voltage than the mains supply. They believe perhaps that a 20 W mains lamp gives much more light than a 20 W 12 V lamp. You can reassure people of this misunderstanding by showing them a system working at night.

In principle solar electricity can run all the appliances people are used to seeing in a town. In practice solar electricity is only cost effective for low-power appliances. Read the earlier section of this chapter on considering alternatives to solar electricity to make sure that solar electricity really is suitable for your customers.

Potential customers may say that the cost of a solar system is too much. Remember to mention the following points:

1. There are no expensive running costs, such as fuel to buy.
2. Customers can take out a loan. The money they regularly spent before on fuel each month can be used to pay back the loan.
3. A solar electric system can start small with one module, one battery, and one appliance. More parts are added later as more money becomes available.

Choice of system to offer

When starting to look for customers, you must have a system to offer and discuss with them. Start with a system that has the following four features:

1. Small – use just one module and one battery.
2. Simple – provide power just for lighting, a cassette player, and a 12 V d.c. television.
3. Reliable – use a medium-size solar module rather than the smallest one

available. Use a better-quality lead–acid battery than the cheapest ones available for cars. Include only a few appliances.

4. Low cost – use a *self-regulating* solar module (explained in Chapter 6) with an *expanded-scale voltmeter* (described in Chapter 13). Use local sources of supply where possible.

Examples of such systems are shown in Figures 1.3(a) and 7.2.

When choosing the solar module, take advice from the supplier for the size of battery to use and the number of appliances it can run. Guidance on these aspects is also given in Chapter 8.

Estimating costs

Electricians who want to sell their services must have a realistic idea of how much a solar system costs, since one of the first questions asked by a customer will be 'What is the price?' Tables 7.1–7.3 show how to calculate the costs for materials, labour, and tools.

Suppliers of solar modules can usually provide all the parts for a solar system. Buying everything from one supplier ensures that all the parts are compatible and discounts may be offered. Disadvantages of one supplier are less choice of parts and higher prices. The solar equipment supplier may be a long distance away in the main town so getting extra parts will be slow and expensive.

Table 7.1 *Calculating the cost of materials.*

Item	Source	Unit cost	Quantity	Cost
	1. 2. (see below)			
	Total cost of parts listed above:			
	Allowances for extra materials (say 10% of above figure):			
	Delivery to site and other transport costs:			
	Total cost of materials:			

Details of sources: 1. Module supplier
                     2. Source of batteries
                     3.
                     .
                     .
                     .

Table 7.2 *Calculating the cost of labour.*

Job category	Hourly rate	Hours required	Cost

Total labour charge:

Incidental expenses (transport, food, accommodation):

Sub-total of labour cost:

Allowance for doing repairs within first year
(say 10% of above figure):

Total cost of labour:

Table 7.3 *Listing the cost of tools that are needed.*

Item	Cost

Total cost of tools:

A list is given below of other types of supplier who should also be approached (see Figure 7.3). Start with suppliers in your nearest town. Ask for prices and details of all the items listed under each type of supplier. Some of the specifications and other details about the items may not mean anything to you but they can be found elsewhere in this book by using the index:

1. Solar equipment suppliers:
    (a) solar modules (ask for datasheet);
    (b) mounting equipment for modules;
    (c) lead–acid and nickel–cadmium batteries;
    (d) control units (ask for a full list of the features);
    (e) fluorescent lamps with inverters;
    (f) low-voltage bulbs and the fittings to hold them;
    (g) low-voltage d.c. appliances, e.g. refrigerators and fans;
    (h) power inverters;
    (i) self-contained systems, e.g. water pumps and electric fencing;
    (j) list of existing users.

2. Electrical shops:
    (a) cables;
    (b) connectors;
    (c) plastic trunking (for surface mounting inside);
    (d) PVC conduit (for outside and underground routes);
    (e) wall clips for cables and conduit;
    (f) wall switches;
    (g) time-lag switch;
    (h) socket outlets and plugs;
    (i) junction boxes;
    (j) fuse boxes, fuses, and MCBs (miniature circuit breakers);
    (k) fluorescent tube lamps;
    (l) lamp fittings sealed from the weather for outside use.

3. Auto-spares shops:
    (a) lead–acid batteries for cars and trucks;
    (b) distilled water and acid for lead–acid batteries;
    (c) battery terminals;
    (d) battery hydrometer;
    (e) fuse holders (in-line type and boxes);
    (f) cables;
    (g) crimp and spade connectors;
    (h) toggle switches;
    (i) 12 and 24 V bulbs with a single filament and bulb sockets;
    (j) tungsten halogen bulbs;
    (k) fog lamps (sealed units for mounting on bumper);

(a)

(b)

Figure 7.3 Examples of suppliers. (Source Peter Thornley.)
(a) Radio repair and electronics shop.
(b) School supplier for science equipment.

(l)   12 V d.c. appliances, e.g. fan motor;
(m)   low-voltage adaptor (plugs into the cigarette lighter socket for running a cassette player);
(n)   voltmeters and ammeters;
(o)   compression springs (for use in a cell holder such as the one in Figure 15.3(b)).

4.   Radio repair and electronics shops:
(a)   switches (at least 1 A rating);
(b)   diodes;
(c)   plugs and sockets for mains and low-voltage electricity;
(d)   screwdriver, pliers, and wire cutters;
(e)   insulation strippers;
(f)   multimeter;
(g)   low-voltage adaptor (plugs into the cigarette lighter socket of a car for running a cassette player);
(h)   nickel–cadmium batteries;
(i)   12 V d.c. television;
(j)   soldering iron and solder;
(k)   voltmeters and ammeters;
(l)   transistors and other electronic components (for making the circuits in Chapters 12–16).

5.   Hardware shops:
(a)   screwdriver, pliers, and wire cutters;
(b)   insulation strippers;
(c)   hammer and wall punch;
(d)   wood saw;
(e)   small and large hacksaws;
(f)   hand drill and drill bits;
(g)   cables;
(h)   mounting materials, e.g. wood, steel and aluminium;
(i)   fencing;
(j)   white paint and paint brushes;
(k)   screws and tacks;
(l)   clips for cables and conduits;
(m)   padlock;
(n)   metal and plastic boxes;
(o)   soldering iron and solder for electronics (not the type for metal workers and plumbers).

6.   School science equipment suppliers:
(a)   voltmeters;
(b)   ammeters;

(c)   nickel–cadmium batteries;
(d)   12 V d.c. bulbs;
(e)   distilled water;
(f)   diodes.

7. Suppliers for boating and caravanning accessories:
(a)   deep-cycle batteries;
(b)   12 V d.c. appliances, e.g. two-way radio;
(c)   power inverters.

8. Workshops for large vehicles such as buses and trucks:
(a)   24 V d.c. bulbs;
(b)   24 V d.c. appliances.

☐ Questions

1. Why is a visit to a working solar electric system recommended before deciding to purchase any solar equipment?

2. When comparing solar electricity to other technologies, what are the three types of cost for a system that should be considered?

3. Solar electricity has many advantages compared to systems using a generator. List three reasons for each of the following advantages:
    (a) Lower running costs.
    (b) Easier to install.
    (c) More reliable.
    (d) More convenient to use.

4. In a generator-based system, why is it usual for all the lights to be left on while the generator is running?

5. How can the power required for lighting in a solar system be kept low so that only a few solar modules are needed?

6. For many countries, solar modules have to be imported, so why might the governments of these countries encourage their use by lower import duty and other assistance?

7. What are the problems of cloudy weather for a solar system?

8. List some of the benefits that potential users can gain by being involved in the design and installation of a solar system.

8 Sizing a solar electric system

When people first consider using solar electricity, they want to know exactly how many appliances can be powered. *Sizing* a solar electric system is to do with this aspect. It is about calculating the number of solar modules and batteries that are needed to run the required number of appliances.

Figure 8.1 summarizes the steps given in this chapter for sizing a solar system. The first step is to add up the daily requirement for electricity of each of the appliances. This is based on the power rating of each appliance and the average length of time it will be used in one day.

The next step in sizing is to calculate how much electricity will be produced by one module. This calculation uses the weather records of sunshine for the site and the current output from one module. There are maps in this chapter of sunshine measurements for most countries which can provide an approximate estimate for the site. If a summary of weather records for the area of the site is available, it can be used to make a better estimate of the daily output expected from a module. A procedure for correcting the measurements according to the tilt angle of the module is given in Appendix B.

The number of modules is then calculated using the daily requirement of appliances and the daily output expected from one module.

Batteries are used in a solar electric system to store electricity generated during the day for use at night. Batteries also store the extra electricity generated during sunny days for use during and after cloudy days. Sizing the batteries is based on the daily requirement for electricity and the number of days of storage that is needed. Battery sizing also depends on the recommended cycle depth for the type of battery to be used.

Limitations of sizing

The procedure for sizing summarized in this chapter gives exact answers for the numbers of modules and batteries that are needed. However, it is important to

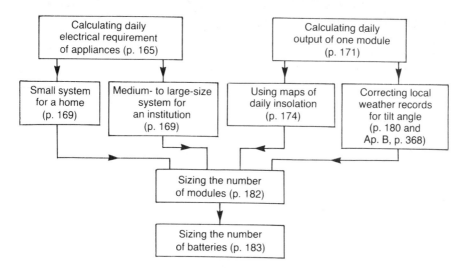

Figure 8.1 Summary of Chapter 8 about sizing a system with cross-references to one appendix (Ap. appendix, p. page references to text).

realize that no sizing procedure is perfect, so the answers cannot be relied upon totally. The main problems with sizing are as follows:

☐ The weather records for the site may not be detailed enough to do an accurate calculation of the module output.
☐ Since the weather records are a summary of the past, they can only suggest what may happen in the future when the solar electric system is operating.
☐ It is difficult to predict accurately how much electricity will be used each day.

One way of overcoming these limitations is to have an excess of modules and batteries which allow for periods of very bad weather, but this will obviously make the system more expensive. For low-cost solar systems, it is best to avoid over-loading the system by starting with very few appliances. If many appliances are installed, users must accept that some appliances may need to be turned off occasionally when the batteries are at a low state of charge.

Daily requirement for electricity

Units of consumption for electricity

For homes connected to a mains utility supply, there is a meter as part of the consumer's control unit. This meter measures the amount of electricity consumed in kilowatt-hours (kW h) or *units*. The utility company sells the mains electricity at a certain price per unit.

The power rating of a typical appliance used in a solar electric system is measured in watts rather than kilowatts. So instead of kW h, the W h (watt-hour) unit of consumption is used for doing calculations of solar electricity use in small solar systems. (The W h unit is one-thousandth the size of the kWh unit.)

To calculate the daily requirement in W h per day for a solar system, you, the system designer, must first list all the appliances that are expected to be used in the system. For each appliance, find its power and decide the amount of time in hours that it will be used each day. The calculation of daily requirement for each appliance is as follows:

$$\boxed{\begin{array}{c}\text{Power of}\\\text{appliance}\\\text{(W)}\end{array}} \times \boxed{\begin{array}{c}\text{Expected daily}\\\text{use of appliance}\\\text{(hours per day)}\end{array}} = \boxed{\boxed{\begin{array}{c}\text{Daily requirement}\\\text{of one appliance}\\\text{(W h per day)}\end{array}}} \qquad \text{(8.1)}$$

The power or wattage of an appliance is usually written somewhere on the outside of the appliance. It can also be found on the electrical tag attached to the cable, or in the instruction book. On light bulbs, there may not be a power figure but only numbers with units of 'V' and 'A'. Multiply these two numbers together to get the power of the bulb in W.

Consumption of mains electricity for a typical home

Electricians and users who are familiar with mains electricity will have some idea about the power requirements of mains appliances. Table 8.1 is an example of the calculation of electrical consumption for a home connected to the mains with a typical range of mains voltage appliances. The total at the bottom of the table shows that this home uses about 6000 W h per day which is six of the kW h units of electricity. When supplied by the mains utility supply or a generator, 6 kW h per day is not too expensive.

The output from a solar cell module of 40 W peak output can reach about 150 W h per day (at the system voltage) at a typical site. Therefore at least forty modules are needed to meet a daily requirement of 6000 W h per day (from 6000 divided by 150). This is a very large number of solar modules for just one home considering that one 40 W module can cost about US$ 300 (at 1990 prices).

Clearly it is not economical to use solar electricity for running some of the appliances that are found in a home connected to the mains or a generator. When sizing for a solar system, the daily requirement can be reduced significantly from the values in Table 8.1. Reductions are made by carefully deciding which appliances need to be run on solar electricity and for how long they really need to be used each day.

Table 8.1 *Typical use of electricity for a home connected to a mains supply. 'Electrical requirement' for each appliance is calculated using Formula (8.1). The total daily requirement of almost 6000 Wh per day is much higher than could be economically supplied by solar electricity.*

Appliances	Appliance power (W)	Expected daily use (hours per day)	Electrical requirement (W h per day)
Four fluorescent tubes, 20 W each	80	3	240
Two filament bulbs, 40 W each	80	3	240
Cassette player	5	4	20
Colour television	50	4	200
Cooling fan	50	6	300
Refrigerator	120	10	1200
Clothes iron	1000	0.25	250
Electric kettle	1000	0.5	500
Electric cooker	3000	1	3000
Total daily requirement of electricity (W h per day):			5950

Estimating the consumption for a solar electric system

Table 8.2 gives details of power and voltage requirements for a range of appliances normally used in solar electric systems. This table should help in deciding which appliances are sensible to consider when designing a solar system. The numbers in the 'Power requirement' column are used for the calculation of electrical consumption in W h per day.

System voltages for solar electricity are usually 12 V d.c. or 24 V d.c. The 'Voltage needed' column shows which appliances are available at these voltages for direct connection in a low-voltage d.c. solar system. 'Below 12' means that a low-voltage adaptor is required and 'Mains a.c.' means that a power inverter is required. (See Chapter 6 for details about voltage adaptors and inverters.)

Lighting

In solar systems where the main use is for lighting, lamps have to be chosen carefully in order to make the best use of the electricity. Fluorescent tube lamps are recommended because they produce at least three times more light than filament bulbs for the same consumption of electricity. This is shown by Table 6.2 which compares efficacy values for four types of lamp. Tube lamps also last longer than bulbs.

In addition to efficacy and expected life, the cost of the lamps and their

Table 8.2 *Details of power and voltage ratings for typical appliances used in a solar electric system.*

Appliances	Power requirement (W)	Voltage needed (V) d.c.			a.c. mains
		Below 12	12	24	
Fluorescent tube and inverter	8–40		×	×	
Filament bulb	8–40		×	×	
Cassette player	2–30	×	×		
Small B/W television	≥12		×		
Small colour television	≥50		×		×
Video cassette recorder	≥30				×
CB radio on receive	≥4		×		
CB radio on transmit	≥10		×		
Cooling fan	≥100		×		×
Small computer	≥10		×		×
Electric typewriter	≥30				×
Siren (to scare intruders)	10		×		
Burglar alarm system	≥1	×			
Soldering iron	30–100		×		×
Electric drill	≥20		×		×
Sewing machine	≥30		×		×
Refrigerator	100–400		×		×
Microwave oven	≥1000				×

fittings should be taken in to consideration. Each fluorescent tube lamp needs its own inverter which makes the whole lamp unit more expensive than a simple 12 V filament bulb and socket. Halogen bulbs with reflectors are a good alternative to fluorescent lamps. Despite the lower efficacy of ordinary filament bulbs, they can be considered where lighting is needed only for short periods, such as bedrooms, toilet, corridors, and store room. In these places, the use of filament bulb lamps can help to keep down the total cost of the installation.

However, where filament bulbs are installed, it is important that they are not left on for longer than they are really needed. In large installations where users may forget to switch them off, time-delay switches which automatically go off after a few minutes are recommended (see Figure 9.6).

For selecting the amount of illumination, Table 6.3 gives recommended lamps and power ratings for a variety of applications. Full details of a formula method which can be used for all applications is given in Appendix A.

Table 8.3 *Example of the electrical requirements of a simple solar electric system for a home. 'Electrical requirement' for each appliance is calculated using Formula (8.1).*

Appliances	Appliance power (W)	Expected daily use (hours per day)	Electrical requirement (W h per day)
Tube lamp for living room	8	4	32
Tube lamp for kitchen	8	3	24
Filament bulb for wash room	10	0.5	5
Filament bulb for bedroom 1	10	0.5	5
Filament bulb for bedroom 2	10	0.5	5
Small B/W television	15	3	45
Cassette player	5	4	20
Total daily requirement of electricity (W h per day):			136

Requirements of solar electricity for a home

In a solar electric system for a home, the typical breakdown of electrical requirements is calculated in Table 8.3.

The total requirement is 136 Wh per day which could be supplied by the single module mentioned earlier that produces 150 Wh per day at the system voltage. The large reduction in requirement from Table 8.1 to Table 8.3 is achieved by removing the high-power appliances and changing the lighting.

Anticipating problems in a solar electric system

In major solar electric installations, such as microwave transmitter stations and warning lights for aircraft, it is essential that power is always available whenever it is needed. These systems are sized with an excess of both solar modules and battery storage. They may also have a back-up generator which takes over from the battery supply when the weather is much cloudier than usual.

In contrast, the systems covered by this book are those which do not have the extra solar modules and batteries to allow for unexpected conditions. It must be appreciated by designers and users that problems will arise unexpectedly.

The main problem is an unusually long period of cloudy weather when the solar modules generate only a small amount of electricity. Another problem might be failure of one of the batteries.

The estimates of daily requirement used to size the system may turn out to be too low. In practice, after the system is installed and operating, electricity is found to be needed for longer or more appliances may get switched on each day.

Lamps originally intended for three hours' use each day may end up being left on all night for security or deterring 'spirits'.

If any of these problems occur, the immediate solution is to switch off some of the appliances so that less electricity is needed. Controlling the number of appliances that can be used is part of the job of managing a solar system. It involves checking the state of charge of the batteries each day. When the state of charge is low, a decision is made to switch off certain appliances. Another aspect of managing the system is to switch on the lighting circuits when it gets dark and switch them off later when people go to bed.

'Essential' and 'non-essential' circuits in medium-size installations

In anticipation of managing a system in the way just described, the appliances can be divided into two groups of circuits at the planning stage. One group is

Table 8.4 *Example of listing the electricity requirements for a medium-size solar system. 'Electrical requirement' for each appliance is calculated using Formula (8.1). The appliances are divided between 'Essential' and 'Non-essential' circuits to give two sub-totals before the overall total at the bottom.*

Type of circuit	Details of appliance	Total power of circuit (W)	Daily use (hours per day)	Electrical requirement (W h per day)	
				Essential	Non-essential
Lighting	Block A, 2 tubes (15 W each)	30	3	90	
Lighting	Block B, 4 tubes (15 W each)	60	3		180
Lighting	Dormitories, 4 tubes (15 W each)	60	1	60	
Lighting	Outside, 6 tubes (8 W each)	48	3		144
Lighting	Toilets, 8 bulbs (8 W each) with time-delay switches	64	1	64	
Sockets	Cassette players, etc.	40	4		160
Sockets	Charger for sealed nickel-cadmium batteries	1.5	12	18	
Sub-totals for each group of circuits (W h per day):				232	484
Total daily requirement for electricity (W h per day):					716

switched off when it is necessary to reduce the load on the system. This group is of non-essential appliances, such as sockets for cassette players and outside lighting. The group of circuits left on are for essential appliances, such as a single lamp in each of the rooms that may normally use two lamps.

In medium-size systems, the two groups of appliances can be wired on separate circuits. This enables the system to be managed effectively because the separate groups of appliances are controlled at a central point. By careful choice of cable sizes, this approach need not be more expensive (see Chapter 5 for calculation of cable cost). Details for building a simple distribution unit with separate switching of circuits are given in Chapter 16.

The job of switching off appliances can also be done by a control unit with the feature of automatic low-voltage disconnect (see Chapter 4). When the state of charge becomes low, a control unit with this feature will automatically switch off the appliance circuits. However, it is inconvenient for all appliances to go off suddenly at the same time. A better arrangement that suits most users is for the non-essential appliances to go off. Note that a low-voltage disconnect works for lead–acid batteries only. For nickel–cadmium batteries, the non-essential circuits are switched off by hand when the batteries are suspected to be at a low state of charge.

Table 8.4 is an example of calculating the total daily requirement of electricity for a medium-size solar system, such as a school. It shows how the circuits can be divided into two groups by putting the 'Electrical requirement' values in separate columns. A guideline to follow on how to group the circuits is for the 'essential' total to be less than half of the 'non-essential' total. The example in Table 8.4 is in accordance with this guideline.

Sizing to a limited budget

The following sections are about sizing the number of modules and batteries to meet a particular electrical requirement. For some people who are planning to install a system, the problem with this approach is cost. These potential users do not have enough money or access to credit for all the modules and batteries that are needed to power the appliances they want to use. In this case, it may be best to start costing the system with a fixed number of modules and batteries, then return to this section and find out how many appliances can be used.

Average daily output from one module

For a system with a generator, sizing is simple because the power output of the generator, specified in watts, is constant. For a solar electric system, sizing is more complicated. This is because the amount of electricity generated each day depends both on the rating of each solar module and on the amount of sunlight reaching the modules through the day.

The procedure for the number of modules is summarized in Figure 8.2.

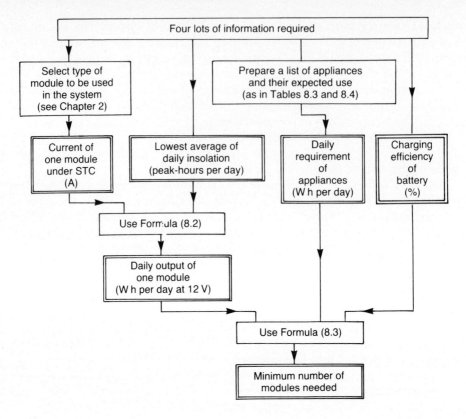

Figure 8.2 Summary of steps for calculating the minimum number of modules needed in a solar system:

☐ steps involved

▣ results at each stage with units in brackets

Daily insolation

Measurements of sunshine and cloud cover are taken as part of the meteorological records kept by weather stations all over the world. Two types of measurement to do with sunshine are daily sunshine measured in hours and *daily insolation* which has various units. Daily insolation is the measurement used to estimate the output from a solar module. It takes into account variations in angle between the sun and a horizontal surface together with the reduction of irradiance owing to cloud cover.

The measurement of daily insolation is also referred to by many other names, such as *daily radiation*, *insolance*, *solar irradiation*, and *global horizontal irradiation*. ('Insolation' is a shortened version of the words INcoming SOLar radiATION.)

Units of daily insolation

At any moment in time, the light intensity or irradiance reaching the front of a module or any surface can be measured in units of watts per square metre (W/m^2) (see Chapter 2). A different unit is used when measuring the total amount of light or insolation reaching the ground over a period of time.

The units used in this chapter for calculating the daily output of a solar module are *peak-hours per day*. Peak-hours are the equivalent number of hours of sunlight at an irradiance of 1000 W/m^2. This value of irradiance is chosen because it is the same value as in the standard test conditions under which the electrical specifications of solar modules are measured (see Chapter 2). The value of 1000 W/m^2 also happens to be about the highest irradiance that can be received on a surface facing the sun directly and when the sun is more than 45° above the horizon.

Peak-hours per day can also be given as kW h/m^2 per day which are the same size. Details and conversion factors of other units are listed in Table B.1.

Module tilt

A solar module is always mounted at a certain angle of tilt from horizontal (see Figure 8.3). The tilt angle should be 15° or more to ensure that rain-water drains off easily, washing dust away with it.

The value of tilt angle is chosen to optimize irradiance on the module throughout the year. A simple way to choose the tilt angle is to set it at the latitude angle of the site. The direction of tilt should be set towards the Equator, which is due south for countries north of the Equator and due north for countries south of the Equator.

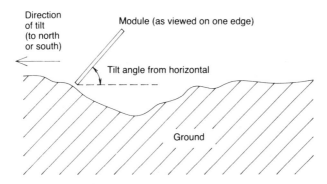

Figure 8.3 How to define the tilt angle of a module. It can be checked using a template with a spirit level or a plumb line, as shown in Figure 10.4.

For sites at higher latitudes than 30°, the tilt angle can be set at the latitude angle plus 15°. This helps to even out the daily electrical output over the year by optimizing the tilt angle for the winter months.

For sites at latitudes between 15°S. and 15°N., a tilt angle of 15° is used. The direction of tilt depends on which half of the year has the cloudiest month. For example, if July is the cloudiest month, modules just north or just south of the Equator should both face north. Alternatively, facing west or east should be considered if mornings or afternoons tend to be cloudy.

Daily output from one module

The maps in Figure 8.4 have sets of curves of average daily insolation for most countries of the world. The averages are over three-month periods and apply to modules tilted at the same angle as their angle of latitude.

For some sites, the country can be found directly on the maps. Otherwise draw pencil lines for the angles of latitude and longitude of the site so that the site is located where the lines cross. For each quarter of the year, choose the nearest curve of daily insolation and follow along this curve to the value of peak-hours per day. A more accurate estimate of daily insolation can be made by judging the position of the site between two curves. This method is used in Example 8.1.

Chapter 2 about solar modules shows how to select a module. At the end of that chapter, there are details about which current to use for sizing calculations. The most appropriate specification to use is the current at a load voltage of 14 V. This current should be under the STC irradiance and air mass but corrected for the actual operating temperature of the cells at midday rather than the standard test condition of 25 °C (77 °F). If this current is not given for the module of interest, another current specification near the top of the list on p.34 should be used.

The daily electrical output from one module in units of *W h per day at 12 V* is calculated using the following formula:

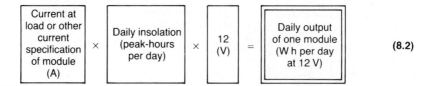

$$\boxed{\begin{array}{c} \text{Current at} \\ \text{load or other} \\ \text{current} \\ \text{specification} \\ \text{of module} \\ \text{(A)} \end{array}} \times \boxed{\begin{array}{c} \text{Daily insolation} \\ \text{(peak-hours} \\ \text{per day)} \end{array}} \times \boxed{\begin{array}{c} 12 \\ \text{(V)} \end{array}} = \boxed{\begin{array}{c} \text{Daily output} \\ \text{of one module} \\ \text{(W h per day} \\ \text{at 12 V)} \end{array}} \qquad \text{(8.2)}$$

Figure 8.4   Maps of daily insolation averaged over three-month periods for most parts of the world. The curves of daily insolation are for modules tilted at the angle of latitude of the site and are in units of peak-hours per day at 1000 W/m². (Based on maps from Report 87-0804.UC-63 of Sandia National Laboratories, Albuquerque, NM 87185, United States.)

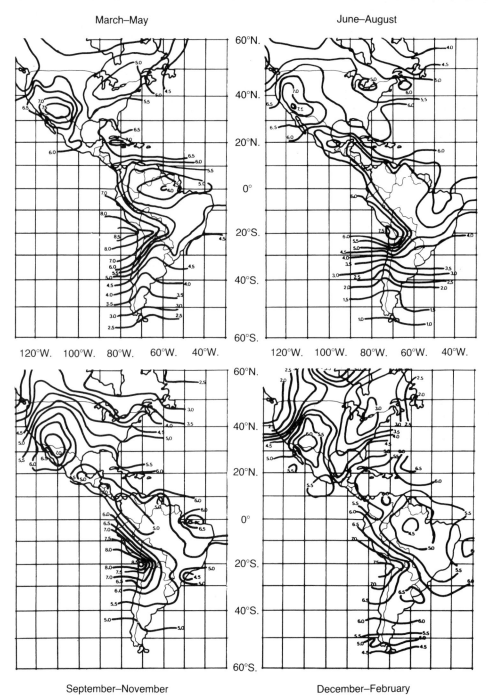

(a) North and South America (longitudes 130°W. to 30°W.).

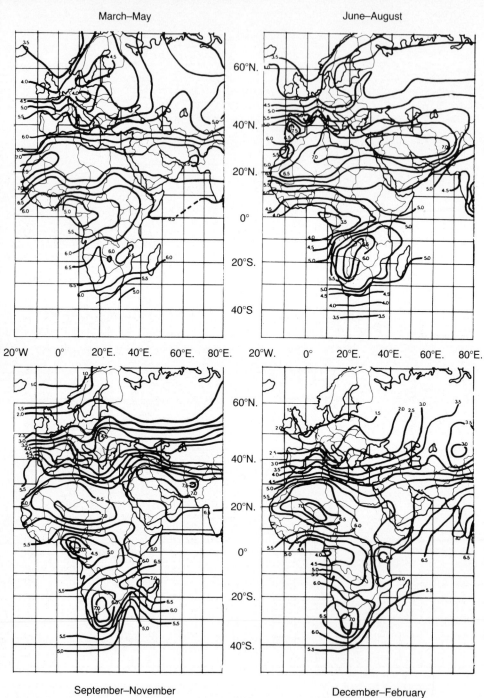

March–May

June–August

September–November

December–February

Figure 8.4(b)   Europe, Middle East, and Africa (longitudes 20°W. to 80°E.).

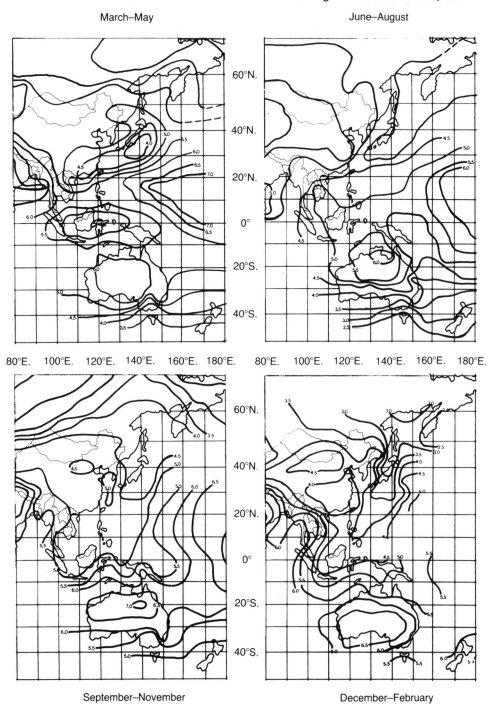

March–May

June–August

September–November

December–February

Figure 8.4(c)   Far East, Australia, and New Zealand (longitudes 80°E. to 180°E.).

The use of 12 V in this formula might be surprising since the output at a module varies from 12 V to over 15 V as a battery is charged up. The value of 12 V is chosen because it is the voltage at which the electricity is actually used by the appliances. For 24 V systems, 12 is still used because allowance for the higher voltage is made later when sizing the number of modules.

Daily insolation values from the maps and results from Formula (8.2) can be summarized together in a table, like the one in Figure 8.5. For the next step of calculating the number of modules required, the period with lowest daily insolation is used. In this way, the system is sized to supply electricity for all seasons including the worst three-month period.

Example 8.1

Modules with a current at load of 3.2 A under STC are going to be used at São Paulo in Brazil at latitude 24°S. and longitude 47°W. (The modules have more than thirty-six cells each so that this current is not reduced if they have to operate at a high temperature.) What will be the lowest daily electrical output of one module averaged over a three-month period?

Referring to Figure 8.4, Brazil is in South America on map (a). For this example, South America is enlarged in Figure 8.5(a) and lines are drawn for the latitude and longitude marking the position of São Paulo. Values from these maps are summarized in the table of Figure 8.5(b).

For March to May, São Paulo is between curves marked 4.5 and 5.0. It is nearest the 4.5 curve, so an average daily insolation of 4.6 peak-hours per day is estimated for this period. Using this value with the current specification in Formula (8.2), the daily electrical output is

$$4.6 \times 3.2 \times 12 = 177 \text{ W h per day at 12 V}$$

The daily electrical output for the other three periods are calculated in the same way and recorded in the table. The lowest value is 157 W h per day at 12 V for June to August. This value should be used for sizing the number of modules.

São Paulo is at a latitude of 24°S. so the module should be tilted at 24° from horizontal and facing north to generate this electrical output. However, to raise the daily electrical output over the winter quarter, the tilt angle should be set at about 40° (from the latitude angle plus 15°).

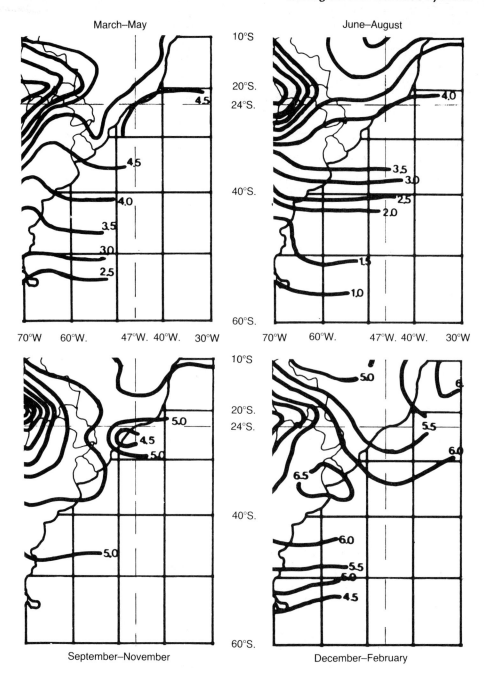

Figure 8.5 Using maps from Figure 8.4 for Example 8.1 of São Paulo in Brazil.
(a) Daily insolation maps enlarged for part of South America showing the latitude and longitude lines that locate São Paulo.

Module details:	make			type		
	current	3.2 A		(conditions:	at load of 14V)	
Site details:	name	São Paulo		position	Brazil	
	latitude	24° S.		longitude	47° W.	

| | Results from each quarterly period | | | |
	Mar.–May	June–Aug.	Sept.–Nov.	Dec.–Feb.
Average daily insolation (peak-hours per day)	4.6	4.1	4.6	5.4
Daily output of one module (W h per day at 12 V)	177	157	177	207

Figure 8.5(b)   Table summarizing results. The values for 'Daily output of one module' are calculated using Formula (8.2).

Limitations of using daily insolation maps

The information in Figure 8.4 gives only an approximate indication of daily insolation. The values on the curves are averaged over three-month periods. There is no indication of how low the daily electrical output might get for one month. Setting the tilt angle of the module at the same angle as the latitude of the site may not be the optimum. On the small scale of the maps, they cannot take into account local variations which can be significant for some sites.

Examples of daily insolation by monthly averages are given in Figure 8.6 for two places at different latitudes. The daily insolation averages are for a horizontal surface and the effect of correcting for tilt angle is shown by the lines.

Ibadan in Figure 8.6(a) is at a latitude of 7°N. but the modules should be tilted at no less than 15°. Since the lowest month is August, the tilt is to the north. Belgrade in Figure 8.6(b) is at a latitude of 45°N. and a tilt angle of 55° is used to maximize output between November and February. This tilt angle means that a potentially high output for May to July is reduced but this is desirable for self-regulated systems to minimize over-charging.

If meteorological records are available for your area of interest, they can be used to give a better estimate of daily electrical output expected from a module. Meteorological measurements are always for a horizontal detector so they need to be corrected for other angles before they can be used for sizing. A procedure is described in Appendix B for correcting these measurements to any required tilt angle.

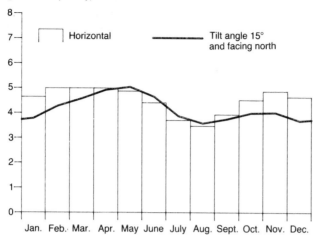

(a)

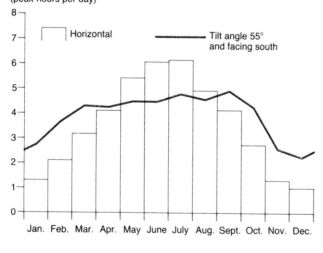

(b)

Figure 8.6 Examples of daily insolation for two sites. Daily insolation as monthly averages on a horizontal surface are shown as bar charts. The thick lines show the result of correcting for a particular tilt angle (using the procedure and tables in Appendix B). These tilt angles are chosen to raise the lowest monthly average and smooth out variations for the whole year.

(a) Ibadan in Nigeria at a latitude 7°N. and longitude 4°E., as an example of a site near the Equator.

(b) Belgrade in Yugoslavia at a latitude 45°N. and longitude 20°E., as an example of a site at a high latitude.

Sizing the number of modules needed

Most appliances are used at night so they draw power from the batteries instead of directly from the solar modules. When sizing the number of modules that are needed, the small loss of electricity when charging the batteries must be included. This is the current or A h charging efficiency. Typical values to use are 80 per cent for lead–acid and 70 per cent for nickel–cadmium batteries.

Here is the formula for sizing the minimum number of modules needed:

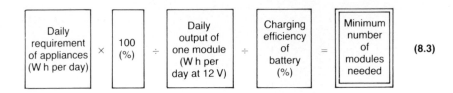

$$\begin{array}{|c|} \hline \text{Daily} \\ \text{requirement} \\ \text{of appliances} \\ \text{(W h per day)} \\ \hline \end{array} \times \begin{array}{|c|} \hline 100 \\ (\%) \\ \hline \end{array} \div \begin{array}{|c|} \hline \text{Daily} \\ \text{output of} \\ \text{one module} \\ \text{(W h per} \\ \text{day at 12 V)} \\ \hline \end{array} \div \begin{array}{|c|} \hline \text{Charging} \\ \text{efficiency} \\ \text{of} \\ \text{battery} \\ (\%) \\ \hline \end{array} = \begin{array}{|c|} \hline \text{Minimum} \\ \text{number} \\ \text{of} \\ \text{modules} \\ \text{needed} \\ \hline \end{array} \quad (8.3)$$

The nearest whole number above this answer should be used. Some systems operate at 24 V to reduce the size of cables used for distribution (see Chapter 5). The same formula applies for these systems but the nearest even number above the answer should be used. An even number of modules is needed because the modules are wired in series pairs for operation at 24 V (see Figure 10.7). When planning to use modules in series, check in the manufacturer's specifications that this is permitted for the particular modules to be used.

Example 8.2

The lowest monthly average of daily electrical output from the module considered in Example 8.1 is 157 W h per day. The daily requirement of appliances for the school considered in the example of Table 8.4 is 716 W h per day. How many modules are needed?

These values are used in Formula (8.3) together with 80 per cent as a typical figure for the average charging efficiency of the batteries:

$$716 \times 100 \div 157 \div 80 = 5.70$$

Therefore the minimum number of modules that are needed is six. If the system voltage is 24 V instead of 12 V, six modules is still OK because it is an even number.

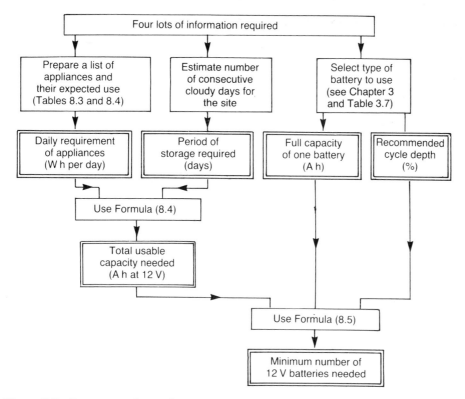

Figure 8.7 Summary of steps for calculating the minimum number of 12 V batteries needed in a solar system:
☐ steps involved
▣ results at each stage with units in brackets

Sizing the number of batteries needed

The steps involved in sizing the number of batteries are summarized in Figure 8.7.

Total usable capacity needed

Batteries charge up during the day ready for use at night. Batteries also smooth out the daily variations of insolation. They do this by storing the excess charge received during sunny days ready for use during cloudy days that follow. The period of storage required should be based on the maximum number of consecutive days with rain or heavy cloud. This could be as low as two days for arid areas, such as Saudi Arabia, but a more typical figure used in sizing small systems at low latitudes is five days. For latitudes above 30°, ten or more days may be necessary.

Another purpose of batteries can be to provide seasonal storage and smooth out variations of daily insolation between months. A battery with a low rate of self-discharge is essential for this purpose. Reserve capacity is calculated in the range of ten to twenty days. Batteries used for storage between seasons spend many weeks at partial charge which causes a reduction of capacity in lead–acid batteries due to sulphation. Therefore use only high-quality lead–acid batteries with depth of cycle less than 50 per cent or vented nickel–cadmium batteries.

The usable capacity required is calculated from the daily electrical requirement and period of storage as follows:

$$
\boxed{\begin{array}{c}\text{Daily} \\ \text{requirement} \\ \text{of appliances} \\ \text{(W h per day)}\end{array}} \times \boxed{\begin{array}{c}\text{Period of} \\ \text{storage} \\ \text{required} \\ \text{(days)}\end{array}} \div \boxed{\begin{array}{c}12 \\ \text{(V)}\end{array}} = \boxed{\begin{array}{c}\text{Total usable} \\ \text{capacity needed} \\ \text{(A h at 12 V)}\end{array}} \qquad \textbf{(8.4)}
$$

Battery specifications

Chapter 3 shows how to select a rechargeable battery from those that are available. For sizing, two specifications are required about the battery which is selected:

1. The full capacity in A h units.
2. The usable depth of discharge recommended for that type of battery, as a percentage.

Since discharge in a solar system is slow, use the capacity specified over 100 hours ($C/100$ or C_{100}) if given. Capacity is also specified for an operating temperature of 20 °C (68 °F). If lower operating temperatures are expected, reduce the capacity by 1 per cent per degree C below 20 °C (0.5 per cent per degree F below 68 °F).

The full capacity of a battery is measured as it is discharged to a specified voltage. However, most types of lead–acid battery should not be cycled over their full capacity otherwise their life is severely shortened. The percentage of charge used on each cycle of a battery is called cycle depth. To obtain the full life of a battery, the cycle depth should not exceed the depth recommended for that type of battery. If the recommended cycle depth is not specified by a battery supplier, refer to Table 3.7 for guidance.

The number of batteries that are needed is calculated from the usable capacity and cycle depth as follows:

$$
\boxed{\begin{array}{c}\text{Total} \\ \text{usable} \\ \text{capacity} \\ \text{needed} \\ \text{(A h at 12 V)}\end{array}} \times \boxed{\begin{array}{c}100 \\ (\%)\end{array}} \div \boxed{\begin{array}{c}\text{Full capacity} \\ \text{specified for} \\ \text{one 12 V battery} \\ \text{(A h)}\end{array}} \div \boxed{\begin{array}{c}\text{Maximum} \\ \text{depth} \\ \text{of} \\ \text{cycles} \\ (\%)\end{array}} = \boxed{\begin{array}{c}\text{Minimum} \\ \text{number} \\ \text{of 12 V} \\ \text{batteries} \\ \text{needed}\end{array}} \quad \textbf{(8.5)}
$$

This calculation is based on nominal 12 V batteries. When batteries have a lower nominal voltage, they are connected in series to form 12 V batteries. Their voltages add for series connection while the overall capacity in A h is the same as for one battery.

For systems operating at 24 V, the wiring arrangement is to connect 12 V batteries in series pairs (see Figure 10.10(c)). In these systems, Formula (8.5) still applies but the nearest even number above the answer should be used. When planning to use batteries in series, check that the higher system voltage is within the limit set by the manufacturer for the particular batteries intended for use.

Example 8.3

The daily requirement of appliances for the school considered in Example 8.2 is 716 Wh per day. The batteries selected for this system each has a capacity of 110 Ah. They are lead–acid batteries intended for deep-cycle operation and can be discharged to a depth of 60 per cent. What is the smallest number of batteries that can be used?

According to Figure 8.7, it is also necessary to estimate the period of storage that is required. Since this information is not given, the typical value of five days is chosen. Using Formula (8.4), the total usable battery capacity needed is:

$$716 \times 5 \div 12 = 298 \text{ A h at 12 V}$$

This answer is used in Formula (8.5) to obtain the total number of batteries needed:

$$298 \times 100 \div 110 \div 60 = 4.52$$

Therefore the minimum number of batteries that are needed is five. If the system voltage is 24 V instead of 12 V, six batteries are needed because six is the nearest even number above 4.52.

☐ *Questions*

1. What are the limitations of sizing for low-cost solar systems?

2. Compared to a system run from a mains supply, why does the electrical requirement have to be much lower for a solar-powered system?

3. Calculate the total daily electrical requirement for the following appliances:
   (a) Two lamps of 8 W each used for four hours.
   (b) One outside lamp of 12 W used for twelve hours.
   (c) One television of 20 W used for three hours.

4. A tube lamp with its own inverter is much more expensive than a light bulb, so why are tube lamps normally recommended for solar systems?

5. 'Peak-hours per day' are units of daily insolation. What do they mean?

6. Why does a module need to be tilted in operation?

7. The centre of Sri Lanka is at 8°N and 81°E. From the maps in Figure 8.4, what is the lowest value of daily insolation over one three-month period?

8. The average daily output from one module at a site is expected to be 130 W h per day at 12 V. How many of these modules are needed for a daily electrical requirement of 900 W h in a system operating at 24 V?

9. What factors should be considered when choosing the days of storage for the battery bank of a solar system?

9 System planning

Planning a solar electric system involves designing the layout and ordering the parts. The stages involved are summarized in Figure 9.1. The modules, control unit, and batteries should all be as close together on the site as is convenient. Short distances between them will reduce the cost of the wire. Also the voltage drop during charging will be low without having to use thick cable.

Once the system sizing is complete and the layout finalized, a full list can be drawn up of components to buy. For systems bought as a single package, the last section of this chapter gives advice on items that should be included.

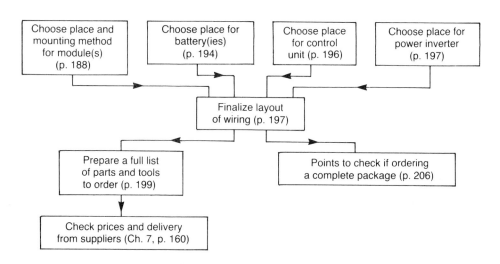

Figure 9.1 Summary of Chapter 9 about planning the layout of a solar electric system with a cross-reference to another chapter (Ch. chapter, p. page references to text).

Solar modules

The place and method of mounting a module or array of modules must be chosen carefully. There are several points to be considered for both aspects.

General position of solar modules

The modules should be close to the control unit and batteries to minimize voltage drop along the cables.

The modules should be upwind from kitchen fires and dusty roads to minimize build-up on the glass of ashes and other dirt carried by the wind. They should be away from where children play and where there is a risk of falling objects, such as stones.

Modules should not be mounted in a place where shadows of big trees or other tall objects can prevent the maximum amount of sunlight reaching them. Even a small shadow on just one cell can affect the performance of the whole module.

Procedure for checking shadows

One way to check for shadows is to stand at the position proposed for the modules with your head at the same level as the modules will be. Look at all parts of the sky that the sun passes across over a year. Table 9.1 lists a number of angles that may be helpful in finding the positions of the sun at various times. While looking at these positions, check that no objects appear between you and the sun that could cast a shadow on the modules.

This is the procedure for using Table 9.1:

1. Stand at the proposed place for the modules.
2. Mark a line on the ground starting at your feet and leading in the direction of north. Use a compass or map to locate north.
3. Select the row in Table 9.1 with the right range of latitude for the site and note the six angles for bearings and angle above the horizon at midday.
4. Use a protractor or compass to find bearing angles from north. Draw lines or place straight objects on the ground for marking the four bearings for sunrise and sunset.
5. Hold one arm out straight and slightly raised so that the tips of your fingers are at about 20 cm (8 in) above eye level. By looking over your finger tips, you are looking at the height of the sun above the horizon at about one hour after sunrise.
6. For sunrise, swing your arm between the bearing angles for 21 June and 21 December. Check for objects above your fingers that might cause shadows.
7. Repeat step 6 for the sunset angles.
8. For the position of the sun at midday, use the angles from the middle pair of

Table 9.1 *Angles of the sun above the horizon at different times of the day and year. These are used for checking that obstacles will not form shadows over the modules. The sunrise bearings are for one hour after the sun has risen above the horizon (horizontal skyline). The sunset bearings are for one hour before the sun reaches the horizon.*

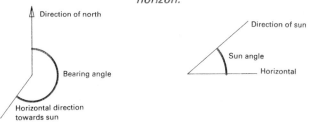

Latitude	Bearing one hour after sunrise		Angle above horizon at midday		Bearing one hour before sunset	
	21 June	21 Dec.	21 June	31 Dec.	21 June	21 Dec.
60 °–50 °S.	35 °	120 °	10 °N.	60 °N.	325 °	240 °
50 °–40 °S.	45 °	115 °	20 °N.	70 °N.	315 °	245 °
40 °–30 °S.	50 °	110 °	30 °N.	80 °N.	310 °	250 °
30 °–20 °S.	55 °	110 °	40 °N.	90 °	305 °	250 °
20 °–10 °S.	60 °	110 °	50 °N.	80 °S.	300 °	250 °
10 °S.–0 °	65 °	115 °	60 °N.	70 °S.	295 °	245 °
0 °–10 °N.	65 °	115 °	70 °N.	60 °S.	295 °	245 °
10 °–20 °N.	70 °	120 °	80 °N.	50 °S.	290 °	240 °
20 °–30 °N.	70 °	125 °	90 °	40 °S.	290 °	235 °
30 °–40 °N.	70 °	130 °	80 °S.	30 °S.	290 °	230 °
40 °–50 °N.	65 °	135 °	70 °S.	20 °S.	295 °	225 °
50 °–60 °N.	60 °	145 °	60 °S.	10 °S.	300 °	215 °

columns in Table 9.1. Face in the direction given by the letter after each angle, which is either due north or due south. Raise your arm above horizontal to the angle given. Ask someone else to stand to one side with a protractor and check that your arm is at about the correct angle. Then sweep your arm around and downwards to the bearings for sunrise and sunset. This should give a rough impression of the sun's path for June and December.

If this procedure identifies objects that will cause shadowing, aim to mount the modules high off the ground or choose a different place and repeat the procedure.

When the sky is covered by clouds, light reaches the modules from all parts of the sky. Even though objects to the north and south will never shade direct sunlight, they can still cause some loss of light from clouds. Modules are best placed in the clearest area that is available at the site in order to receive the most light.

Mounting arrangement

There are several aspects to remember for the mounting arrangement:

- ☐ Rigid and secure.
- ☐ Accessible for cleaning.
- ☐ Kept cool.
- ☐ Tilt angle.
- ☐ Tilt direction.
- ☐ Tracking option

A variety of mounting methods is shown in Figure 1.2. Modules can be mounted on a frame at ground level set in concrete and an example is shown in Figure 9.2(a). A fence surrounding the modules is required to prevent damage from people and animals. There must be sufficient clearance between the fence and the solar array to avoid shading any of the solar cells.

The alternative to mounting at ground level is on a pole or a roof (see Figure 9.2(b)). The direction of tilt should be to the north or south to within 20°, which may restrict the choice of roof. Also check the local building regulations.

Solar cells produce less electricity when they are hot. The mounting should be positioned where the wind can help to cool the module. Mounting directly on a roof made of iron sheets is not recommended because the sheets become very hot in direct sunlight.

Modules generate most electricity when facing the sun directly but the position of the sun in the sky changes through the day. The mounts shown in Figure 9.2 are the stationary type where the modules only face the sun directly a few times a year. To improve the positioning of the modules, their angle can be changed to follow the sun across the sky and this is called *tracking*. Full tracking mounts that ensure the modules face the sun all through the day and for every day of the year are quite complicated. A simple version that improves the angle between the modules and the sun is shown in Figure 9.3.

Mounting hardware

Solar modules are intended to be fully exposed to all weather conditions and the mounting hardware simply supports the modules outside in the sun. Important features of mounting hardware are that it is strong enough to withstand storm-force winds and that the modules are held securely. Also each module should be held flat so that there is no twisting force applied along its length.

(a)

(b)

Figure 9.2 Examples of methods for mounting modules.
(a) Large array of modules mounted on an aluminium frame. The array is surrounded by a high fence to keep unauthorized people and animals away.
(b) Module mounted on a roof using a wooden frame.

Modules should be set at a tilt angle from horizontal of 15° or more. The minimum tilt of 15° ensures that rain-water does not build up and instead helps to wash dirt off. At latitudes higher than 15°N. or 15°S., there is an optimum tilt angle for each site which depends on the weather conditions through the year. For latitudes between 15°N. and 15°S., modules should be tilted at 15° and in the direction north or south for the cloudiest month. See Figure 8.6(a) as an example and Appendix B for further details.

Even with rain draining off, the glass face of each module requires regular cleaning to maintain the best performance. Access to the modules should be planned at this stage. A ladder is required for modules mounted on a roof or pole. Access should be safe so that there is no risk of falling and the person doing the job feels comfortable. Note that cleaning must be done frequently to keep the modules at their peak performance. If none of the users feels confident to go up a pole or on a roof, a ground-level mounting should be considered instead.

For a large array of modules, gaps should be left between modules to enable effective cleaning by hand. Gaps also allow the wind to blow through without putting unnecessary strain on the support.

For systems operating at 24 V, mount each pair of series connected modules together. Since the cells in thin-film modules are arranged as parallel strips (see Figure 2.4), the modules should be mounted with the strips running vertically from top to bottom. If the strips run horizontally, any build-up of dirt will cover the bottom strip and seriously affect the performance of the whole module. With the other types of modules, the long side can be horizontal or at the tilt angle, whichever is most convenient on the mounting structure.

Materials used for the mounting hardware can be wood (Figure 9.2(b)), steel (Figure 9.3), or aluminium (Figure 9.2(a)). Steel is available in box, angle, and 'T' section and can be welded or bolted together. The steel must be galvanized or painted to prevent rusting. Aluminium is more expensive but has the advantages of being lighter for its size than steel and soft for drilling and cutting. Aluminium does not rust so does not require painting. Mounting hardware is usually available from suppliers of solar equipment in the form of kits made up of aluminium sections which bolt together.

Modules are attached to the mounting hardware by screws and nuts through the angled section of the module frame. If it is necessary to drill extra holes in the frame, it is important to protect the back of the module from possible damage during drilling. Protection can be provided by covering the back with a piece of wood.

Sometimes the junction boxes on the modules are difficult to reach when the modules are attached to the support structure. When this is so, it is helpful to have a junction box on or near the support structure. This provides a convenient point where the main cable to the control unit and cables to the separate modules are all connected. A junction box can be seen at the bottom of the tracking stand in Figure 9.3. Junction boxes must be weather-proof if mounted outside.

(a)

(b)

(c)

(d)

Figure 9.3 Up to four modules mounted on a simple tracking stand which rotates about a vertical axis.

(a) Front. (Source BP Solar.)

(b) Side.

(c) Back.

(d) Locking mechanism.

Batteries

There are several points that must be considered when choosing a place to put the batteries:

☐ Moderate temperature.
☐ Ventilation.
☐ Security.
☐ Protection.
☐ Access.

Temperature

It is important to keep the batteries at a moderate temperature. The optimum range is 15–25 °C (60–80 °F) while the maximum is 10–35 °C (50–95 °F).

In hot climates, the batteries should be away from direct sunlight and as cool as possible. In cold climates, low temperatures are not as serious but the batteries should be kept close to living-quarters to avoid the lowest temperatures.

To prevent temperature differences developing across a battery, avoid both direct sunlight and positions next to heaters and pipes for radiators or steam. Batteries can be partially buried or insulated if temperature differences might be a problem.

Ventilation

During the charging of vented batteries, small amounts of hydrogen gas are produced. Hydrogen is like bottle gas used for cookers, and burns easily. If there is no space above the batteries for the hydrogen to escape, it may collect there and create a danger of explosion. Therefore vented batteries must be in a place that is well ventilated. This means that there must be some opening to the outside of the building, such as a vent, through which air can flow freely.

A single battery in a small system serving a home releases very small amounts of hydrogen and can be positioned in living quarters quite safely. Sealed batteries do not release any gases under normal operation so they do not have any special requirements for ventilation. A large bank of vented batteries should be positioned away from living quarters, and gases from them should not be allowed to enter air vents to the living-quarters or heating and cooling systems.

Even with good ventilation, it is still necessary to keep burning and sparking materials away. Never allow smoking cigarettes near vented batteries at any time. Do not store where flammable gases and vapours may exist, such as paraffin (kerosene) and bottle gas.

Security

Batteries are expensive items of equipment and useful for other purposes. Therefore their position must be secure so that they are safe from theft. Also batteries should be secure from tampering by unauthorized people and children.

Theft of batteries which look suitable for vehicles can be a problem. One solution is to use a battery bank made up from separate 2 V cells in groups of six instead of 12 V batteries. This makes transfer to a vehicle less tempting.

Protection

The batteries should be covered so that metal tools and other objects cannot fall on them by mistake. If the batteries are not in a box, a strong wooden stand or other support should be used. This keeps each battery off the floor and a lid protects the terminals and connecting wires. The tops of the batteries should be easily accessible for routine cleaning and for measuring the state of charge. Also, the batteries should be kept horizontal.

The box and floor should be resistent to spillage of electrolyte (acid for lead–acid batteries and alkali for vented nickel–cadmium batteries). A strong plastic tray can be put under each battery to contain spillages from damaging other equipment. This is especially important if there is a risk of contaminating a water supply.

Vented cells produce a small amount of mist when over-charging. This settles on any surfaces near the vents so these must also be coated to avoid damage. For a wooden stand, the wood can be protected by two coats of *epoxy paint*. This is two-part paint that is sold for use on floors, and is very strong. The paint is supplied as two parts in separate tins which are mixed together just before use.

Access

Clear access must be available to install the batteries and carry out maintenance. If batteries are heavy, provision for handling equipment should be provided. The place should have good illumination. A lamp may need to be installed on a separate circuit so that the batteries can be inspected if there is a problem at night.

Possible positions for batteries

Recommended places in a home are a store which has good ventilation. A hallway could also be used as long as children cannot interfere or the battery is secure in a box with a lock. In a school or other institution, any well-ventilated room which can be locked is suitable. An example of one is shown in Figure 9.4.

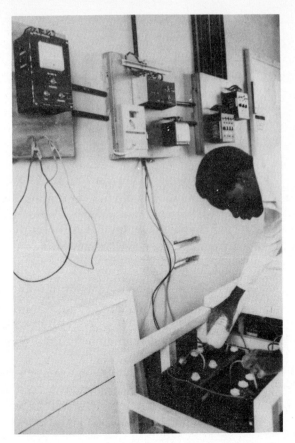

Figure 9.4   Example of a room with batteries and control units serving a school solar system. Slots in the wall provide good ventilation over the batteries. The batteries are supported in pairs on wooden stands. The lid for the first stand is leaning against the wall while the batteries are topped up with distilled water.

Control unit

The control unit acts as the main junction point between the modules, batteries, and appliances, as shown in Figure 1.3. It contains the main switches, fuses, indicator lights, and sometimes meters to show how well the system is operating. There may also be a timer that is set each day for the lighting circuits.

Easy access is required to the control unit for adjustment of the controls and for inspecting the indicators. Therefore the unit should be mounted on a wall in an accessible place. However, in a system for an institution, access to switches may need to be restricted to prevent tampering.

Control units contain manual and automatic (relay operated) switches.

These produce a small spark when opened. Manufacturers of the control units recommend that the units are not mounted too close to vented batteries unless the ventilation is very good. If the battery is in a box, the control unit should certainly not be mounted inside the same box.

Power inverter

For a large power inverter of more than 100 W capacity, a large current is drawn from the batteries. Therefore the inverter should be sited as close as convenient to the batteries to keep the cable short. Also a thick cable should be used to make sure the voltage drop is less than about 1 V. The smallest size of cable for a voltage drop of 1 V is calculated from the following formula:

$$\boxed{\begin{array}{c}\text{Cable} \\ \text{length} \\ \text{(m)}\end{array}} \times \boxed{\begin{array}{c}\text{Output} \\ \text{power} \\ \text{(W)}\end{array}} \times \boxed{\begin{array}{c}100 \\ (\%)\end{array}} \times \boxed{\left(\dfrac{0.04}{\text{A m}}\text{V mm}^2\right)} \div \boxed{\begin{array}{c}\text{Input} \\ \text{voltage} \\ \text{(V d.c.)}\end{array}}$$

$$\div \boxed{\begin{array}{c}\text{Inverter} \\ \text{efficiency} \\ (\%)\end{array}} = \boxed{\begin{array}{c}\text{Smallest} \\ \text{cable for 1 V} \\ \text{drop (mm}^2\text{)}\end{array}} \quad \textbf{(9.1)}$$

From the output of the inverter, wiring must comply with standards and regulations for mains voltage. This means using fittings intended for mains voltage and an earthing system. Refer to electrical installation manuals for full details.

If the system includes a circuit with socket outlets for low-voltage d.c. appliances, a different style of socket outlet and plug is essential to avoid confusion with connections to circuits at mains voltage.

Detailed layout of wiring

Careful design of the circuit layout throughout the installation is important and the following factors should be noted:

☐ Prevent the voltage drop being too high while minimizing cost by using short runs of the optimum thickness (see Chapter 5).
☐ Choose routes through and between buildings for ease of installation.
☐ In medium-size installations, arrange the appliances in separate circuits for effective management of which appliances can be used (see Chapter 8 and Table 8.4).

Generally the shortest routes for the main cables are chosen once the places for the modules, batteries, control unit, lamps, and power outlet points are fixed.

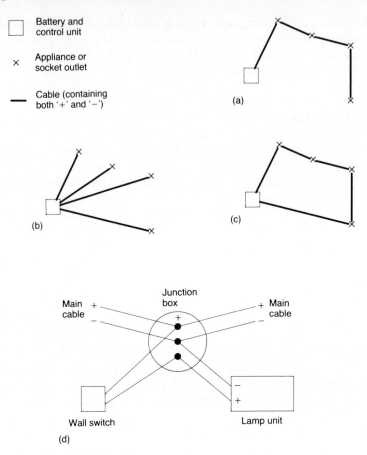

Figure 9.5 Wiring circuits.
(a) Radial circuit for one cable supplying several appliances.
(b) Star circuit with separate cables for each appliance.
(c) Ring circuit for socket outlet points around a building.
(d) Loop-in circuit for a lighting cable. This is used when the switch is separated from the lamp fitting.

The most common circuit is called *radial* with one cable for a group of appliances (see Figure 9.5(a)). Radial circuits are used either for several lamps or several outlet points. For fixed appliances that draw a high current, a *star* circuit should be used with a separate cable to each appliance (see Figure 9.5(b)).

For several outlet points around a group of rooms, a ring circuit may be suitable. In a *ring* circuit, the outlet points are linked by a cable that starts and ends at the control unit (see Figure 9.5(c)). This provides two routes for current to flow to any point on the ring so there is no restriction on where appliances are plugged in.

In large installations, there is a choice of how the lamps are controlled. It is recommended that there is at least one main circuit switch. This enables appliances to be turned off without any possibility of being turned on by mistake. A design for a control unit with separate switches for several circuits is given in Chapter 16. Dividing the lamps into separate circuits enables control at one point and is a good way of reducing electricity consumption during bad weather.

If switches are required for each lamp, try to buy lamp fittings with integral switches. This simplifies wiring, reduces the number of wiring joints, and may reduce cost. The switch may be a rocker type for a wall-mounted lamp or a pull cord for a ceiling mounting.

In a large installation, it may be desirable to put switches on the wall, as for mains systems. However, these are unnecessary if lamps are always left on when the circuit is switched on. If a wall switch is required for a lamp in a lighting circuit, the switch can be wired by a *loop-in* system (see Figure 9.5(d)). The main cable runs through a number of junction points. At each junction, there is one cable running to the lamp fitting itself and another cable to a switch on the wall. The wire from the switch to the lamp fitting loops through the junction box.

Checklist of parts and tools required

Table 9.2 is a list of all parts that may be needed for a solar electric system. A list of tools and other useful items is given in Table 9.3.

The rest of this section gives details about small items that are not covered in the earlier chapters.

On–off switches

Figure 9.6 shows some examples of switches used in mains systems. These switches can also be used in solar systems after first checking the current rating. This shows how well the contact surfaces of a switch can tolerate the small spark or electric arc that is formed when the switch is opened. In switching a.c., the arc does not last for long. It stops at the instant the voltage changes polarity which is after less than a hundredth of a second of opening the switch. In switching d.c., the arc lasts longer because it is only stopped when the contacts are a few millimetres apart. If the arc continues for long, it can burn the contacts and shorten their life.

For 24 V d.c. systems, the same current rating at mains voltage a.c. marked on the switch should be used. For 12 V d.c. systems, the current rating can be doubled. The quick make-and-break type of switch with a snap action is the most suitable for switching d.c. (see switch 3 in Figure 9.6). A toggle and spring mechanism inside the switch produces a quick movement in making and

Table 9.2 *Checklist of items required for installation of a solar electric system.*

Items	Specifications
Modules:	
Solar cell module	W_P, V_{OC}, number of cells
Securing bolts and nuts including spares	Material (galvanized steel, stainless steel, aluminium)
	8 mm (⅜ in)
Mounting frame	
Ladder with padlock and chain	
Batteries:	
Battery	A h capacity, type, voltage of each
Acid (for dry-charged lead–acid batteries)	Litres/pints/gallons
Distilled or deionized water	Litres/pints/gallons
Ring clamps for terminals	One pair for each battery
Box, stand, or platform	
Petroleum jelly or other grease	
Sodium bicarbonate (baking powder)	
Control	
Control unit	
Fuse holder	
Spare fuses or fuse wire	
Meter unit	
Sub-board	
Distribution	
Fixed cable	Size 2.5–20 mm²
	Length (metres/feet/yards)
Flexible cable	Size 1.5–10 mm²
	Length (metres/feet/yards)
Surface-mounting clips and nails	
Plastic trunking and nails	20 or 25 mm
PVC conduit tubing and couplers	
PVC glue	
Metal clamps with bars and screws for conduit	
Connector strip	
Crimp connectors or ring terminals	
On–off switches	Surface mounting with patress box
	Flush mounting with recessed box
	Panel mounting

Table 9.2 *Checklist of items required for installation of a solar electric system.*

Items	Specifications
Time-delay switch	
Socket outlet	Surface, flush, panel
Plug	
Adaptable metal box with rubber grommets	
Appliances:	
Tube lamp with inverter and perhaps own switch	Power rating, voltage
Bulb with fitting	Pendant with ceiling rose
	Wall mounting
Spare tubes	
Spare bulbs	
Low-voltage adaptor	
Outside lamp enclosure/housing	

breaking contact. The quick make prevents contact bounce and the quick break prevents the arc from lasting long and burning the contacts.

Time-delay switches

For the best use of the charge stored in the batteries, appliances should only be left on for as long as they are actually needed. Places such as toilets and store rooms are visited for only a few minutes each time so their lights should be turned off when leaving. In institutions, it may be difficult to encourage users to do this so switches with a built-in timing mechanism are recommended.

A time-delay switch is closed by hand and the mechanism inside opens the switch automatically after a few minutes. This sort of switch is often found in the corridors and stairways of hotels. The switches stay closed long enough for people to pass through so it helps to reduce the electricity bill of the hotel.

In a solar system, the total cost of a time-delay switch with a low-cost filament bulb should be compared to the cost of a tube lamp and inverter that provide the same amount of light using less power (see Chapter 6). Choose the cheaper option.

Plugs and socket outlets

Sockets at power outlet points are useful for connecting portable appliances into the main circuit, such as cassette players, televisions, and small lamps. The socket outlet is attached to a wall and connected to the fixed wiring. The plug is

Table 9.3 *Checklist of tools and useful items for installing and servicing solar electric systems.*

Tools for servicing only

Multimeter (preferably digital, otherwise analogue)
Current shunt (20 A, 200 mV)
Battery hydrometer in protective case
Thermometer 0–60 °C (30–140 °F) in protective case
Screwdrivers (small and large; flat blade and cross-end)[1]
Pliers (cutting, stripping, flat nose, and long nose)[1]
Adjustable spanner[1]
Set of Allen keys (for screws with hexagonal sockets)
Marker pen and tie-on or self-adhesive labels (for marking cables)
Insulation tape
Paint brush

Extra tools and materials for installing

Tape-measure and chalk
Compass and protractor
Spirit level and plumb line
12 V d.c. electric drill or hand drill
Set of high-speed drill bits (for wood and metal)
Set of tungsten-tipped bits (for masonry)
Long masonry drill bit 13 mm × 400 mm (0.5 × 15 in)
Hammer[1]
Wall punch
Wood chisel
Gimlet
Shovel (for digging holes and trenches)
Small hacksaw
File (rat tail and flat)
Mason's trowel
Cement
Spring for bending PVC pipes
Stiff wire for threading cables through pipes
Silicone mastic or pitch
Two-part epoxy glue
Heavy-duty adhesive tape
Knife
Crimping tool (for spade connectors)
12 V soldering iron
Electrical solder
Plastic gloves and goggles or face shield
Plastic funnel and plastic tubing (for filling vented batteries)

---

[1]With insulated handles.

Figure 9.6   Examples of switches suitable for use in solar electric systems (current rating at mains voltage given in brackets): **1** smooth-action on-off switch (5 A); **2** time-delay on-off switch (10 A) with setting range up to ten minutes; **3** quick make-and-break on-off switch (6 A) with cover removed to show mechanism; **4** two-pole, two-way toggle switch (3 A) for panel mounting on a box.

the movable part and is connected to the appliance by a flexible cable. A range of suitable plugs is shown in Figure 9.7. A few points should be noted when choosing the type of socket to use in a solar installation.

With d.c. electricity, it is important to maintain the correct polarity of the conductors. Reversing the polarity by mistake will cause some appliances not to work and may even damage them. Therefore two-pin plugs and sockets that can be fitted in two different ways should not be used, since only one way is correct. Three-pin plugs with round or square pins are suitable. Although the earth connection is not used, the earth pin ensures that the plug fits the socket in one way only with no risk of reversing polarity.

There is a standard plug for 12 V d.c. which is based on the cigarette lighter in cars, although the plug and socket fittings may not be locally available. This type of plug has the positive at the tip and the negative at the side.

A similar type is used for the d.c. input to electronic appliances, such as cassette players, and is called a *power-in* or *jack plug*. Polarity of the contacts on a jack plug is not standardized. When wiring one of these plugs, the polarity of the socket on the appliances should be checked first. This is indicated by a picture on the appliance next to the socket (see Figure 14.1).

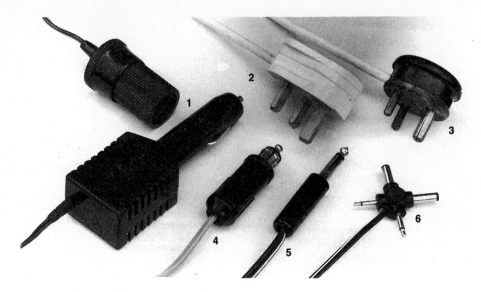

Figure 9.7   Examples of plugs suitable for use in solar electric systems: **1** plug and socket in the same size for cigarette lighters in vehicles, **2** three-pin square with internal fuse; **3** three-pin round; **4** small-size car lighter, **5** 6.4 mm (0.25 in) jack connector (two-pole); **6** four-way plug with (clockwise from cable) 2.5 mm (0.1 in) sub-miniature jack plug, 2.1 mm (0.08 in) power-in-plug, 2.5 mm (0.1 in) power-in plug, 3.5 mm (0.14 in) miniature jack plug.

The current rating of the plug and flexible cable should be high enough for the appliance they serve. The current drawn by an appliance is calculated from the following formula:

$$\boxed{\begin{array}{c}\text{Power rating}\\\text{of appliance}\\\text{(W)}\end{array}} \div \boxed{\begin{array}{c}\text{System}\\\text{voltage}\\\text{(V)}\end{array}} = \boxed{\begin{array}{c}\text{Current drawn}\\\text{by appliance}\\\text{(A)}\end{array}} \quad\quad (9.2)$$

It is good practice to protect a portable appliance, such as a cassette player or fan motor, by its own fuse. The fuses in the control unit of 10 A or more are only meant to protect the main cables which carry current to several appliances at once. Appliances such as cassette players may have their own fuse fitted in the case. For other appliances, a fuse can be fitted in the plug (plug 2 in Figure 9.7) or by using an in-line fitting (see Figure 4.2(b)).

For the rating of fuse, use the nearest current rating of available fuses above the answer from Formula (9.2). Some appliances draw a higher current just after being switched on. This is called a *current surge* and is usual for motors. Either use a *slow-blow* type of fuse at the correct rating or an ordinary fuse of double the current calculated from Formula (9.2).

Avoid confusion with mains plugs

With low-voltage appliances, it is important not to connect them to a mains socket by mistake. If this happens, the high voltage will burn the appliance out and, more seriously, metal parts that are exposed may become live with mains voltage.

This mistake could be avoided by writing something like 'low voltage only' on the appliance. However, it must be accepted that most users find electrical terms such as 'volts', 'd.c.' and 'live' very confusing and do not appreciate some of the important differences between mains and solar systems. Some users may only be guided by the shape of plugs and other fittings rather than by electrical characteristics, such as voltage, which cannot be seen. If a plug looks as if it can possibly fit a socket, many users will try fitting them together and switching on. This will be done before reading any labels or seeking advice.

If at all possible, the type of socket used in solar installation should be different from the one normally used for mains installations in the locality. This makes it difficult for appliances to be plugged into the wrong supply accidentally. It is particularly necessary where a power inverter unit for running mains voltage appliances is also in use. The socket on the inverter should be of the mains type.

Cables

A selection of cable types is shown in Figure 5.2. Cables made with seven or more strands are preferred because a single strand can break more easily after bending. Flexible cable should be used in all places where the cable is not fixed in one position but intended to move. This includes connections to modules on a tracking mount, such as down the central tube of the tracking mount in Figure 9.3.

Surface mounting with clips or enclosed wiring in conduit pipes can both be used. Between buildings, routeing underground is preferable to overhead cables which are much more likely to be damaged. The cable should either be designed for underground laying or protected from water by a sheath, such as PVC conduit (see Figure 9.8). With glued joints between each length of pipe, the cable is then well protected from moisture in the ground and mechanical damage. At the buildings, the pipe can be bent by heating and routed up the side wall passing under the roof at the top. In this way, no rain can get into the pipe and the cable remains dry. Alternatively the pipe can pass through the wall lower down and be sealed with cement and mastic.

Joints between cables and at 'T-offs' can be made with plastic connector

Figure 9.8 PVC conduit for protecting cables that run underground between buildings.

strip. Larger sizes are needed than is usual for lighting circuits in mains wiring because of the larger cables. A set of connector strips is shown in Figure 9.9. Spade connectors are also suitable and the appropriate crimping tool should be used for a reliable grip on the cable.

Ordering a system as a complete package

A complete package is a good way to buy a system, although not necessarily the cheapest. An example of the parts included is shown in Figures 1.3 and 7.2.

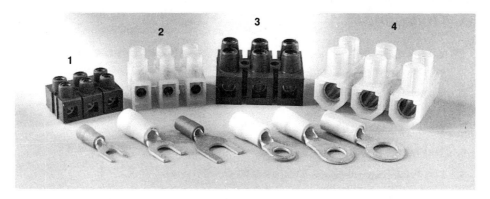

Figure 9.9 A range of connector strips, spade connectors, and eyelet connectors. Details of connector strips: **1** 2.6 mm diameter holes for 4 mm² cable; **2** 3 mm diameter holes for 6 mm²; **3** 5.5 mm diameter holes for 10 mm² cables; **4** 7 mm diameter holes.

Check the following aspects when comparing systems:

- ☐ Total generating capacity of solar modules in peak watts (W_P).
- ☐ Type of mounting hardware for modules.
- ☐ Total capacity of batteries in ampere-hours (A h) and whether vented or sealed.
- ☐ Features on the control unit, such as automatic disconnection of loads when the batteries are low and lightning protection.
- ☐ Number and power rating of appliances.
- ☐ Expected use of appliances for a specified value of daily insolation in peak-hours or kW h/m² per day.
- ☐ Length of cables and inclusion of fixtures.
- ☐ Tools needed for assembly and maintenance.
- ☐ Spare parts.
- ☐ Documentation.

Specify that the units are to be packed in containers which are small enough to be easily handled and transported in small vehicles. The packing should protect the units and parts against all weather and handling conditions during transport to the site.

There are extra requirements for suppliers exporting parts to the country of the site. The supplier should arrange for the equipment to be comprehensively insured for its full value. Goods should be insured right up to delivery at the site. The minimum requirement for insurance cover is that it should extend from the time the equipment leaves the supplier's premises until clearance from customs at the point of entry into the country of installation.

☐ *Questions*

1. Why do the modules, batteries, and control unit need to be positioned close together?

2. Why does it matter if any part of a solar array is shaded when in operation, even if it is only over one cell?

3. What is a tracking mount?

4. Why is good access for users required to the modules?

5. List five features required of the place for the batteries.

6. A power inverter with an efficiency of 70 per cent is used in a 12 V system and powers a 200 W appliance. If the length of cable from the batteries is 5 m, calculate the smallest size that can be used.

7. What is a time-delay switch and where is it most useful in a solar system?

8. Portable appliances that work at low voltage should never be directly plugged into a mains socket. How can this be prevented?

$\boxed{10}$ Installation

The sections covered by this chapter are summarized in Figure 10.1. Safety is very important. Before starting any installation work, take careful note of the safety precautions listed at the start of this chapter. Installation should only be performed or supervised by personnel who have experience of electricity and fully understand these precautions.

For users, it is necessary to check that the installation work is done correctly. Details to check are given at the end of this chapter.

Safety precautions and warnings

Solar electric systems can contain hazardous materials and generate high voltages. Safety is very important in order to avoid accidents and damage to expensive equipment. For the protection of yourself and others, follow the safety precautions given in this section very carefully. Make sure that everybody working with your system reads and understands this safety section, or has it explained to them.

Some examples of safety warning signs are shown in Figure 10.2. They are clearer than written instructions and should be put up near the modules, in the battery room and over sockets.

In case of accident

Prepare a safety notice, like the one in Figure 10.3(a), with translations into local languages. It should be left at a place for quick and easy reference in the event of an accident. A first-aid kit should be available at the installation. Check that someone knows what the items in it are for and how to use them.

When installing a medium or large system and any system with a power inverter, there is a risk of electric shock. Prepare a notice like the one in

209

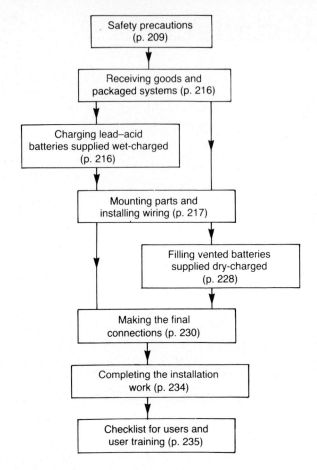

Figure 10.1   Sequence of the steps for the installation of a solar electric system (p. page references to text).

Figure 10.3(b). Make sure someone at the nearest health centre knows how to treat persons suffering from electric shock.

Electricity

The terminals of a module are live when the front face is illuminated by sunlight or artificial light although the electrical output of one module is not dangerous. However, if the modules are incorrectly wired in series, voltages could be obtained that are potentially lethal. Some systems, such as for powerful water pumps, have all the modules wired in series for operation above 50 V.

The same problem of incorrect series connection applies to batteries. In

Figure 10.2 Safety warning signs to put up around an installation.
(a) Near the modules.
(b) By the batteries.
(c) Over sockets at power outlet points.

addition, batteries can deliver hundreds of amps into a short circuit producing a lot of heat.

Electrical precautions include the following:

☐ Remove all metal from hands, wrists, and neck (rings, watch with metal strap, metal necklace, etc.) to avoid accidental shorting of exposed metal parts that are live.

☐ Take care when making connections to battery terminals. Use tools with insulated handles. Sparks can cause a fire.

☐ Never bypass the fuse nearest to the batteries.

☐ Work on the modules of an array in early morning or late evening. If working at midday, cover all the modules with a thick sheet or cloth.

☐ When examining a new system, find out the operating voltage. Measure the voltage of connections with a voltmeter before touching them.

Solar modules

Care is required when handling modules. In modules made up of crystalline solar cells (examples in Figures 2.2 and 2.3), the cells are thin fragile discs connected

IN CASE OF ACCIDENT

Electrolyte on SKIN

Wash skin immediately with water. Remove contaminated clothing.
Wash skin again with water.

Electrolyte in EYES

Wash out eyes with clean water for at least ten minutes. Ask for immediate medical attention.

Electrolyte in MOUTH

Drink as much clean water as possible. Do NOT try to vomit. Ask for immediate medical attention.

Electrolyte SPILLED

Sprinkle sodium bicarbonate (baking powder) onto the affected area.
Wash down with plenty of water.

FALL from roof or high place

Do not move person. Ask for immediate medical attention.

(a)

Figure 10.3   Safety notices. These should be translated into the local languages and put up in prominent places for immediate reference in the event of an accident.
(a)   The advice about electrolyte does not apply to systems with sealed batteries. The advice about falls applies to systems with modules mounted above the ground on a roof or pole.
(b)   Only required when installing several modules or where a power inverter is used.

by delicate strips of metal. When they are assembled into the module, they are well protected by the hard glass on the front. However on the back of the module, the cells are covered only by a thin sheet of plastic.

Hitting the back of a module with a hard object, such as a screwdriver, can easily break a cell or connection and destroy the whole module. Also, the back should be protected from damage by sharp objects. If cuts are made in the surface, moisture can seep in and this will slowly destroy the solar cells.

Modules are often mounted in high places so guard against falls.

Precautions when handling modules include the following:

☐   Modules should always be carried and transported packed in a box that protects both the front and back.

☐   During transport, secure modules in a vertical position and do not rest other objects on top.

IN CASE OF ELECTRIC SHOCK

Victim STILL IN CONTACT with source of shock

Quick action is essential.

DO NOT touch directly a victim who is still in contact with the electric source
(to avoid an electric shock to yourself).

Pull on the victim's clothes. Otherwise push or pull the victim out of contact
with the source of shock using:

wooden stick
dry rope
leather belt
dry clothes or blanket used as a rope

Cushion fall as victim is pulled free.

Check for a pulse. If the heart has stopped beating, hit the victim's chest once to restart it.

Seek medical attention immediately.

Victim NOT BREATHING

Lie victim down and give the kiss of life as follows:

Tilt victim's head back and check victim's mouth is clear.

Pinch victim's nose closed and blow four breaths into the victim's mouth.

Let the victim's chest fall.

Continue breathing into the victim's mouth at normal breathing speed.

Seek medical help.

BURNS to skin

Cool burns immediately with plenty of clean cold water.

Cover burns with a clean dry cotton sheet.

Seek medical attention.

(b)

☐ Modules should never be stored flat on the ground. They may be stepped on or objects may fall on them.

☐ If it is necessary to drill extra holes in the frame, take great care not to punch through into a cell. Use a piece of wood between the frame and the plastic covering.

☐ The mounting structure should be square so that it will not cause the modules to twist when they are attached.

☐ Make sure that access to high places is safe. Use ladders of the correct length that are positioned against a wall at a stable angle.

☐ Never walk on a sheet metal or tile roof. Always lie a ladder or plank up the slope of the roof which is secured by a rope taken over the roof top and tied at ground level.

Batteries

The electrolyte in batteries can burn skin and cause blindness. It is also very damaging to clothes and tools. Take careful note of the instructions given in Figure 10.3(a) if an accident occurs.

Lead–acid batteries that have vents should be supplied dry-charged so that they can be filled with acid at the site of the installation. This avoids the risk of spilling electrolyte and damage from a deep discharge caused by self-discharge. As dry-charged, the battery is also slightly lighter for ease of carrying. Delay filling the batteries until just before they are needed in the system.

Lead–acid batteries can be supplied *wet-charged* for convenience if the journey from the supplier to the site is short and easy. After a battery is filled, acid should never be emptied out. Filled batteries must be transported with great care.

Lead–acid batteries produce hydrogen gas when being charged. This gas can explode when ignited by a cigarette or a naked flame.

Precautions include the following:

☐ Handle batteries with care.

☐ Do not let children touch them.

☐ Keep batteries upright at all times. (Does not apply to fully sealed batteries.) Do not carry batteries on your head.

☐ If carrying handles are not fitted, do not lift batteries by the terminals or connections. Use carrying straps or a sling with handles. Otherwise lift by the bottom corners.

☐ During transport, cover wet-charged batteries with a solid plastic board or plywood to avoid any risk of shorting the terminals.

☐ Never bring a glowing cigarette or naked flame near batteries. This applies even if the place they are in is well ventilated and the batteries are not being charged.

☐ Use tools with insulated handles to prevent accidental shorting of terminals.

☐ Wear glasses or protective goggles and old clothes when handling the electrolyte.

☐ When handling electrolyte, keep a bowl full of water on one side.

☐ If acid gets on to tools, wash them with water, rub dry, and coat steel parts with grease.

☐ Check that the lids on electrolyte containers are tightly closed before moving them.

☐ Store unused electrolyte in a safe place. Label the container with the warning signs for 'Corrosive', 'Poison', and 'Keep upright', as shown in Figure 10.2.

☐ Do not use electrolyte containers for storing drinking-water.

A *neutralizing solution* should be prepared which is always available to be poured on spilt acid to make it safe. The neutralizer is a solution of *sodium bicarbonate*. This is also known as *bicarbonate of soda* and is the main ingredient of baking powder. The solution is made by mixing together about 100 g of sodium bicarbonate for each litre of water (or 2 oz for each pint). To use the neutralizing solution, pour on the spilt acid and keep pouring until foaming has stopped. Afterwards wash the area clean with ordinary water.

Voltage and polarity of d.c.

For mains systems, there is generally only one voltage rating for the appliances available in a country. For the low d.c. voltage used in solar electricity, there are many voltages in use.

The electrical supply in a solar electric system is d.c., and correct polarity must be maintained in all connections. This means that one wire is always positive, usually the red one, and the other wire is negative, usually the black one. Some d.c. appliances will be damaged if the wires are connected the wrong way.

Where possible, choose control units and appliances containing electronics that are protected against reverse polarity of connections:

☐ Appliances that are connected directly into the system must have the correct voltage rating. Check this rating when ordering and collecting the appliances.

☐ A voltage adaptor is needed for any appliance rated for a voltage below the system voltage.

☐ When repairing or making alterations to a system, do not assume that a red wire always links positive terminals. Sometimes mistakes are made or a previous electrician might have run out of one colour of wire.

☐ Label wires before disconnection so that they are reconnected correctly.

Inverters for fluorescent tube lamps

The inverter for a fluorescent tube converts low-voltage d.c. to high-voltage a.c. necessary to operate the tube. Poor-quality inverters can be damaged if the polarity of their connections is wrong or if a tube is not fitted:

☐ Check the polarity of wiring to an inverter before switching on for the first time.

☐ Always make sure a good tube is fitted to an inverter before switching the power on.

☐ Do not attempt to repair broken inverters. They produce dangerous voltages.

Receiving goods

If parts are collected directly from a supplier, check that all parts containing electronics work before taking them away. This applies to inverters and control units. Also make sure that wet-charged and sealed batteries are fully charged.

The following points should be checked as the parts for an installation arrive:

1. Inspect the outside of the packages for damage that might have occurred during transport.
2. Unpack parts and check for damage. Damaged parts should be repaired or replaced by the supplier. Damage that occurred during transport should be covered by insurance.
3. Note the date that the equipment left the supplier. Sealed batteries or batteries supplied wet-charged should be unpacked immediately and recharged.
4. Store equipment indoors in an area that is clean, cool, dry, and secure. Do not stack equipment. Make a note of the date when the next charge is required for filled batteries that will be left in storage.

If there is a delay before the batteries can be installed, they should be stored near a charging point from a generator or the mains supply. Charging can also be done from a module put in the sun, but care is necessary to protect the module from damage while unsupported.

Packaged systems

Check that the following documents are included with the system:

☐ A complete list of all parts that should be in the package, including spares and tools.

☐ Assembly instructions.

☐ Operating instructions.

☐ Instructions and a timetable for routine tasks and maintenance.

☐ Identification of all parts to help when ordering replacements.

Apart from the main items, other items that should be included in the package:

☐ Consumables and spares for parts that will need replacing during two years of operation. Examples are distilled water for vented batteries and fuses.

☐ Spares of items that are likely to get lost or broken during transport, such as screws, nuts, and tube lamps.

☐ Special tools as appropriate, such as Allen or socket keys, box spanners, and a funnel for topping up vented batteries.

Mounting parts

Solar modules

It is often easiest to make the electrical connections to modules when the modules are flat on the ground rather than mounted on the support structure. If this is the case, the modules and support structure are only prepared at this stage ready for permanent mounting of the modules during the wiring stage.

The modules should be attached to the support structure with screws through the frame. The usual screw size is 8 mm (⅜ in) diameter. Try to use holes already drilled in the frame. If existing holes need to be enlarged or extra holes added, protect the back of the module from damage with a piece of wood while drilling. Also lie the module on a flat surface so that there is no bending force on the module while drilling. For the position of the junction boxes when mounted, see the later section on 'Series and parallel connections of modules.'

Setting the direction of tilt to north or south has to be accurate only to within 20° of the right direction. If the modules are mounted on a roof, adjustment of the direction may not be possible.

The direction of tilt can be checked using a compass to show the direction of north. To set the direction, stand in front of modules. Hold the compass level and turn yourself until the compass shows that you are facing due north or south as appropriate. Look up at the modules and estimate whether any adjustment is needed.

Another method is to use the direction of the shadow from a vertical pole. Wait until the sun is at the highest position in the sky when the shadow is shortest. This is not exactly at 12 noon because of the position in the time zone and seasonal variations (caused by changes in the speed of the earth around the sun).

Ensure that the support structure sets the modules at the correct tilt angle (as defined in Figure 8.3). The tilt angle can be checked using a template with a spirit level or a plumb line. The template is a triangle with the shape shown in Figure 10.4(a). Using 500 mm (20 in) for the length of one side, the length of the other side is given in Figure 10.4(b) for a number of tilt angles. Cut the template from a stiff material, such as cardboard or wood, that will not scratch the glass.

Figure 10.4(c) shows a spirit level or a plumb line being used to set the template in the correct position. The gap between the module and the long side of the template indicates the amount of adjustment required to the tilt angle.

Leave the modules off the support structure ready for wiring as described later.

Control unit

Control units should be securely attached to a wall at eye level. One method is to attach them to a wooden sub-board with the connections taken behind the hinged panel of the sub-board (see Figure 9.4). Otherwise attach the unit directly to a wall with screws into plastic or wooden rawl plugs. If the wall is not hard enough for rawl plugs, use threaded rods through the whole thickness and put nuts on both sides of the wall. Mark where the holes have to be drilled by putting the regulator on the wall and checking its position with a spirit level.

Wiring the system

The first stage of wiring can be done by an electrician or any other person who has experience of wiring mains-type systems. It involves connecting all the circuits for the appliances and laying the wires ready for connection to the solar modules, batteries, and control box. The final connections are made in a particular order to prevent damage to equipment. The correct order of connections is described in the next section.

Figure 10.4   Template for setting and checking the tilt angle of modules.
(a)   Outline of template.
(b)   Table of dimensions for a range of tilt angles.
(c)   Method of using template with a spirit level or plumb line on a module. In this example, the tilt angle of the module needs to be increased.

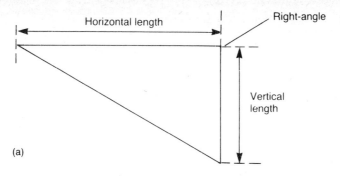

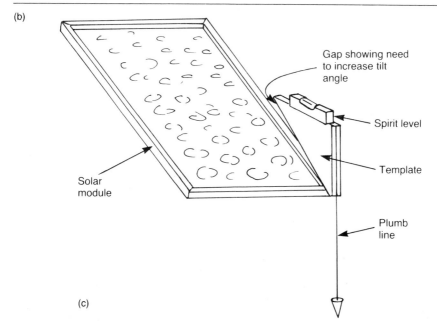

(a)

Tilt angle	Lengths of sides			
	Dimensions (mm)		Dimensions (in)	
	Horizontal	Vertical	Horizontal	Vertical
15°	500	135	20.0	5.4
20°	500	180	20.0	7.3
25°	500	235	20.0	9.3
30°	500	290	20.0	11.5
35°	500	350	20.0	14.0
40°	500	420	20.0	16.8
45°	500	500	20.0	20.0
50°	420	500	16.8	20.0
55°	350	500	14.0	20.0
60°	290	500	11.5	20.0
65°	235	500	9.3	20.0
70°	180	500	7.3	20.0
75°	135	500	5.4	20.0
80°	90	500	3.5	20.0
85°	45	500	1.7	20.0

(b)

(c)

Installing cables

Cables should never be loose but always fixed at close intervals or threaded through conduit. Cables can be attached with clips or heavy-duty adhesive tape.

When a cable passes through a hole in a roof, the hole round the cable should be sealed with silicone mastic or pitch to prevent leaks. Corrugated steel roofs should only be pieced on the top of a ridge. If a cable passes through a false ceiling, it should be secured to the solid supports of the ceiling.

Along a wall, first mark a line on the wall with chalk. The cable should take the shortest route possible, but always in horizontal or vertical directions. Cables should be fixed at regular intervals of 200–300 mm (8–12 in) which can be marked off along the chalk line. Keep the cable taut while putting the wall mounts and cable in place.

For routes outside, the cable should be laid in a trench which is at least 500 mm (20 in) deep. The cable should be designed for use underground or threaded through PVC conduit (see Figure 9.8). Do not stretch the cable in the trench or conduit. Leave it slack so that it is not under strain when the trench is filled in.

Making good connections

All the electrical connections should be made with care since many faults are caused simply by loose connections. Never connect wires just by twisting them together and wrapping with insulating tape. Always use proper connectors in junction boxes with connector strips.

The voltage drop at connections between wires depends on how well the connections are made. Good connections avoid any additional voltage drop at these points. A few bad connections in one circuit will prevent some of the appliances from working properly when all appliances are on and the circuit is carrying the full current.

A good connection has firm metal-to-metal contact between all strands of the wires being joined. Wires must be properly prepared before insertion into connector terminals, switches, and other fittings. After removing the insulation, the wire should be trimmed to leave just the right amount of bare wire. When trimming flexible cable, care must be taken not to cut any of the small strands.

The best connection between two wires is to twist them together and insert the twisted pair into one end of the connector (see Figure 10.5). In a 30 A connector strip, the hole is large enough for a pair of 2.5 mm^2 wires twisted together in this way. For larger cable sizes, the connector is used in the usual way with the twisted end of each wire inserted into opposite sides of the connector. Where more than two cables meet, the strands from one wire can be divided between two adjacent connector terminals.

The screws should be tight enough for a secure connection without being so tight that the screws cut through any strands. Tug each wire to ensure that it is connected securely.

Figure 10.5 Methods of joining stranded cables: **1** twisted and put in one side of a connector block; **2** spliced joint that is half completed.

Where possible, connections should be made in accessible places so that they can be checked and tightened at a later date. For connections that will become inaccessible later, such as long runs underground, it is necessary to use a more permanent method of joining. This is shown in Figure 10.5 and involves splicing the individual strands. A spliced connection is finished off by wrapping with insulation tape.

Connections to the solar modules

No wires should be connected to the modules at this stage but the wires can be prepared.

Connections to modules are either to screw terminals in junction boxes or to a pair of wires that are already sealed into the back. Junction boxes have a gland fitting which seals onto the cable or conduit to prevent water leaking into the box.

Some modules have diodes fitted in the junction box (see Figure 10.6). Check their identity with the module instructions before preparing the connections. Bypass diodes should always be left in place. If the control unit already contains a blocking diode or has some means of preventing discharge at night, any blocking diode on the module should be removed.

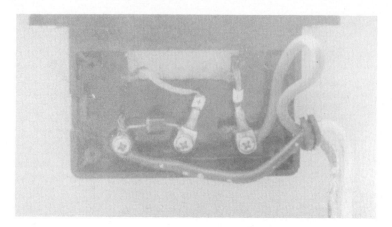

Figure 10.6 Example of a junction box with the cover removed on a module. This box contains a blocking diode connected to the positive output of the module. If the blocking diode is not required at the module, the wire is connected directly to the '+' screw terminal instead.

Series and parallel connections of modules

When there is more than one module, connections between the modules are necessary to put them either in series, in parallel, or a combination of series and parallel. Examples of these connections are shown in Figure 10.7. It is very important to understand the connections and to avoid the risk of making the wrong series connections by mistake.

Parallel connections are used to increase the current output of the array of modules. They are made by connecting like terminals (negatives connect to negatives and positives connect to positives). For modules with separate junction

---

Figure 10.7 Connecting arrays of modules.
(a) For a system voltage of 12 V and modules with separate terminal boxes for positive and negative. Connection of a blocking diode, if required, is shown using a connector strip. (The current rating of the diode must be greater than the total short circuit currents of the modules.)
(b) For a system voltage of 12 V and modules with a single terminal box each.
(c) For a system voltage of 24 V and modules with separate terminal boxes for positive and negative.
(d) For system voltage of 24 V and modules with a single terminal box each. If bypass diodes are not already fitted in the modules, the positions are shown. (The current rating of the diode must be greater than the short circuit current of the module in which it is used.)

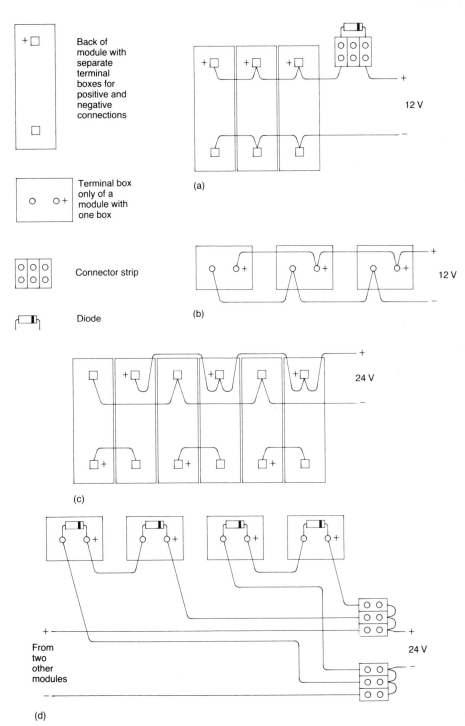

Back of module with separate terminal boxes for positive and negative connections

Terminal box only of a module with one box

Connector strip

Diode

(a)

(b)

(c)

(d)

12 V

12 V

24 V

24 V

From two other modules

boxes for positive and negative, all the positives should be at one end for ease of connection (see Figure 10.7(a)). Figure 10.7(b) shows the arrangement for modules with single junction boxes. It also shows use of a single diode if blocking diodes are not provided in each module or a control unit. Make sure that the end of the diode with the stripe is connected towards the control unit.

Modules are connected in series to increase the system voltage. The positive of one module is connected to the negative of the next module. When grouping modules with series connections, modules in the same group must have the same current output and be mounted next to each other on the support structure. They should also be of the same type so that their outputs are exactly matched when generating electricity.

Figure 10.7(c) shows the arrangement for 24 V operation using modules with separate junction boxes. The modules alternate in direction to keep the wires short. For modules with single junction boxes, the parallel connections between series groups of modules should be made in a separate junction box to avoid mistakes (see Figure 10.7(d)).

Bypass diodes

For systems operating at 24 V or higher, bypass diodes are required for each module. If bypass diodes are not already fitted in modules by the manufacturer, they can be added across the terminals as shown in Figure 10.7(d). Silicon diodes should be used with a higher current rating than the maximum short circuit current of the other series-connected module and a breakdown voltage greater than 16 V. Make sure that the stripe end of the diode is connected to the positive.

When the voltage of the modules is less than the system voltage, Figures 10.7(c) and 10.7(d) show that parallel connections are made after modules are grouped in series up to the system voltage. If it is necessary to have parallel modules within series strings, add an extra diode between the positive and negative of each parallel group. This diode should have the capacity to conduct the total current of the whole parallel group of modules. A heat sink (see Chapter 12) may be necessary to ensure that the diode does not over-heat when in use. This large extra diode is required because the small internal diodes in each module may not share current equally in this arrangement.

Battery connections

No wires should be connected to the battery at this stage but the connections can be prepared.

The brass terminals used for batteries in vehicles have a large hole to accept the thick cable that leads to the starter motor. This hole is too large for a good connection to be made with the sizes of wire used in solar electric systems. Instead the wires should be twisted and wrapped around the screw heads on the

(a)

(b)

Figure 10.8 Connections to batteries.
(a) Wires twisted around screws on a brass terminal clamp.
(b) Spade connector crimped on to wire.

terminal, as shown in Figure 10.8(a). This is necessary to ensure maximum contact with the terminals when the screws are tightened.

Another method of connection is by *spade connectors*, as shown in Figure 10.8(b). They are often used for wiring in vehicles because the connections are quick to make, neat, and reliable. Joining the spade connector to the end of a wire requires the correct crimping tool. The joint can be made by squeezing with pliers and soldering but it is not as strong. If tools are not available at the installation or are inconvenient to carry there, the wires could be prepared before hand elsewhere.

Battery clips, of the type shown in Figure 10.9, should not be used as a permanent means of connection. There is a fire risk because the clips could easily

Figure 10.9   Battery clips should not be used!

touch and cause a short circuit. Also a voltage drop is introduced by poor contact to the terminals.

Series and parallel connections of batteries

When there is more than one battery, connections between the batteries are necessary to put them either in series, in parallel, or in a combination of series and parallel. Examples of these connections are shown in Figure 10.10.

Series connections are used to increase voltage. The positive of one battery is connected to the negative of the next battery (see Figure 10.10(b)). Batteries are connected in series to reach to system voltage. When grouping batteries with series connections, batteries in the same group must have the same capacity. If possible, they should also be the same type and the same age so that they charge and discharge in the same way. When series-connected batteries are not matched, the effective capacity of the group is decided by the smallest.

Parallel connections are used to increase the A h capacity of the battery bank. They are made by connecting like terminals so that negatives connect to negatives and positives connect to positives (see Figure 10.10(a)). When the voltage of the batteries is less than the system voltage, parallel connections are made after batteries are grouped in series up to the system voltage (see Figure 10.10(c)).

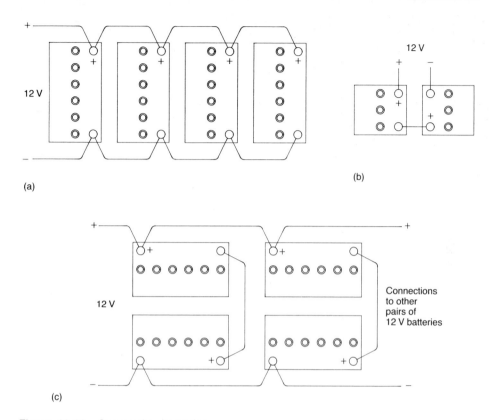

Figure 10.10 Connecting batteries.
(a) Parallel connection of 12 V batteries for a system voltage of 12 V.
(b) Series connection of two 6 V batteries for a system voltage of 12 V.
(c) Series and parallel connection of 12 V batteries for a system voltage of 24 V.

Connections to the control unit

No wires should be connected to the control unit at this stage but the wires can be prepared.

There is a great variety of different control units with their own system of connections. The instructions supplied with the unit should be read carefully before any wires are prepared.

The usual system of connections is pairs of terminals for cables to the modules, batteries, and load circuits. Terminals for the charging current from the solar modules may be marked 'array'. This name describes the way a group of modules is neatly arranged on the mounting structure to face the sun.

For the batteries, there may be two pairs of terminals marked 'battery' and 'battery sense'. The battery sense pair are required so that the control unit can accurately measure or 'sense' the voltage across the battery terminals. The battery voltage is used for regulating the charging current and triggering the low-voltage disconnect (for control units fitted with these features).

When the cable to the batteries is more than a few metres long or connecting several batteries, there will be a significant voltage drop along the cable when it carries a high current. This means that the voltage measured at the control unit will be less than the voltage across the battery terminals. A separate cable should link the battery terminals directly to 'battery sense' (see Figure 4.5). The cable can be as small as the test leads used for a voltmeter since it carries a very small current.

One advantage of having sense wires is that the true voltage of the battery is checked even if connections carrying the current have deteriorated.

In small systems, the 'battery sense' terminals can be linked directly to the 'battery' terminals at the control unit. This is when there are only one or two batteries at less than 2 m (6 ft) from the control unit.

There is usually one pair of terminals marked 'load' to supply the appliances. If there are several pairs of terminals, they can be used for separate circuits serving different groups of lamps and power outlet points. A relay may be included for a low-voltage disconnect of the loads or alarm circuits. The relay connections are called *voltage free* and can be used just like any other switch. An example of the connection for disconnecting circuits is shown in Figure 4.12.

Filling dry-charged batteries

Batteries that are supplied dry-charged should be left empty until just before they are needed in the system.

Prepare for filling in the following way:

☐ Read the safety warnings at the start of this chapter.

☐ Fill batteries outside or where spilt electrolyte will not cause damage.

☐ Keep children and other onlookers away.

☐ Wear glasses, goggles, or a full face shield.

☐ Wear plastic gloves.

☐ Wear old clothes and shoes so that damage to them from electrolyte does not matter.

☐ Keep a bowl of clean water nearby.

To fill the battery, remember that sulphuric acid which forms the electrolyte is not thick like oil but pours in the same way as water. Filling the batteries requires some care to avoid spilling or splashing.

Figure 10.11   Filling a lead–acid battery with electrolyte using a syphon tube. Note that plastic gloves (not shown) should be worn when handling electrolyte.

When filling from small containers of about one litre, pour the electrolyte in through a plastic funnel. When filling from a large container such as a twenty-litre or five-gallon jerry can, the electrolyte can be syphoned out through a plastic tube, as shown in Figure 10.11. The easiest way to stop the flow through the syphon when moving between cells is with a finger. If plastic gloves are not available, the tube should be pinched to stop the flow. Any splashes on skin should be washed off immediately in the bowl of water.

Fill each cell almost to the top. Leave for about ten minutes for air trapped between the plates to escape, then fill to the maximum level. If a maximum level is not marked, leave a clearance from the top of the cell inside of about 10 mm (½ in). Finally screw the vent caps on and wash the top of the batteries with clean water.

Leave the full cells for at least twenty minutes before measuring the voltage between the terminals. If the voltage is less than the nominal value, the battery is faulty and should be replaced. See Tables 3.2 and 3.4 for voltages expected for cells and batteries.

Final connections

The final connections should be done carefully. Follow instructions from suppliers where given and the guidance in this section. If possible, get help from someone who has some experience in installing solar systems successfully.

Before starting the final connections, the following jobs should be complete:

- ☐ Modules ready for mounting on their support structure.
- ☐ Batteries charged and in place.
- ☐ Fixed appliances and socket outlet points wired up to the control box but not connected to it.
- ☐ All cables cut and fixed in position but no connections made to batteries, control unit, or modules.

The order of final connections is as follows:

1. Measuring electrical output of modules (open circuit voltage, short circuit current) and completing installation of the solar array.
2. Connecting batteries.
3. Connecting the solar array to the control unit.
4. Connecting circuits for the appliances.

Installation and wiring of solar array

The exact order of steps for completing the wiring to the modules and attaching the modules to the support structure is not definite. It varies with the type of connections, number of modules in the solar array, and ease of working on the support structure.

Making the connections to the back of the modules is usually easiest with the modules laid glass side down on level ground. Use the packing material as protection to avoid damage to the glass. The modules are then attached to the support structure before completing the wiring to the control unit and batteries.

Here are some points to note:

- ☐ Ensure that the ends of the wires in the main cable to the control unit are covered so that they cannot touch each other or any other connections and bare wires.
- ☐ When working on the electrical connections of a module that is installed, try to work early in the morning or late in the evening when modules generate low currents. If work must be done around midday, cover the front of the module with a thick sheet or cloth.
- ☐ If series connections are required between modules, make these bringing

each series group of modules up to the system voltage. Measure the voltage of each series group. (If covers are being used, remove these for the measurement and then replace.) If the measurement is not above the system voltage, check the connections.

☐ Once the wiring is complete, measure the voltage of the whole solar array. (If covers are being used, remove these for the measurement and then replace.) If the measurement is not above the system voltage, check the connections.

For small systems with just one module, it is not essential to measure the electrical output of the module during installation. However, making measurements is recommended, especially for a solar array which has several modules. These measurements help check that the wiring is correct and help in solving problems that might arise when one part of the solar system fails to work properly.

Open circuit voltage of each module

Measuring the voltage of each module is a check of all the internal connections between the solar cells in a module. Measurements should be taken when there are no clouds covering the sun:

1. Use a voltmeter with a scale of 15 V or more.
2. Locate the positive and negative connections of the module. These are either two wires, two terminals in a single junction box, or separate junction boxes. For junction boxes, attach test leads from the terminals to the voltmeter. If a blocking diode is fitted, make the measurement on the module side of the diode.
3. If the module is on the ground, move it so that the glass front is facing the sun. Check that none of the cells in the module is shaded.
4. Record the voltage measurement in a log book.

This is a measure of the open circuit voltage (V_{OC}) and should be compared with the specification in the datasheet. For a module that can charge a 12 V system, V_{OC} should be 17–20 V. Modules designed to charge 6 V systems should have a V_{OC} of 8–10 V.

If a module reads a low voltage, check any bypass diodes that are fitted. A diode connected the wrong way or shorted internally will make the voltage low. If the voltage remains low after repeated measurements, replace the module.

Short circuit current of each module

This measurement requires a meter with a current scale of 5 A or more. It can also be measured using a voltmeter with a *shunt* resistance. A typical size of shunt converts a 200 mV scale for reading 0–20 A. These shunts are available for maximum currents of 10 or 20 A. An alternative shunt for a 5 V scale is shown in Figure 13.6(a).

Connect the test leads of the meter to the positive and negative terminals of one module as for the measurement of open circuit voltage. Record the current measurement in a log book. The measurement of short circuit current (I_{SC}) shows how well the module converts light into electricity. Since the short circuit current depends on the exact lighting conditions, record the time of day, date, and clearness of the atmosphere (clear, hazy, dusty, thin cloud, or mist) with the current measurement.

If the modules are all of the same type, their I_{SC} values should be very close. For any module with a very low value, repeat the measurement. If I_{SC} is still low, replace the module.

Connecting batteries

1. If series connections are required, make these, bringing each series group of batteries up to the system voltage.
2. Measure the voltage of each series group. If it is not at the system voltage, check the connections. If any individual battery has too low a voltage, it must be replaced.
3. If 'battery sense' wires are being used, connect these to one battery or series group of batteries and at the control unit. The control unit should now indicate full charge. Disconnect these wires.
4. Make the main positive and negative connections for the battery wires at the control unit.
5. Ensure that the bare ends of the positive cables are well clear of the positive terminals of the batteries.
6. Fit the negative cables to each series group of batteries first. Tighten each clamp just enough to hold it on to the terminal.
7. Take one positive cable and briefly touch it against the positive terminal on one battery. There may be some small sparks or no sparks at all. Any sign of a large spark suggests a problem in the wiring to the control unit or in the control unit itself. Check these parts.
8. If there are no sparks from the test in step 7, proceed to fit all the positive cables to the positive terminals. Reconnect the sense connections from step 3.

Connecting the solar array to the control unit

Try to work early in the morning or late in the evening when the solar array only generates a low current. If work must be done around midday, cover the front of the solar array with a thick sheet or cloth. Make sure that the array is completely covered, taking care not to scratch the surface of the glass fronts as the cover is pulled across.

1. Make the negative connection for the solar array cable at the control unit.
2. Briefly touch the positive wire of the solar array cable against the positive terminal on the control unit. There should be no sparking. Any sign of a large spark suggests a problem in the wiring to the control unit or in the control unit itself. Check these parts.
3. If there are no sparks from the test in step 2, proceed to connect the positive wires securely.
4. If a cover was used, remove it.
5. If there is a charging indicator on the control unit, it should now show charging. (Some control units have a slight delay in operation when they are first connected so the charging indicator may not light up immediately.) Measure the voltage at the control unit. It should be above the system voltage.

Connecting circuits for appliances

1. Turn off all lighting switches.
2. Fit tubes and bulbs in all lamps.
3. Unplug any appliances from socket outlet points.
4. Turn off circuit switches or remove main fuses.
5. Complete the negative connections for the appliance circuits.
6. Touch one positive wire for the appliance circuits against the positive terminal on the control or junction box. Watch for sparks. If there are any, check that all appliances are off. Repeat the touching test. If there are still sparks, inspect all the wiring to the appliances for mistakes.
7. When the touching test does not give sparks, complete the positive connection.
8. Turn on the load circuits by switches and fuses in the control box.
9. In each room, turn on the lamps. If the lamp does not light, turn off immediately and leave for later examination. Leave on lamps that do work.

Testing failed tube lamps

1. Disconnect the positive connection to the inverter.
2. Turn on at wall switch if fitted. Use a voltmeter to check the polarity and measure voltage between the positive wire disconnected in step 1 and the negative. Wrong polarity (red wire is negative) or zero voltage indicates a

wiring fault. Check the wiring. Also check the fuse in the control unit in case it has blown.

3. When the voltage is correct, reconnect the positive to the inverter. If the tube lamp still does not work, proceed through the following checks:
   (a) Replace the tube with one that definitely works.
   (b) Measure the voltage at the terminals of the inverter with a tube fitted. If the voltage is too low, check for bad connections that could introduce a high voltage drop along the wires.
   (c) Remove inverter and test directly across a battery with tube lamp fitted. If it still does not work, replace.

4. With all appliances on, check for dim lamps. This indicates excess voltage drops because of poor connections or cables that are too thin. To check for voltage drops in a circuit, leave all the appliances on and measure the voltage at any points in the circuit where positive and negative are accessible. Record your measurements on a map of the installation.

Checking polarity of outlet points

If sockets are used, a convenient way to check the polarity is by using a plug with its cover removed to expose the contacts. Check the polarity and measure the voltage. If the polarity is wrong, find the place where a red wire is connected to black by mistake.

Before connecting appliances, check the polarity of the wiring in the plug. Then connect the appliances and make sure they work.

Finishing off

☐ Check that all lamps, power outlet points, and appliances work as expected.

☐ Turn on all the lamps and appliances. At the main switch on the control unit, turn the appliance circuits off and back on. This ensures that the rating of the main fuses is not too low.

☐ Switch all the appliances off. Then remove each clamp from the battery terminals in turn. Coat each clamp with petroleum jelly or some other available grease. Wipe away excess from the contact surfaces. Refit to the battery terminal, twisting slightly to ensure metal-to-metal contact between the clamp and the terminal. Tighten up the clamp. Do not over-tighten since the clamp needs only to be firm enough to prevent movement.

☐ Replace the lids of the junction boxes on the modules and elsewhere. If a rubber gasket is used, make sure it is properly located. Do not over-tighten the screws holding each lid on. Seal any holes that may let in rain-water with silicone mastic or pitch.

☐ Cover all bare wires.

☐ Paint any exposed parts that require protection from the weather.

☐ Mark each battery with a different letter (A, B, C . . .) for ease of record keeping (see Table 11.1).

☐ If a ladder is used to reach the modules, make sure that it is locked away to prevent unauthorized access to the modules and theft.

☐ Complete documentation (see below).

☐ Plan for the first service after one month and then at twelve-month intervals.

System documentation

Documentation means making a written record of all the essential details about the system. The purpose is to enable spares to be ordered and people to be contacted when repairs are required. It should also list all the main parts so that new parts can be easily specified and ordered if the system is expanded.

The details can be kept in one *log book* which belongs to the system. This book should also record when maintenance tasks are carried out and any other notes about the system. Here is a list of the first details to include:

1. Date of installation.
2. Names and addresses of all people involved in the installation of the system. These are the designer, supplier, and installer.
3. Names and addresses of the nearest sources of simple spares such as fuses, tube lamps, and light bulbs.
4. Description of the equipment (see the list of questions in Chapter 7 for when visiting a working system).
5. Appropriate maintenance schedules (see Figure 11.1).
6. How to identify faults and actions to take (see Table 11.3).
7. How to contact the nearest electrician for repairing faults.

Checking the installation

Here is a checklist that should be made by the user when the installation is complete:

1. Can the modules be reached easily and safely for cleaning?
2. Are the modules protected from damage by unauthorized people and animals?
3. Are the batteries placed so that they are out of direct sunlight?
4. Is there good ventilation around the batteries (if they are the vented type)?

5. Can the batteries be reached easily for inspection and maintenance?
6. Are the batteries mounted in protective cases with their tops covered?
7. Are all the cables firmly attached or hidden?
8. Do all the appliances work at the same time?
9. If indicators are fitted on the control unit, do they show that the batteries are being charged?

User training

Training of the users is required for systems installed by an electrician. In medium- to large-size installations, the electrician should ensure that there is one user who takes responsibility for managing the system every day. The electrician is responsible for carrying out the following training:

1. Identify the main parts of the system and ensure that the user understands their basic operation.
2. Explain the operation of the system on a daily basis.
3. Explain the routine tasks listed in the maintenance schedules.
4. Ensure that the user understands what to do if a fault arises.

The first point is covered by Chapter 1, while Points 2 to 4 are dealt with in the next chapter. The main parts of a solar system are as follows:

1. Solar array.
2. Battery bank.
3. Control unit.
4. Lighting circuits.
5. Circuits for other appliances.

The electrician who installed the system should explain the function of all switches, indicators, and meters on the control unit. He or she should locate the positions of all the fuses and ensure that spares are left, including a tool for removing the clamps from a battery.

New users are sometimes uneasy about working with electrical appliances. Electricians should emphasize that a system operating at 12 or 24 V is like a vehicle or a large torch and there is no risk of electrocution.

☐ *Questions*

1. What action should be taken if electrolyte splashes into someone's eye?
2. Under what conditions is the voltage from a solar array or bank of batteries dangerous?

3. How should spilt electrolyte be cleaned up?

4. If solar modules are mounted in a high place, how is safe access ensured?

5. What precautions should be taken when transporting solar modules?

6. When the parts are first received, why is it important to check the despatch date?

7. Why is it necessary to know the latitude of a site?

8. Why is all the wiring installed first without making any connections to the modules, batteries, or control unit?

9. Describe the procedure for making measurements of voltage and current.

10. How is the total short circuit current of the solar array related to the short circuit current of each module in the array?

11. What information is recorded in the system log book?

11 Maintenance

This chapter is divided into four sections:

1. Regular maintenance.

2. Servicing.

3. Replacing and adding parts.

4. Problem-solving guide.

The regular maintenance tasks are specifically for users and are quite straightforward. Servicing and replacing parts require a higher level of competence and are for skilled users and electricians. Instructions in the problem-solving guide are marked according to whether they are for users or electricians.

Regular maintenance

A solar electric system requires regular maintenance to ensure proper operation and the full life of the components. The maintenance tasks do not require special expertise so can be carried out by a user with minimal guidance. Attention to lead–acid batteries is particularly important because lack of maintenance can reduce their life drastically.

A number of maintenance schedules are given in Figure 11.1 for solar modules, lamps, and various types of batteries. To identify the type of battery used in the system, refer to the summaries given at the end of Chapter 3. Details about each of the maintenance tasks are given in this section.

Solar cell modules

Monthly maintenance • Clean the front of the modules.
• Check for shadowing of the modules, especially between 8 a.m. and 4 p.m. This may require moving obstacles or cutting back trees and bushes.

(a)

Lamps

Monthly maintenance • Inspect tubes and replace those that have black rings at the ends.
Every six months • Clean the reflectors.

(b)

Batteries

Daily • Check that the charging indicator is on when it is sunny.
• Check the state of charge from a state-of-charge meter. When it is below x,[1] take steps to reduce use of appliances.

Weekly • If the state of charge is less than 50% for more than two weeks, a decision must be taken on how to relieve the batteries:

Either Reduce daily use of electricity by a half so that the batteries gradually charge up each day.

Or Take the batteries for charging elsewhere.

Every six months • Check the level of electrolyte and top up with distilled or deionized water if required.
• If the batteries have never been at full charge for the last six months, plan for an equalization charge.

Battery removed from system • Take for charging to full capacity.
• Recharge every six months while in storage.

(c)

[1]x = 20% for low-antimony plates or 50% for antimony-free plates.

Figure 11.1 Examples of maintenance schedules that can be put up on a wall for users to follow. Details about each of the maintenance tasks are given in the text. See Table 11.2 for voltages corresponding to particular states of charge of lead–acid batteries.
(a) Solar modules.
(b) Lamps.
(c) Low-maintenance vented lead–acid batteries with either low-antimony or antimony-free plates.

Batteries

Daily   • Check that the charging indicator is on when it is sunny.

Every six months   • Check the level of electrolyte and top up with
                     distilled or deionized water if required.
                   • If the batteries have never been at full charge
                     for the last six months, plan for an
                     equalization charge.

(d)

Batteries

Daily   • Check that the charging indicator is on when it is sunny.
                   • Check the state of charge from a state-of-charge meter.
                     When it is below 50%, take steps to reduce use of appliances.

Weekly   • If the state of charge is less than 50% for more than two
                     weeks, a decision must be taken on how to relieve the batteries:

                     Either Reduce daily use of electricity by a half so
                             that the batteries gradually charge up each day.

                     Or   Take the batteries for charging elsewhere.

Battery removed from system • Take for charging to full capacity.
                             • Recharge every six months while in
                               storage.

(e)

Figure 11.1   (continued)
(d)   Vented nickel–cadmium batteries.
(e)   Sealed lead–acid batteries (gelled and starved electrolyte).

```
┌─────────────────────────────────────────────────────────────────────────┐
│                              Batteries                                    │
│                                                                           │
│  Daily              ● Check that the charging indicator is on when it is  │
│                       sunny.                                              │
│                     ● Check the state of charge from a state-of-charge    │
│                       meter. When it is below x,¹ take steps to reduce    │
│                       use of appliances.                                  │
│                                                                           │
│  Weekly             ● If the state of charge is less than 50% for more    │
│                       than two weeks, a decision must be taken on how to  │
│                       relieve the batteries:                              │
│                                                                           │
│                       Either   Reduce daily use of electricity by a half  │
│                                 so that the batteries gradually charge    │
│                                 up each day.                              │
│                                                                           │
│                       Or       Take the batteries for charging elsewhere. │
│                                                                           │
│  Every six months   ● Check the level of electrolyte and top up with      │
│                       distilled or deionized water if required.           │
│                     ● If the batteries have never been at full charge     │
│                       for the last six months, plan for an                │
│                       equalization charge.                                │
│                                                                           │
│  Battery removed from system  ● Take for charging to full capacity.       │
│                               ● Recharge every month while in storage.    │
│                                                                           │
└─────────────────────────────────────────────────────────────────────────┘
```

(f)

[1] For SLI batteries with high-antimony plates, $x = 80\%$ for a reasonable life or 50% for a short life.
For traction batteries that have high-antimony plates, $x = 20\%$.

Figure 11.1 continued
(f)   Vented lead-acid batteries with high-antimony plates for SLI use or traction.

Log book

Keeping records of how well the system performs is an important activity, especially for solar systems in institutions. Records help users to keep a check on the performance of the system. They also provide important information to an electrician who is servicing the system or repairing a fault.

There are two sorts of records. A daily record is kept by the user. An example of the information recorded is shown in Table 11.1(a). The other sort of record is of maintenance carried out by the user or an electrician. Details recorded are measurements made on the modules and batteries (see Table 11.1(b)). These records can be combined in one log book with documentation of the system, as listed at the end of Chapter 10.

Table 11.1 *Examples of record sheets for a log book that is always kept with a system.*
(a) Daily record.

Date	Number of appliances used	State of charge[1]	Comments	User[2]
		low 11.7 V	Auto-disconnect at 8.40. Only circuits A and B used. Charging indicator not come on. Topped up electrolyte. Cleaned battery terminals. Cleaned modules.	

[1]Reading taken one hour after switching on lighting circuits.

[2]Initials of user who completes the entries for that evening.

(b) Maintenance record for vented batteries.

Date: Measurements made by:

Battery	Cell[1]	Voltage (V) Battery Cell[2]	Specific gravity	Temperature in one cell of battery	Specific gravity at 25 °C (77 °F)[3]	Comments and actions taken
A	1					
	2					
	3					
	.					
	.					
	.					

[1]Counting from positive end.

[2]For batteries with exposed connections between cells.

[3]Corrected using Table D.4.

Cleaning modules

When the glass front of a module is dirty, less light reaches the solar cells so less electricity can be generated. Although modules are mounted with a slope, rain does not wash off all the dirt. Only regular cleaning of the glass ensures that the modules are always working at their best performance. Cleaning is recommended every month, especially when conditions are dusty, and certainly no less frequently than every three months.

Figure 11.2 Cleaning the glass of a module by hand with plenty of clean water.

The procedure for cleaning modules is as follows:

1. .For modules on a pole or the roof, make sure that the access is safe. If the existing means of access are not secure, provide a better method.
2. Do not clean the modules in bright sunshine. When the weather is very clear with few clouds, clean only in the early morning or late evening when the sun is low.
3. Use plenty of clean water. Do not add any soap powder because particles in the soap might scratch the glass. The glass can be rubbed using a soft cloth, sponge, or just bare hands as in Figure 11.2. Remove rings and wrist-watch and check the cloth for bits to avoid scratching.
4. Start cleaning from the highest parts and work down the slope. Do not stand or lean heavily on the modules.
5. Make sure that all the dust and dirt is removed. Any water caught in the ridge at the bottom should be clean.

Check for shading

Shading of any part of an array of modules reduces the amount of electricity generated, even if the shadow falls across only one cell.

Cut back bushes and trees that may have started to shade the solar array between 8 a.m. and 4 p.m. If the bushes and trees belong to someone else, seek permission from the person responsible and explain why the cutting is required. Do not cut down more than is necessary. For modules mounted on the ground within an enclosure, ensure that the enclosure is weeded regularly.

Make sure that nothing is put in front of the modules that may cause a shadow. If new buildings cause shading, it may be necessary to move the modules to a new position. This requires the help of whoever installed the system.

Inspecting lamps

Regular attention to each tube lamp is required to prevent damage to the inverter that powers it. Cleaning lamps also ensures that electricity is used effectively for illumination:

☐ Inspect the condition of tube lamps. A tube with a black ring at its end is approaching the end of its life and should be replaced.

☐ Check the performance of tube lamps at night when the batteries are not at the charging voltage. Tubes that do not come on immediately or blink are weak or old. Although a tube may still work satisfactorily after flashing a few times, it should be replaced to avoid damaging the inverter. Low-quality inverters can stop working permanently if used with a faulty tube.

☐ Inspect reflectors for dirt. They should be clean and shiny so that light is directed efficiently without any unnecessary loss:
(a) Switch off lighting circuit.
(b) Remove tube.
(c) Clean reflector. Stainless steel reflectors can be cleaned using a cloth moistened in soapy water and polished to a good shine with a dry cloth.
(d) Inspect the connections and outside of the inverter. Clear away any material left by insects.
(e) Refit tube.
(f) Switch on circuit to check that the lamp is still working.

Checking state of charge

Maintenance of batteries is not really needed on a daily basis. However, for lead–acid batteries, it is a good idea to check the state of charge from the voltage.

Types of meter for indicating state of charge are shown in Figure 4.4(b). For reliable readings, the state of charge should be measured at the same time each day. When most use of electricity is for lighting in the evening, a good time for measurement is one hour after sundown. This hour of use allows the batteries to reach a more standard condition than while on charge during daylight. For a

Table 11.2 *Conditions for lowest state of charge that are recommended for various types of lead–acid batteries.*

Type of battery	Lowest values recommended for end of discharge (measurements for 25 °C (77 °F))			
	State of charge (%)	Voltage (V) at load		Specific gravity
		12 V	24 V	
SLI for cars to achieve: [1]medium life	80	11.8	23.6	1250
short life	50	11.5	23.0	1200
Heavy-duty SLI Antimony-free	50	11.5	23.0	1200
Low antimony Fully sealed Traction	20	10.8	21.6	1150[2]

[1]Two sets of conditions according to how long the battery is required to last before replacement.

[2]Cannot be measured for sealed batteries.

system in an institution, measurements should be recorded in a system log book (see Table 11.1(a)).

Table 11.2 gives a summary of characteristics for the lowest state of charge of various types of lead–acid battery. Some lead–acid batteries, such as the Delco 2000, include a simple internal hydrometer which indicates when the state of charge is below 65 per cent.

For self-regulating systems, make sure that electricity continues to be used during the summer when there is more charging. This minimizes over-charging and the need to top up the electrolyte in vented batteries.

Low state of charge

If the state of charge is low for more than two weeks, a decision must be taken as to how to relieve the batteries. Continued use results in partial charging which shortens the overall life of all lead–acid batteries. There are two options:

1. Reduce daily use of electricity by at least a half. This enables the batteries gradually to charge up each day.
2. Take the batteries for charging elsewhere such as the nearest town.

For the second option, half the batteries in a battery bank can be taken for charging first. After these are returned, the other half of batteries can be taken. Retaining some of the batteries enables the system to be used to some extent at least. However, use of appliances must be reduced to avoid deep discharge while half the batteries are away.

Topping up electrolyte of vented batteries

Regular topping up is required for vented batteries, which includes the types described as 'low maintenance'. Topping up is never required for sealed batteries.

For batteries that have a central tapping to power a low-voltage appliance (see Chapter 6), cells between the tapping and the positive end may require extra water. If these cells do not require extra water, the battery should have an equalizing charge every few months. This is necessary to bring the cells back into balance (see the following section on servicing).

Access to the cells is by separate vent caps for each cell which are unscrewed or by a plastic strip that clips onto the top and is pulled off to reveal the holes.

Use only distilled or deionized water. Never use ordinary drinking-water even though it may look very clean. Over the life of a vented battery, the total volume of water added may be much higher than the original volume of acid. Levels of impurities in water for topping up should be very low since any impurities accumulate as water is lost during gassing. Most impurities increase the rate of self-discharge. Topping up with acid is required only in exceptional circumstances and is certainly not part of routine maintenance (see Appendix D).

Rain-water can be used as long as it is collected directly by a plastic funnel. Do not use the run-off from a roof. Distilled water can also be made over a fire from clean water using the system shown in Figure 11.3.

Water for batteries should be stored in glass or plastic bottles, never in steel or galvanized containers. Label the bottles clearly to prevent use for other purposes by mistake.

The procedure for topping up electrolyte with distilled water is as follows:

1. Check the level of electrolyte in each cell. If the case is transparent or translucent, look from the outside. There should be two marks showing the maximum and minimum levels. Filling is required when the level is nearer the minimum mark. If the level cannot be seen from the outside, remove the caps for all the cells. The level should never fall below the top of the plates.
2. Use a plastic bottle with a spout or pour through a plastic funnel.
3. Do not fill up until the cell overflows. If the level cannot be seen from the outside, fill to 13mm (0.5 inch) above the plates or to just below the top inside the cell. Liquid should not come up inside the hole for the cap.
4. Replace all caps. Clean and dry the top of the batteries.
5. Replace the protective covers over the batteries.

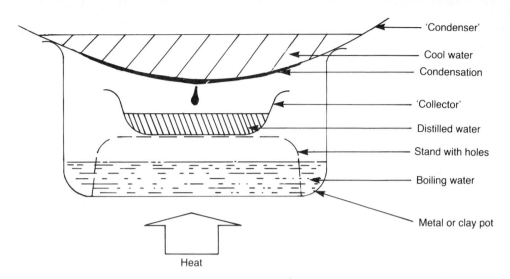

Figure 11.3 Method of making distilled water over a fire. Try to use glass or enamelled dishes for the condenser and collector. This avoids the risk of adding impurities from the surfaces of metal dishes. Store distilled water in glass or plastic bottles.

Servicing

After one month of operation, the installation electrician should carry out a service. This is then repeated after every twelve months.

Here is a list of service tasks for an electrician or expert user. Record observations, measurements, and actions taken in the system log book (see Table 11.1(b) as an example):

1. For vented batteries, measure the specific gravity of the electrolyte (see p. 248 for procedure). If there is variation between them of more than twenty units, organize an equalizing charge at 14.5–15.0 V for each 12 V battery. This involves either switching off most of the appliances for several days or taking the batteries for charging elsewhere.
2. Inspect daily records of state of charge. If the state of charge is very low, organize for the batteries to be charged immediately. If the state of charge is not very low but has not been full for many weeks, organize for an equalizing charge at 14.5–15.0 V for each 12 V battery.
3. Wipe the tops of the batteries clean with a damp cloth. (Dirt on the top can increase self-discharge.) Inspect the sides and bottom of each battery for cracks and leaks.
4. Loosen the clamp on each battery terminal and check for corrosion. If the clamp is too tight to move because of corrosion, do not force off with a hammer. First remove the corrosion using the procedure detailed on

page 250. One way to check for poor contact is to measure the voltage between exposed metal surfaces on the clamp and the terminal. The measurement is made when there is a full charging or full load current and the voltage should be less than 0.1 V. If the voltage is higher, there is contact resistance from corrosion and the clamp should be removed for inspection.

5. Check for shading of the solar array between 8 a.m. and 4 p.m. Organize for vegetation to be cut back as required. If shadows are caused by a new building, it may be necessary to move the modules to a new position.

6. Inspect the support structure of the modules. Repair or strengthen weak parts. Paint exposed metal. Check that the modules are still firmly attached. Tighten screws. On a tracking mount, grease the moving parts. Check for wear on cables owing to rubbing against an edge or sharp object.

7. Tighten the screws in all electrical connections.

8. Inspect the condition of walls inside rooms. Renew coating with white paint to maintain effectiveness of the illumination.

If the performance of a battery is suspected, its rate of self-discharge and capacity can be measured using the procedure in Appendix D. This involves disconnecting the battery from the system. Checking the performance while connected to the system is unreliable because there is always a charging or discharging current which affects the measurements. When disconnecting wires, label each wire before disconnection and cover the bare end with insulating tape to avoid accidental shorting. Record all measurements made in the log book.

If the performance of the modules is suspected, their electrical output can be measured. However, this should only be required after checking thoroughly the condition of the batteries and all connections between the modules and batteries. The performance is checked by measuring the open circuit voltage (V_{OC}) and short circuit current (I_{SC}) in bright sunshine. The procedure is the same as for the installation instructions in Chapter 10. Remember to label each wire before disconnection and to cover the bare end to avoid accidental shorting. Record measurements made in the log book.

Measuring specific gravity for vented batteries

For vented batteries, it is necessary to make regular measurements of the specific gravity of the electrolyte in each cell. These measurements are useful for checking the condition of cells in a battery and estimating state of charge.

Measurement of specific gravity is made using an object that floats in the liquid being measured, called a *hydrometer*. The hydrometer has a scale of marks along the side and the level it floats at shows the density or specific gravity of the liquid.

The name *battery hydrometer* refers to the whole instrument of a hydrometer float that is fitted inside a glass container for drawing up liquid, as shown in Figure 11.4. This makes it easy to sample electrolyte from each cell without spillage.

Another type of battery hydrometer has several balls instead of a long float. The number of balls that float to the top of the liquid shows the specific gravity. This is easier to use than the type shown in Figure 11.4, but much less accurate.

The procedure for using a battery hydrometer is as follows:

1. Prepare a page in the log book or elsewhere to record the measurements (see Table 11.1(b)).
2. Check that the hydrometer is clean. Any dirt or old liquid should be rinsed out with distilled water.
3. Unscrew and remove the caps from each cell.
4. Squeeze the rubber bulb and insert the rubber extension tube into one cell, ensuring that the end of the tube is well below the level of electrolyte.
5. Release the bulb slowly so that sufficient electrolyte is drawn up into the tube for the hydrometer to float freely. If there is insufficient electrolyte to make the hydrometer float, the cell may need to be topped up with distilled water first.
6. Air bubbles on the hydrometer will cause inaccurate readings. If any bubbles are present, squeeze and release the bulb so that liquid washes down and up the hydrometer.
7. To make an accurate measurement, hold the battery hydrometer vertical. Bend down so that your eyes are level with the top of the liquid, like the person in Figure 11.4(a). The surface of the liquid has a curved shape called a *meniscus*. The correct reading is the position on the hydrometer scale that is level with the bottom part of the meniscus, as shown in Figure 11.4(c).
8. Squeeze the bulb carefully so that all the liquid is returned to the cell without spilling any.
9. Record your measurement of specific gravity in the log book.
10. Repeat steps 4 to 9 for all the other cells.
11. Replace the vent caps and wash away any electrolyte on top of the batteries with ordinary clean water.
12. Wash the end of the rubber tube with a little distilled water and wipe dry. Store the battery hydrometer in a place that is clean and secure.

Quick measurements of specific gravity give a general indication of the condition of a cell in a vented battery as follows:

above 1250   fully charged
1200–1250   about half charge
1150–1200   low
below 1150   cell is dead

For a more accurate assessment of state of charge from specific gravity

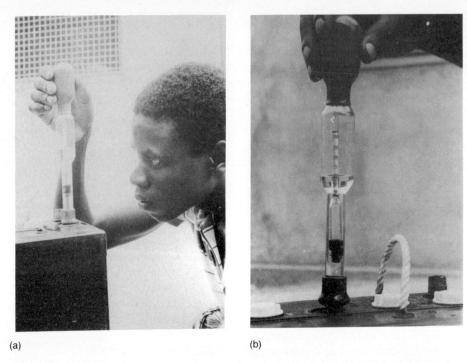

(a)   (b)

Figure 11.4 Battery hydrometer for measuring specific gravity of acid electrolyte in vented lead–acid batteries which are vented. (The electrolyte in sealed batteries cannot be checked.)
(a) Drawing up liquid from one cell and reading the position of the hydrometer float inside the glass tube.
(b) Detail of the hydrometer float inside the glass tube showing the shape of the meniscus where the measurement of specific gravity is read. The reading shown is 1295.
(c) Parts of a battery hydrometer and level of meniscus for taking measurement.

measurements, see Appendix D. If the temperature of the batteries varies by a lot at different times of year, the specific gravity measurements can be corrected to a reference temperature. This requires measuring the temperature of the electrolyte in one cell and using the correction procedure given in Appendix D.

Removing corrosion from battery connections

When the clamp on a battery terminal is difficult to remove, this is usually because there is a build-up of corrosion. Bad corrosion on connections is indicated by a build-up of white powder around the clamp, as shown in Figure 11.5.

Do not force the clamp off otherwise the battery terminal will be damaged.

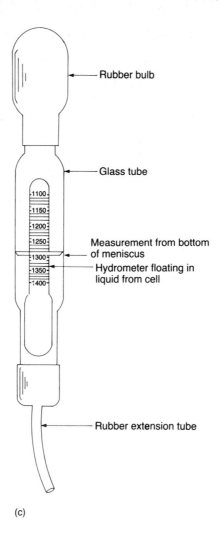

Rubber bulb

Glass tube

Measurement from bottom of meniscus

Hydrometer floating in liquid from cell

1100
1150
1200
1250
1300
1350
1400

Rubber extension tube

(c)

Instead, loosen the corrosion according to the following procedure:

1. Remove the protective grease from the connection with a solvent such as paraffin (kerosene) or petrol.
2. Make up about 0.5 litres (1 pt) of neutralizing solution, as described on p. 215.
3. Brush neutralizing solution on to the metal parts until the clamp can be easily removed from the battery terminal.
4. Clean the contact surfaces of the battery terminal and clamp with neutralizing solution. Sandpaper or a knife can be used to get a smooth surface.

Figure 11.5 Example of corrosion on a battery terminal.

5. If the ends of the cable are corroded, cut back to good wire and remake the connection to the clamp.
6. Coat the clamp and bare strands of the cable with grease, such as petroleum jelly.
7. Wipe off excess grease from the inside of the clamp where it contacts with the battery terminal. Fit the clamp to the terminal, twisting slightly to ensure metal-to-metal contact between the clamp and the terminal. Tighten up the clamp. Do not over-tighten since the clamp needs only to be firm enough to prevent movement.

Changing and adding parts to a system

Parts may need to be replaced or added for the following reasons:

☐ Replace faulty or old parts.
☐ Correcting for undersizing.
☐ Expanding the system.

    A good guide to undersizing of a system is the condition of the batteries as recorded over several months. If the batteries often reach a low state of charge but only for short periods each time, the total capacity of the battery bank should be increased. This is done by adding batteries to the battery bank in parallel. If the batteries are frequently at a low state of charge, more modules should be added in parallel to the solar array.

    It is often found that undersizing is caused by a higher use of electricity than originally planned. This can be checked by repeating the sizing procedure given in Chapter 8 according to the actual pattern of use. Undersizing because of greater use is corrected by adding extra modules and batteries.

When replacing or adding parts, follow the same procedure for making connections in Chapter 10 as if the system is being installed from the start again. Remember to label each wire before disconnection and cover the bare end to avoid accidental shorting. Take note of the following points about each part.

For batteries, try to replace with exactly the same type of lead–acid or nickel–cadmium battery. Do not mix different types in the same battery bank otherwise batteries of one type will never reach full charge. In series-connected groups of batteries, make sure that the added battery has the same capacity.

New modules should have cells made of the same type of silicon as in the existing modules (either single crystal, polycrystalline, or thin-film). Use modules with the same number of cells or the same open circuit voltage specified under standard test conditions. In systems operating at 24 V or higher, modules should be carefully matched to the other series-connected modules in the same group.

Check the voltage rating of appliances and control units before connecting.

When expanding a system, check that the control unit has sufficient current capacity for both charging and switching the circuits when the appliances are all on. The design for a unit to increase the current rating of a relay is given in Chapter 16. Otherwise instead of expanding one system, consider forming a separate system.

Problem-solving guide

Various problems that can occur are listed in Table 11.3. For each problem or symptom, a number of possible causes are suggested, together with a test and corrective action.

When dealing with a problem, start with the first cause listed for that problem. Proceed in order through all the causes. Record results of tests and corrective action taken in the log book. Faults caused by poor maintenance are marked by 'M'. These can be corrected by the user. Complicated problems may require more expertise to carry out the tests and corrective action. These are marked with 'E' for expert user or electrician.

If after doing all the tests the problem is still not corrected, start at the first test and check everything again. If the problem continues after doing all the tests twice, call an electrician or the supplier.

Testing continuity of cables

If a break along a cable is suspected, the continuity can be checked by joining the two wires of the cable at one end and measuring the resistance at the other end. A high resistance or open circuit shows that there is damage in one of the wires.

Table 13.3 *Problem-solving guide:* (*M*) *maintenance task that can be done by users;* (*E*) *task for expert user or electrician.*

Problem: **No charging current**

Indications ☐ Solar charge indicator does not come on even when there is direct sun.
☐ Voltage of a 12 V system does not go above 11.5 V.
☐ Voltage of a 24 V system does not go above 23 V.
☐ Blocking diode on control unit does not get hot.

Possible causes	Test	Solution
Poor connections to battery	Feel whether connections are loose	Tighten loose clamps
	Look for signs of corrosion such as white powder	(M) Clean connections
	(E) Measure voltage between clamp and terminal	(M) Clean connections
Fuse blown in control unit	Remove fuses and check or inspect their continuity	Replace blown fuse
Short circuit or break in wires between modules and control unit	(E) Inspect connections at module and control unit	Tighten loose connections
	(E) Disconnect wires at both ends and check for continuity	Repair damaged section or replace wires
Damaged module	Inspect front of module for broken connections and corrosion	
	Inspect back of module for damage	(E) Replace module if defective
	(E) Measure V_{OC} and I_{SC} in full sunshine, and compare to specified performance	

Table 11.3 (continued)

Problem: **Batteries at low state of charge**

Indications ☐ Warning indicator for low state of charge comes on.
☐ Load automatically disconnected by control unit.
☐ Voltage in 'low' section of expanded-scale voltmeter.

Possible causes	Test	Solution
Over-use of electricity	Check if any appliances were left on by mistake	Turn off appliances and leave batteries to charge up
Poor connections to battery	Feel whether connections are loose	Tighten loose clamps
	Look for signs of corrosion such as white powder	(M) Clean connections
	(E) Measure voltage between clamp and terminal	(M) Clean connections
Dirty modules	Check when modules were last cleaned	(M) Clean glass
Fuse blown in control unit	Remove fuses and check continuity	Replace fuse
One cell in a battery has a fault	(E) Measure specific gravity and voltage of each vented cell where possible	(E) Replace battery
Self-discharge of batteries is high	(E) Measure rate of self-discharge	(E) Replace battery

---

Problem: **Excessive over-charging**

Indications ☐ Vented batteries need to be topped up more often than expected.
☐ Voltage often above 14.5 V at midday for a 12 V system.
☐ Voltage often above 29.0 V at midday for a 24 V system.

Possible causes	Test	Solution
Faulty control unit	(E) Measure voltages at control unit when modules are in bright sunshine	(E) Replace faulty control unit
	Check operation of control unit according to manufacturer's instructions	

Table 11.3 (continued)

Faulty recombination cap	Feel temperature of cap	Replace caps that are cold
Under-use in a self-regulated system	Compare actual use to expected use	If actual use low, use more electricity each day

Problem: **No power to appliances**
Indications ☐ Appliances fail to come on.
          ☐ Tube lamps fail to come on and bulbs are dim.
          ☐ One lamp fails to come on.

Possible causes	Test	Solution
Automatic disconnection by control unit	Check status of control unit	Reduce consumption of electricity
Circuits for appliances not turned on at control unit	Check control unit	Switch on circuits
Switches in rooms not turned on	Check all switches are in the on position	Turn on all switches
Bulb or tube is broken	(No test)	Switch off circuit and replace with a good tube or bulb
Fuse corroded or blown	Remove fuses and check continuity	Replace blown fuse and ensure holder is clean
Voltage too low to operate inverter for tube lamp	Turn off other appliances to see whether lamp starts to work	(E) Improve quality of all connections
Inverter broken	(E) Check whether there is full system voltage at connections to inverter	(E) Replace inverter
Damaged cables	(E) Measure voltage at access points along cable	(E) Repair or replace section that has excessive voltage drop
Voltage drop along cable is too high	(E) Check sizing of cable for loads	(E) Add extra cable or reduce total load on cable

Table 11.3 (continued)

Problem: **Fuse keeps blowing, even after replacement**

Possible causes	Test	Solution
Fuses are wrong rating	Check required rating in system documentation	Fit correct rating of fuse
Faulty appliance	Turn off all appliances, replace fuse, then turn on appliances one by one until fuse blows	(E) Repair faulty appliance
Appliance has high starting current	Check whether appliance contains a motor	Use higher rating fuse or a slow blow type of fuse
Short circuit	(E) Disconnect wires at both ends and check for continuity	(E) Repair damaged section or replace wires
Too many appliances connected at one time	Add up power rating of appliances in circuit and calculate the maximum current using Formula (5.2)	If current is too high, reduce use or number of appliances on circuit

The procedure for checking continuity is as follows:

1. Disconnect and label the positive and negative wires at both ends of the cable.
2. At one end of the cable, twist the two wires together to make electrical contact.
3. At the other end of the cable, measure the resistance between the two wires. High resistance (above 100 Ω) indicates damage or a break. Look for damage and repair or replace the cable as required.
4. To reconnect, first make sure that the wires at the measuring end in step 3 cannot touch each other.
5. Untwist the wires at the other end and reconnect according to their labels.
6. Reconnect the remaining wires.
7. Check indicators on the control unit and appliances to make sure that the circuit is complete.

☐ *Questions*

1. Why is it recommended to check the state of charge of lead–acid batteries every day?

2. Why is regular cleaning of modules necessary and what precautions must be taken when cleaning them?

3. What action should be taken when lead–acid batteries are not in use after being disconnected from a solar system?

4. What problems are caused by loose or corroded terminals in a solar electric system?

5. Which types of batteries require topping up?

6. Describe how to loosen a battery clamp if it is difficult to remove from the battery terminal.

7. What is an 'equalizing charge'?

8. What information is provided about a vented battery by measurements of specific gravity?

9. What does 'undersizing of a system' mean and how is it recognized?

Part Three

Building electronic units

12 Introduction to electronic components and circuit building

Designs for a number of simple electronic circuits are given in Chapters 13–16. For readers unfamiliar with electronics, this chapter describes all the components used in those circuits. Sufficient details are given here to enable the simple circuits to be built and tested. The last part of this chapter lists the tools that are needed and gives general guidance on how to build the circuits. Tables 12.5 and 12.6 summarize the symbols used in the circuit diagrams and component layouts.

If more details are required on how the components and circuits work, refer to the electronics books listed in Appendix F.

Measuring electricity

Two important measurements are voltage and current. Before using a meter, always check that the expected voltage or current is not more than the maximum range of the meter. For meters with several ranges, a good precaution is to start with the highest range and switch down ranges while measuring until the reading is in the middle of a range.

Voltage

Voltage is measured in units of volts (V) using a voltmeter or the voltage scales of a multimeter. It is always measured by putting the test probes of the multimeter on two points in a circuit. The meter is now in parallel with that part of the circuit between the probes.

When measured across the supply, voltage shows how much electrical 'pressure' is available. When measured across a component in a circuit, it shows that the component is connected to the supply.

There are many examples of voltmeters used in a circuit. Figure 4.4(a) shows a voltmeter connected across a battery for measuring voltage during charging or when supplying the appliances. Figure 12.7(b) shows a voltmeter connected across one component called a Zener diode.

Current

Current is measured in units of amperes, also known as amps (A) with an ammeter or the amp scales of a multimeter. It can also be measured using a voltmeter with a *shunt* and this method is described in Chapter 13 and in Figure 13.6(a).

Current is always measured by first disconnecting part of the circuit where the current is to be measured. The test probes of the meter are connected to the two disconnected ends. The meter is now in series with the components on each side and electricity is flowing through the meter. Current is a measure of the 'intensity' of electricity flowing and gives an indication of how much electricity is being used by that component.

Figure 2.5(d) shows an ammeter used for measuring the current flowing from a dry-cell battery to a bulb. Figure 15.6(c) shows how a voltmeter can be used to measure current by connecting it across a shunt made up of four resistors.

Resistors

All conductors of electricity have some *resistance* to the flow of current through them. This means that when a current flows, there is a drop in voltage between the ends of the conductor and heat is produced. *Resistors* are useful in electronic circuits because the drop in voltage is related to the current by a simple formula called *Ohm's Law*. The formula is:

$$
\boxed{\begin{array}{c}\text{Current through}\\\text{the resistor}\\\text{(A)}\end{array}} \times \boxed{\begin{array}{c}\text{Resistance of}\\\text{the resistor}\\(\Omega)\end{array}} = \boxed{\boxed{\begin{array}{c}\text{Voltage drop across}\\\text{the resistor}\\\text{(V)}\end{array}}} \qquad \textbf{(12.1)}
$$

Some examples of resistors are shown in Figure 12.1(a).

Units of resistance

The unit of electrical resistance is the *ohm* which is shortened to the omega sign, Ω. Resistors are available in a wide range of resistances ranging from less than one ohm to over a million ohms.

The resistance value of a resistor is usually given in a coded form without the

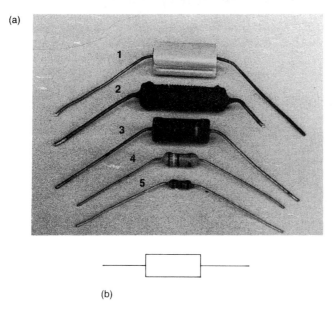

(a)

(b)

Figure 12.1   Resistors.
(a)   Examples of resistors with a range of power ratings: **1** 4 W; **2** 5 W; **3** 1 W;
4 0.5 W; **5** 0.25 W.
(b)   Circuit symbol (as used for the circuits in this book).

Ω sign. For small values, the decimal point is placed by R. Examples are 2R7 for 2.7 Ω and 150R for 150 Ω. For large values, K is placed between the thousands and hundreds and M is placed between the millions and thousands. Examples are 3K3 for 3300 Ω, 56K for 56 kΩ (56 000 Ω) and 1M8 for 1 800 000 Ω.

Only certain values of resistance are available and these are known as *preferred values*. The *E12 range* of preferred values is 10, 12, 15, 18, 22, 27, 33, 39, 47, 56, 68 and 82. Each of these preferred values is available in decade multiples. For example, 47 refers to 4R7, 47R, 470R, 4K7, 47K, 470K, and 4M7. Suppose that resistances of 6.4, 32, 950, and 4200 Ω are needed. The nearest resistors that can be used from the E12 range are 6R8, 33R, 1K0 and 3K9.

Some suppliers may only stock a small selection from the E12 range. The preferred values that are most common are 10, 15, 22, 33, 47, and 68.

The resistance of a resistor is shown either by coloured bands or by a number marked on the body. The code for the coloured bands is given in Figure 12.2. Examples of the colour coding are orange/orange/red for 3K3 and brown/green/gold for 1R5. Often the markings are not clear and a resistance meter should always be used to check the approximate value of resistance before using the resistor in a circuit.

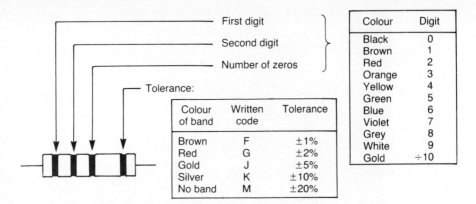

Colour	Digit
Black	0
Brown	1
Red	2
Orange	3
Yellow	4
Green	5
Blue	6
Violet	7
Grey	8
White	9
Gold	÷10

Colour of band	Written code	Tolerance
Brown	F	±1%
Red	G	±2%
Gold	J	±5%
Silver	K	±10%
No band	M	±20%

Figure 12.2 Position of coloured bands on the side of some resistors and the coding key for the colours. For resistors with a code instead of coloured bands, the last letter in the code is the tolerance, as listed in the tolerance table.

The fourth band of a colour-coded resistor is for *tolerance*. This is the maximum percentage difference of the actual resistance of the resistor compared to the value marked on the side. General-purpose resistors have a tolerance of ±5 per cent or higher, while close tolerance resistors are ±2 per cent or less.

Using the resistance scale of a multimeter

Digital multimeters are very simple to use for measuring resistance. They are self-zeroing and give a clear indication of the resistance value. An example of one is shown in Figure 4.4(b).

The more common and less expensive sort of multimeter is the analogue type with a moving needle (examples in Figures 12.6 and 12.7). Here is the procedure for using an analogue multimeter to measure resistance:

1. Set the control knob to the resistance setting.
2. Plug the leads in the correct sockets for measuring resistance.
3. Connect the ends of the test leads together. The needle should swing over to the right which is the zero end of the scale.
4. There should be a knob somewhere on the multimeter for setting the needle exactly on zero at the right-hand end of the scale. The knob is adjusted now while keeping the test leads in contact with each other. If the needle cannot be adjusted to zero, the battery inside the meter needs to be changed. Do not leave the leads connected longer than necessary otherwise the battery discharges too quickly.
5. Connect the ends of the test leads to each end of the resistor that is being measured. Take care when reading the resistance scale because the

numbers increase from right to left and the spaces along the scale vary in size.

6. If there are two or more resistance scales, the zeroing adjustment (steps 3 and 4) must be done whenever you switch from one scale to another.

7. When the meter is not in use, switch to a voltage or current scale. This disconnects the battery for the resistance scale from the leads so that the battery cannot become discharged by mistake.

Connecting resistors in series and in parallel

Each of the circuits in the following chapters has a table listing the components that are required. For most circuits, the exact value of resistance is not important and a range of resistances is given in the tables. In a few cases, it is necessary for the resistance to be exact. When the choice of resistors is limited, the required resistance can be achieved by using more than one resistor and connecting them in series or in parallel (see Figures 12.3(a) and (b)).

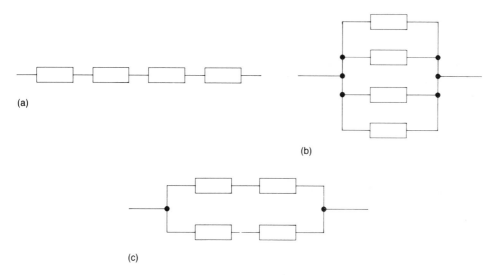

Figure 12.3 Arrangements of resistors to get exact values of resistance or to increase the power rating.
(a) Connection of four resistors in series. The total resistance is calculated using Formula (12.2). (The total resistance is higher than the resistance of any of the individual resistors used.)
(b) Connection of four resistors in parallel. The total resistance is calculated using Formula (12.3). (The total resistance is lower than the resistance of any of the individual resistors used.)
(c) Series/parallel connection of four resistors. When all the resistors are the same, the total resistance is the same as for one, while the total power rating is four times greater than the power rating of one.

For series connection, the values of each resistor are simply added together to get the total resistance:

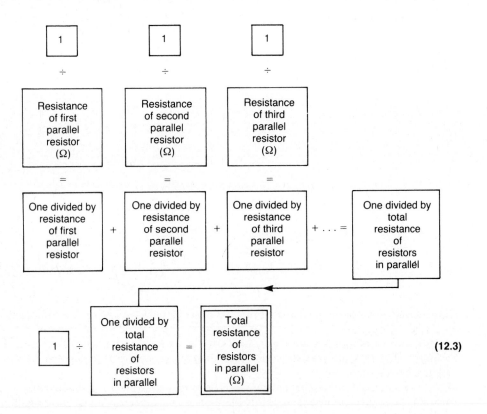

For parallel connection, the calculation of total resistance is more complicated but parallel connection may be the only choice in some cases. The calculation involves three steps:

Note that adding an extra resistor in series increases the total resistance, while adding an extra resistor in parallel reduces the total resistance.

Example 12.1

Suppose there are four different resistors with resistances of 330R, 680R, 1K0, and 2K2.

What is the total resistance when they are connected (a) in series, (b) in parallel?

(a) From Formula (12.2) for series connection, the total resistance is:

$330 + 680 + 1000 + 2200 = 4210 \, \Omega$

Therefore the four resistors in series can be used as a 4K2 resistor.

(b) From Formula (12.3) for parallel connection of resistors, the first step is to divide each resistance into 1:

$1 \div 330 = 0.003 \, 03$

$1 \div 680 = 0.001 \, 47$

$1 \div 1000 = 0.001 \, 00$

$1 \div 2200 = 0.000 \, 45$

Next, these values are added together:

$0.003 \, 03 + 0.001 \, 47 + 0.001 \, 00 + 0.000 \, 45 = 0.005 \, 95$

Finally, this answer is divided into 1:

$1 \div 0.005 \, 95 = 168 \, \Omega$

Therefore the four resistors in parallel can be used as a 170R resistor.

Power rating

The dimensions of a resistor depend not on its resistance but on how much power it can dissipate (heat it can produce) without becoming too hot. Typical dimensions of resistors for a range of power ratings are given in Table 12.1.

It is important to check that the power rating of a resistor is sufficiently high for it to be used. This is done by calculating the maximum power that the resistor will dissipate for its place in a circuit. The calculation uses either the maximum voltage that will be across the resistor or the maximum current that will be required to flow through the resistor. With either of these values, the maximum power is found using one of the following two formulas, as appropriate:

$$
\boxed{\begin{array}{c}\text{Maximum voltage}\\\text{drop across}\\\text{resistor}\\\text{(V)}\end{array}} \times \boxed{\begin{array}{c}\text{Maximum voltage}\\\text{drop across}\\\text{resistor}\\\text{(V)}\end{array}} \div \boxed{\begin{array}{c}\text{Resistance}\\\text{of}\\\text{resistor}\\(\Omega)\end{array}} = \boxed{\begin{array}{c}\text{Maximum power}\\\text{dissipated}\\\text{in resistor}\\\text{(W)}\end{array}} \quad \textbf{(12.4)}
$$

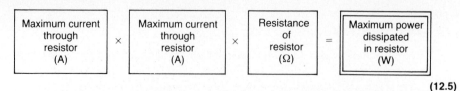

$$\begin{array}{|c|}\hline \text{Maximum current through resistor (A)}\\\hline\end{array} \times \begin{array}{|c|}\hline \text{Maximum current through resistor (A)}\\\hline\end{array} \times \begin{array}{|c|}\hline \text{Resistance of resistor } (\Omega)\\\hline\end{array} = \begin{array}{|c|}\hline \text{Maximum power dissipated in resistor (W)}\\\hline\end{array}$$

(12.5)

When resistors of equal resistance are connected in series or in parallel, the power that must be dissipated is shared equally between them. This is one way of using resistors with a low power rating in a circuit which requires a high power dissipation. The power rating of one size of resistor can be increased by four times using the arrangement in Figure 12.3(c).

Light bulb

When a resistor is required to dissipate 5 W or more, a filament light bulb can sometimes be used instead. Bulbs do not obey Ohm's Law so they cannot be used to control a voltage or current. Their best application is in reducing the power dissipation of a transistor (described later in this chapter). Figure 14.5 is an example of this use. When using a bulb, the voltage must not exceed the specified value otherwise the filament will blow.

Potentiometers

In some circuits, it is necessary to adjust the resistance of a resistor. *Variable resistors* and *potentiometers*, or *pot* for short, are used for this and some examples are shown in Figure 12.4(a). A common use for potentiometers is the volume control on a radio.

Potentiometers have three terminals. Two of the terminals are connected to the ends of a resistor inside the potentiometer which has a fixed resistance. The third terminal is connected to a piece of metal that slides along the length of this resistor, as emphasized by the circuit symbol for a potentiometer (see Figure 12.4(b)).

Table 12.1 *Typical dimensions of resistors for a range of power ratings. The power calculated from Formula (12.4) or (12.5) must not exceed these ratings.*

Power rating (W)	Typical dimensions			
	Diameter (mm)		Length (mm)	
0.25	2	(0.08 in)	6	(0.25 in)
0.5	3	(0.12 in)	9	(0.35 in)
1	6	(0.25 in)	15	(0.60 in)
2	9	(0.35 in)	24	(1.0 in)

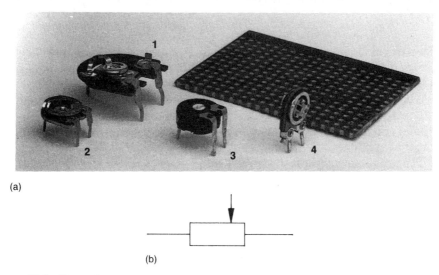

(a)

(b)

Figure 12.4 Potentiometers.
(a) Examples of potentiometers which can be mounted on the stripboard shown which has holes spaced at 2.5 mm (0.1 in). Types and power ratings: **1** standard horizontal (0.25 W); **2** miniature horizontal (0.1 W); **3** miniature enclosed horizontal (0.15 W); **4** miniature vertical (0.1 W).
(b) Circuit symbol (as used for the circuits in this book).

The potentiometers shown in Figure 12.4(a) are only adjusted when the circuit is being tested, so are sometimes known as *presets*. They are mounted directly on the circuit board and the position of the slider is set by a small screwdriver. Larger potentiometers, such as volume controls, are frequently adjusted in normal use and this is done by a knob attached to a shaft.

Potentiometers are available in a small number of resistances with preferred values of 10, 22, 47, and 50. For example, if an adjustable range of 0–1800 Ω is needed, a 2K2 potentiometer should be used.

The size of potentiometers depends on their power rating, as for resistors. The miniature sizes shown in Figure 12.4(a) are rated at 0.1–0.15 W.

Most potentiometers are *linear* which means that the resistance varies uniformly as the sliding contact is adjusted. In *logarithmic* potentiometers, the resistance increases rapidly at one end of the sliding range and this type is intended for use as a volume control. Linear potentiometers are preferred for the circuits in this book but old volume controls which may be the logarithmic type can also be used.

Another type of potentiometer is called a *rheostat*. Rheostats are designed to dissipate several watts of power and are frequently used in school science laboratories. One rheostat can be used as a constant load when measuring the capacity of a battery (see Appendix D).

Diodes

Three sorts of diode are used for the circuits in the following chapters. They are *ordinary diodes*, *Zener diodes*, and *light-emitting diodes* (LEDs). Examples of all three sorts are shown in Figure 12.5(a).

What all these diodes have in common is that they only allow current to flow through them in one direction for low values of voltage. This is like the function of a non-return or one-way valve in a water system that only allows water to go through a pipe in one direction.

The active part of most diodes is a small piece of silicon, the same material used for solar cells. The silicon is given a treatment called doping to make two slightly different regions called *p-type* and *n-type*. (The names 'p' and 'n' refer to the type of charge responsible for conduction of electricity in that part of the silicon.) The area where the two types meet is called the *pn junction*. Wires are connected to each end and the diode is sealed in hard plastic to protect it from water and mechanical damage (see Figure 12.5(b)).

The positive end where current enters is called the *anode* and is marked 'A' on diagrams. The other end is called the *cathode* and is marked 'K.' One way to remember that current comes out of the cathode end is by the shape of the circuit symbol on that side which looks like the letter K and an arrow-head (see Figure 12.5(c)).

To make a diode conduct, the anode must be at a higher voltage than the cathode. This is called a *forward bias* voltage and it needs to be about 0.7 V for diodes made of silicon. Quite unlike resistors, this voltage stays almost constant for a wide range of currents that flow through the diode. In the analogy with a water valve, forward bias for a diode is like the spring on the valve which must be pushed a little before it can open wide.

Ordinary diodes

Ordinary diodes are used, for example, in radios to convert AM radio signals to sound signals. Large diodes are used in the power supplies of televisions and other electronic appliances. In these applications, they act as rectifiers for converting a.c. into d.c.

In a solar system, a diode is often used to prevent the battery discharging through the solar module at night. It is called a *blocking diode* when used this way. The output voltage of the solar module needs to be at least 0.7 V higher than the charging voltage of the battery in order to put the diode in forward bias and make it conduct electricity.

The voltage drop across a diode in forward bias can be made use of. When a voltage appears across the blocking diode, it can turn on a small lamp in the control unit showing that a current is flowing from the module. Another use for

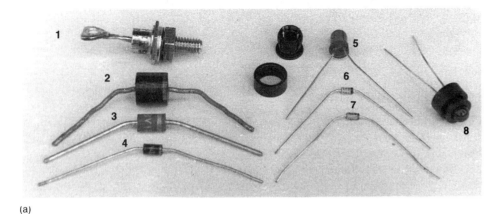

(a)

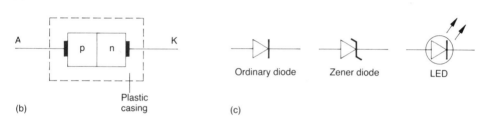

Plastic
casing

(b)

(c)

Figure 12.5 Diodes.

(a) Examples of ordinary diodes, Zener diodes, and LEDs (light-emitting diodes). All diodes are shown with the cathode on the right: **1** stud mounting with DO-4 case (16 A); **2** 5 A diode; **3** 3 A diode; **4** 1N4000 series diode (1 A); **5** LED (0.2 in); **6, 7** 0.5 W Zener diodes; **8** LED fitted in the parts for panel mounting.

(b) Arrangement of connections and pn junction (A anode, p p-type material, n n-type material, K cathode).

(c) Circuit symbols.

the voltage drop in forward bias is in a simple circuit which enables a small radio to be run from a 12 V battery (see Figure 14.3). In this circuit, the voltage is reduced in steps of 0.7 V by connecting the appropriate number of diodes in series between the battery and the radio.

Diodes made of germanium and Schottky diodes have a forward bias voltage of about 0.3 V. The lower bias voltage means that they are a good substitute for the ordinary silicon sort when used as a blocking diode (see Table 2.1).

The size of a diode depends on the maximum current that it can carry in the forward direction without becoming too hot. High-power diodes that can pass a high current are made as a screw called a *stud* so that they can be attached to a piece of metal (see Figure 12.5(a)). The metal is called a heat sink because it helps to dissipate heat from the diode. The heat sink itself is kept cool by the surrounding air which should be allowed to flow over it easily.

Identifying the cathode end

The cathode end of a diode is marked on the diode body by a narrow, painted band. If this band is not clear, the cathode end can be checked using any resistance scale of an analogue multimeter.

When a current from the meter flows through the diode in the forward or conducting direction of the diode, the needle on the meter moves more than half way across (see Figure 12.6). When the diode is connected to the meter terminals the other way round, the needle should hardly move at all. If both ways of connecting the diode give similar movements of the needle, this means the diode is damaged and should be thrown away.

On any resistance scale, the polarity of the terminals on an analogue meter is reversed and current comes out of the negative terminal. After finding the way of connecting the diode that makes the needle swing furthest, the cathode is the end connected to the positive terminal of the meter.

Digital multimeters can also be used to identify the cathode wire of a diode. There are various types of digital multimeter and their instruction booklets should be read carefully to find out what the display shows when testing a diode. If the instructions are not available, the response of the meter can be tested using known components. For most types of digital multimeter, a low number is displayed when the cathode is connected to the negative terminal.

Zener diodes

Like ordinary diodes, Zener diodes conduct when forward biased and do not conduct when reverse biased (cathode connected to a positive voltage). However, when the reverse voltage is above a certain value called the *breakdown voltage*, current does flow through the Zener diode. Over a range of reverse currents, this breakdown voltage stays fairly constant so a Zener diode is used in a circuit to regulate voltage.

Ordinary diodes can also conduct when put in reverse bias but they are not intended to be used this way. A breakdown voltage is specified for them which should be higher than the maximum voltage used in the circuit. Ordinary diodes with a breakdown voltage of 50 V or more, which is usually the case, are suitable for the circuits in this book.

The breakdown voltage of a Zener diode is set when the diode is made. Zener diodes are available with a range of breakdown voltages from 2 V upwards and the value is marked on the side as part of the type number. A code is used for the

Figure 12.6   Using the resistance scale of a multimeter to check a diode. The cathode of the diode is connected to the positive terminal to put the diode in forward bias. The needle is more than half-way along the scale showing that the diode is OK.

breakdown voltage in which the decimal point is replaced by a V, so a breakdown voltage of 8.2 V is marked as 8V2.

Zener diodes are usually encased in coloured plastic and the cathode is identified by a band at one end. The cathode can also be identified using a multimeter in the same way as an ordinary diode.

To check that a Zener diode is in good condition and to measure its breakdown voltage, the equipment needed is a 12 V battery, a resistor, and a voltmeter. The arrangement for doing the measurement is shown in Figure 12.7 and the meter should show the value of the breakdown voltage. If the meter shows 12 V, this means that:

☐   the breakdown voltage is higher than 12 V, or
☐   the Zener is an ordinary diode, or
☐   the diode is damaged.

The size of a Zener diode depends on its power rating, not on its breakdown voltage. The examples shown in Figure 12.5(a) have a low rating of 0.25 W.

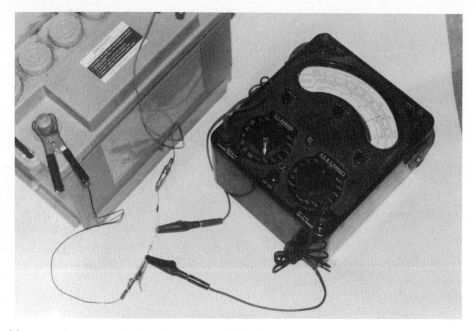

(a)

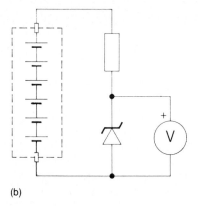

(b)

Figure 12.7   System for measuring the breakdown voltage of a Zener diode using a
12 V battery, a multimeter on one of the voltage scales. and a resistor of more than 470R.
(a)   Arrangement of equipment. The cathode of the Zener diode must be connected to
the positive terminal of the meter.
(b)   Circuit.

Low-power Zener diodes can be used for the circuits in the following chapters because the current through the Zener diode is always limited by a resistor in series with it. The maximum current can be calculated as follows:

Power rating of Zener diode (W)	÷	Breakdown voltage of Zener diode (V)	=	Maximum current allowed for Zener diode (A)

Light-emitting diodes

Light-emitting diodes (LEDs) are made of gallium arsenide or gallium phosphide rather than silicon. These materials give off light when the diode is forward biased and the pn junction is sealed in transparent plastic to let the light out (see Figure 12.5(a)).

The main use of LEDs is as indicator lamps since they are not powerful enough to provide general illumination. They are found on some cassette players and on calculator number displays that can be read in the dark. LEDs are available in red, green, and yellow, with red being the most common. Compared to small torch bulbs, LEDs have no filament to break so they rarely need to be replaced and are permanently soldered into circuits.

For mounting round LEDs neatly in a panel, they are normally supplied with a pair of plastic rings which are shown in Figure 12.5.

To produce light, an LED needs a forward bias voltage of about 2 V, higher than for silicon diodes. They can be run from any voltage above 3 V but the current must be set by a resistor connected in series, called a current-limiting resistor (see Figure 12.8).

For the standard size LED of 5 mm (0.2 in) diameter, the maximum current is specified as 0.03 A although they are bright enough with just 0.01 A (10 mA). The resistance of the current-limiting resistor is calculated using the following formula (based on Ohm's Law) for 0.01 A current:

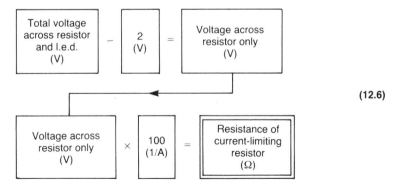

(12.6)

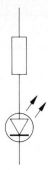

Figure 12.8   Use of a resistor in series with an LED to limit the current. For a current of 0.01 A, the resistance of the resistor is calculated from Formula (12.6).

Example 12.2

What resistance and power rating of resistor is needed to run an LED directly from a 12 V supply?

Using Formula (12.6), the resistance needed is:

$12 - 2 = 10$ V
$10 \times 100 = 1000$ Ω

Therefore a 1K0 resistor is suitable.

To calculate the lowest power rating of resistor that can be used, the maximum voltage across the resistor is 13 V when the batteries are on charge up to 15 V. Using Formula (12.4), the maximum power dissipated in the resistor is:

$13 \times 13 \div 1000 = 0.17$ W

The smallest resistors have a power rating of 0.25 W. Therefore any rating of 1K resistor of 0.25 W or larger is suitable.

Constant current LEDs are available which contain a current-limiting circuit inside. These LEDs can be supplied by any voltage between 2 and 18 V without the need for a series resistor. If they can be obtained, they are clearly easier to use than standard LEDs.

Identifying the cathode of an LED

LEDs are used in forward bias so the cathode must be negative. The cathode wire of an LED is identified by a small flat part on the side of the round body (see 5 in Figure 12.5(a)) or by the wire with the largest end visible through the plastic.

The resistance scale of an analogue multimeter cannot be used to identify the cathode. This is because the 2 V forward bias required for an LED is higher than the voltage of the battery inside the multimeter. When an LED is connected either way round to a multimeter on the resistance setting, the needle does not move. Digital multimeters can be used to identify the cathode of an LED because their resistance scale operates at a higher voltage than for analogue meters. The response of a digital multimeter should be tested with a known LED first.

The operation of an LED can be checked by connecting it to a supply voltage of 3 V or more with a current-limiting resistor of the appropriate resistance for that voltage (resistance calculated from Formula (12.6)).

Transistors

Transistors are vital components in many electronic circuits, such as the circuits for amplifiers and televisions. Although the operation of a transistor is rather complicated to understand in detail, transistors are not difficult to use for the circuits in this book. If more details are required than are given here, refer to specialist books on electronics listed in Appendix F.

A transistor is made out of one piece of silicon, like the ordinary silicon diode. It is then doped to give three regions in a line that alternate between n-type and p-type material. The regions are called the *collector*, *base*, and *emitter*, and are each connected through the casing to a wire on the outside (see Figure 12.9(a)). Examples of transistors are shown in Figure 12.10(a).

The full name for this sort of transistor is *bipolar junction transistor*. It is available in two types called *npn* and *pnp* according to the order of the layers. In the circuit symbol for a transistor, an arrow signifies the emitter wire and the direction of the arrow indicates the type of transistor (see Figure 12.9(b)).

There is another sort called a *field effect transistor* or FET but it is not used for the circuits in this book.

The most important characteristic of a transistor is that a small current flowing through the base wire controls a much larger current crossing the base region between the collector and the emitter. This property makes transistors very useful as amplifiers. For the circuit designs in this book, transistors are used to control either a voltage or a current, or are used simply as a switch (called a solid-state switch).

A transistor has two pn junctions since there are three different regions of p-type and n-type material. It is sometimes helpful to regard a transistor as an ordinary silicon diode and a Zener diode connected together (although a transistor cannot actually be made this way). The npn type is like two diodes connected by their anodes and the pnp type is like two diodes connected by their cathodes (see Figure 12.9(c)).

Some high-power transistors contain two transistors in one casing and are called a *Darlington pair* (see Figure 12.9(d)). They have internal connections so only three or four wires are needed on the outside.

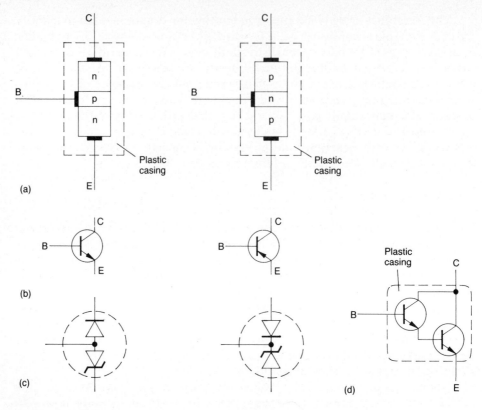

Figure 12.9   Details of transistors (C collector, B base, and E emitter).
(a)   pn junctions.
(b)   Circuit symbols.
(c)   Equivalent as an ordinary diode and a Zener diode.
(d)   Darlington pair of npn transistors in one case with three wires.

Identifying the wires and type of a transistor

Some common arrangements for the base, collector, and emitter wires are shown in Figure 12.10(b). However, unless the wire arrangement is provided by the supplier, it is best to check the arrangement for each transistor.

One procedure for doing this check treats the transistor as if it is two diodes in the way shown in Figure 12.9(c). The base wire and type of transistor (npn or pnp) can both be identified using the resistance scale of a multimeter. The collector and emitter wires are distinguished from each other by putting each junction in reverse bias using a 12 V supply and a resistor, as for the Zener diode test in Figure 12.7.

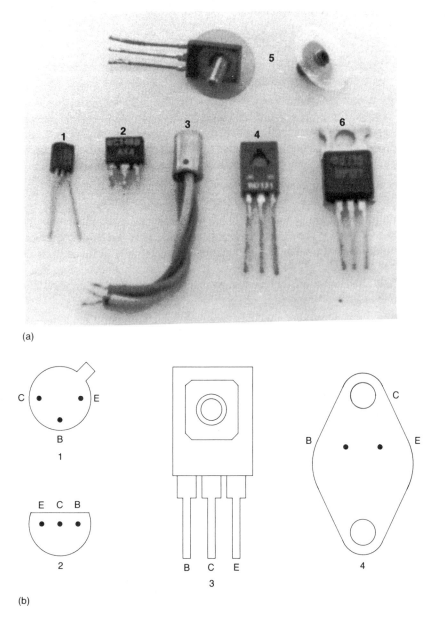

(a)

(b)

Figure 12.10 Transistors.
(a) Examples of transistors; **1–3** low power; **4** high power; **5** high power with mica
washer for isolating the bare metal; **6** Darlington pair.
(b) Common arrangements of wires, as viewed looking at the ends of the wires.
Codes for the type of case: **1** TO5, TO18; **2** TO92; **3** TO126; **4** TO3 (C here is the case).

The procedure is as follows:

1. Draw out a table, like the ones in Table 12.2.
2. Looking at the ends of the wires, draw an outline of the transistor at the top of your table, like the pictures in Figure 12.10(b) and Table 12.2.
3. There are six different ways of connecting the positive and negative leads of the meter to the three wires of the transistor under test. Try each of these different connections looking for pairs of connections with least resistance (needle swings furthest to the right). When a low-resistance pair is found, write '+' and '−' signs in the table under the wires connected to the meter.
4. Find another pair of connections with low resistance and write '+' and '−' signs for this connection in the next row of your table.
5. From steps 3 and 4, one of the three wires should have either two '+' signs or two '−' signs. This identifies the base wire. For an analogue meter, two '−' signs show that it is an npn transistor while two '+' signs show that it is a pnp transistor. Using a digital multimeter on the setting for testing diodes, the cathode is connected to the negative for conduction. Therefore two '+' signs indicate npn while two '−' signs indicate pnp.

Table 12.2 *Examples of the procedure for identifying the connections and type of a transistor. See Figure 12.6 for diode test and Figure 12.7 for Zener diode test. (This example is for an analogue meter which affects the signs for the diode test.)*

		Example 1			Example 2		
Picture of connections							
Diode test — The two arrangements that show low resistance		−	+		−	+	
		−		+		+	−
Conclusion	Base	B				B	
	Type	npn			pnp		
Zener diode test — Base negative			+12 V	+8.4 V	+0.7 V		+0.7 V
Base positive			−0.7 V	−0.7 V	−6.2 V		−12 V
Conclusion			C	E	E		C

6. Connect the base through a resistor of more than 470R to the negative terminal of a 12 V battery supply, as for the Zener diode test (see Figure 12.7).

7. Choose one of the other two wires and connect it to the positive terminal of the battery.

8. Measure the voltage across the transistor and record the value in your table.

9. Use the other wire and repeat steps 7 and 8, putting the voltage measurement in the same line of your table.

10. Change the connection of the base so that it is connected through the resistor to the positive terminal of the battery.

11. Repeat steps 7 to 9 with the unknown wires connected to the negative terminal of the battery and the voltmeter connections reversed. Record your measurements in the next line of your table.

12. How to use the four voltage measurements made in steps 8, 9 and 11:
    (a) The one at 12 V (the voltage of the battery) indicates the collector wire.
    (b) A measurement in the range 5–10 V indicates the emitter wire and the value measured is the breakdown voltage of the BE junction in reverse bias.
    (c) The two remaining measurements are for the junctions in forward bias and both measurements should be less than 2 V. Table 12.3 shows how the forward bias voltages can be used to identify the material of the transistor or whether it is a Darlington pair.

In some countries, Zener diodes and ordinary diodes in low-power ratings are more difficult to obtain than transistors. By collecting a number of transistors and measuring the breakdown voltage of the BE junctions in reverse bias, you now have a selection of Zener diodes. The BC junction of a transistor in forward bias can be substituted for an ordinary low-power diode.

Table 12.3 *Use of forward bias voltages from Table 12.2 to identify the material and type of a transistor.*

BE junction (V)	BC junction (V)	Material
0.3	0.3	Germanium
0.7	0.7	Silicon
1.4	0.7	Darlington pair of silicon transistors

Transistor specifications

In electronics catalogues, there is a very wide range of type numbers and specifications listed for transistors. The only details of concern here are the following:

☐ *Material* – silicon (avoid germanium).
☐ *Type* – npn or pnp, as needed in the circuit (avoid field effect transistors).
☐ *Power rating* – low or high power, as needed in the circuit.
☐ *Cost* – low.
☐ *Wires* – long.

There are two important specifications to do with the size of a transistor:

☐ Maximum current through the collector or $I_{C(max)}$.
☐ Maximum power dissipation for the whole transistor or P_{max}.

Typical values for these specifications are given in Table 12.4 which can be used as a guideline when selecting transistors from a catalogue.

Table 12.4 *Typical values of maximum collector current $I_{C(max)}$ and maximum power that can be dissipated by the whole transistor P_{max}.*

Rating of transistor	$I_{C(max)}$	P_{max}
	(A)	(W)
Low power	≤0.2	≤0.3
High power	≥3	≥15

High-power transistors

When a transistor is dissipating a high power, it becomes quite hot. The temperature of the case must be kept below about 125 °C (260 °F) to avoid damage to the silicon part inside.

High-power transistors have a metal plate included as part of their casing to help the dissipation of heat (see Figure 12.10). A hole in the plate enables the transistor to be firmly bolted to a larger piece of metal that acts as a heat sink. The heat sink itself is kept cool by the flow of air over its surface. A thin layer of a paste called *heat sink compound* can be smeared between the transistor and the heat sink to improve the conduction of heat away from the transistor.

Figure 12.11   Examples of two integrated circuits: **1** 741 op-amp in DIL (dual in-line) casing; **2** DIL socket; **3** voltage regulator.

Figure 14.9 shows a high-power transistor attached to the edge of a circuit board. In this position, the transistor can be bolted to a heat sink when the board is being mounted. Figure 14.6 shows a metal box used as a heat sink for a high-power transistor soldered to a tag strip.

A problem to beware of with high-power transistors is that the metal part is usually connected internally to the collector. This puts the metal used as a heat sink at the same voltage as the collector.

If there is a risk of the heat sink accidentally touching other metal parts and causing a short circuit, the metal of the transistor should be electrically isolated from the heat sink. Figure 12.10(a) shows a mica washer and a plastic bush that are used for this purpose. The mica washer goes between the transistor and the heat sink, while the plastic bush insulates the screw from the metal parts of the transistor. An alternative to mica is silicone rubber reinforced with fibreglass.

Integrated circuits

An *integrated circuit* (IC) is one component that contains many transistors and other components in a single compact form. The circuit inside the IC is designed to do a certain function without the need for many other components on a circuit board. Common applications of ICs are in calculators and digital wrist-watches.

There is a very wide variety of ICs available for performing different tasks. Two types of ICs used for the circuits in the following chapters are an *op-amp* and a *voltage regulator* (examples shown in Figure 12.11).

Op-amps

The full name for an op-amp is *operational amplifier* and the circuit function is as a high-gain amplifier for the difference in voltage between two wires. (The term 'operational' is historical, referring to the main application of this circuit design when first introduced of performing mathematical operations, such as addition

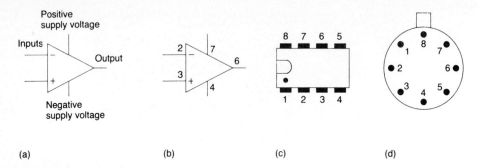

Figure 12.12   Details of a 741 op-amp.
(a)   Standard circuit symbol.
(b)   Pin numbers on circuit symbol.
(c)   Pin numbers on an eight-pin DIL (dual in-line) casing, as viewed looking at the top with the wires pointing away.
(d)   Pin numbers on a TO99 metal can, as viewed looking at the ends of the wires.

of two signals.) Op-amps are versatile components and are used in many different circuits, such as radios and stereo amplifiers. The circuit applications in this book are more straightforward and the cheapest type of op-amp is adequate.

The symbol for an op-amp is a triangle with two inputs on the left and one output on the right (see Figure 12.12(a)). Two connections are also needed to power the circuit inside, which are shown going up and down from the sides of the triangular symbol. Other connections on the case are not used.

The most common type of op-amp is the *741* made in a *dual-in-line* (DIL) case. There are four connections on each side with the pins numbered in an anti-clockwise direction, as shown in Figure 12.12(c). The starting corner for pin 1 is identified by a dot or a U-shaped cut-out. Another type of case is round with pin 8 identified by a tab on the side (see Figure 12.12(d)).

An op-amp can be soldered directly onto a circuit board. It is better, though, to solder on a DIL socket instead, such as the one shown in Figure 12.11, which the op-amp can plug into. This avoids the risk of damaging the op-amp by over-heating with the soldering iron and allows the op-amp to be replaced easily.

Voltage regulators

Voltage-regulating ICs usually have three wires and look very similar to a high-power transistor. The wires cannot be identified by a simple test so it is important to obtain full details of the wire arrangement at the time of purchase.

There are two sorts of voltage-regulating IC with three wires. The simplest sort has a fixed voltage output but the choice of fixed voltages that are available is limited to 5, 12, and 15 V.

The other sort of regulating IC has an adjustable output voltage. The

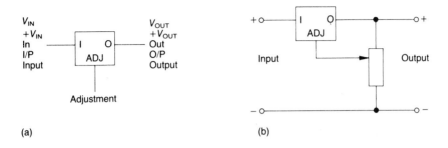

(a)

(b)

Figure 12.13 Details of voltage-regulating ICs that have an adjustable output.
(a) Circuit symbol with lists of names that are often used to label the wires.
(b) Circuit diagram for using a potentiometer to set the output voltage from the IC.

voltage is either set at one value by a pair of resistors or made adjustable using a potentiometer (see Figure 12.13(b)). A range of resistances is suitable when using a pair of resistors and a method for calculating them is normally provided with the regulator. For most regulators, the adjustment connection operates at a reference voltage of 1.25 V relative to the output wire. Suggested values for the resistances are given in the following chapters.

A fixed voltage-regulating IC with a 5 V output can also be used as an adjustable voltage regulator. The 'common' or 'ground' wire is used like the 'adjustment' wire in Figure 12.13(b). The reference voltage is 5 V.

Sometimes capacitors are shown in the circuits suggested by the IC manufacturers. Capacitors are not really necessary for the applications in this book where the supply is already a smooth d.c. However they can be included if recommended by the IC supplier.

Relays

A *relay* is an automatic type of switch which is controlled by an electrical input. Its main application is where a small current is required to control a switch that can carry a much higher current. Unlike the other components described in this chapter, a relay has parts that move (see Figure 12.14(a)).

A relay is used in most vehicles for the electric starting system. The starter motor draws a very high current which means that the wires connecting it to the battery must be thick and short. A relay is mounted along one of the thick wires to the motor so that a small switch can be used next to the steering wheel for the ignition key. When the ignition key is turned, it switches current to the relay which in turn switches a much larger current to the starter motor.

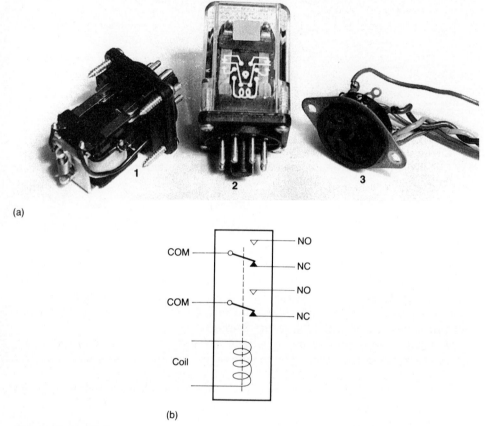

(a)

(b)

Figure 12.14 Relays.
(a) An example of a two-pole, eight-pin relay: **1** with cover off; **2** with cover on and details of pins; **3** eight-pin relay socket.
(b) Arrangement of connections for a two-pole relay: COM common, NO normally open (closed when coil is energized), NC normally closed (open when coil is energized).

Operation

Relays contain a small coil or electromagnet that becomes magnetic when a current flows through it. In this state, the relay is said to be 'energized' and the magnetic force pulls on the moving part of a switch to open and close a number of contacts. When the coil current is switched off, the moving part is released and pulled back to its normal position by a spring.

Two of the terminals on a relay are for the coil while the rest are for the switch contacts (see Figure 12.14(b)). The terminals are labelled according to the 'normal' state of the relay when there is no current flowing through the coil. 'NC' stands for normally closed and 'NO' stands for normally open with 'COM' marking the common connection. The terminals can be checked by using the resistance scale of a multimeter to show continuity between terminals in the normal and energized states of the coil.

In a *latching relay*, the spring is replaced by a second coil for resetting the moving part. Each coil is only energized when it is necessary to change the state of the switch contacts.

Some control units for solar systems include a relay to switch off the load circuits automatically when the battery is at a low state of charge. The current rating of the switch contacts in this relay is specified on the control unit or in the instruction sheets. If the total current of the load circuits is higher than this rating, one solution is to add another relay. Details for doing this are given in Chapter 16.

Specifications

There are four main specifications for a relay:

1. Voltage rating of coil.
2. Current needed to energize the coil.
3. Current rating of the switch contacts.
4. Number of poles of wires that can be switched.

The main use of relays in solar systems is to control the load circuits. For this application, the rating of the coil should be d.c. and at the system voltage (usually 12 or 24 V). The current requirement of the coil is related to the rating of the switch contacts and the number of poles. The current rating of the switch contacts should be higher than the maximum current required by the circuits that they control. However, do not use a relay with an unnecessarily high switch rating otherwise current is wasted in the large coil that is required to activate the switches.

Tools

A few tools and materials are essential for building and checking electronic circuits. Here is a list of them, with some examples shown in Figure 12.15:

☐ Small multimeter, 'AVO' or digital multimeter with scales for d.c. volts and resistance. A d.c. amps scale of 5 A is also useful but not usually included in small multimeters.

☐ Small electric soldering iron with a power rating between 25 and 50 W.

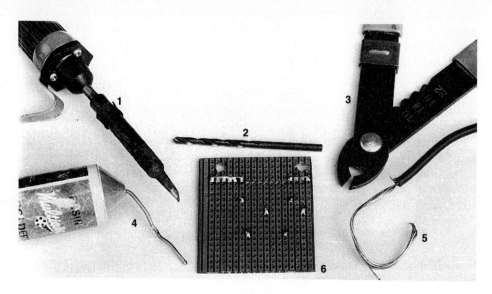

Figure 12.15   Tools and stripboard with copper tracks: **1** tip of a 25 W soldering iron; **2** 3 mm drill for making breaks in the copper track, **3** wire cutters; **4** electrical cored solder; **5** copper wire for making links across tracks; **6** stripboard with 2.5 mm (0.1 in) spaced holes as viewed from the side with copper tracks. The large holes, links across tracks and breaks in the tracks, are for one of the circuits in Chapter 13.

☐   A d.c. supply of 12 V for doing tests. This can be provided by any of the following:
   (a) Lead–acid car battery.
   (b) Eight dry cells (torch batteries) connected in series.
   (c) Pair of 6 V radio batteries connected in series.

☐   Fine-nose pair of pliers.

☐   Pair of wire cutters.

☐   Desoldering tool or solder sucker which sucks up molten solder is useful for removing components from a circuit board.

☐   Electrical cored solder which contains rosin flux (through the middle).

☐   Tag strip for small circuits.

☐   Stripboard with copper tracks for larger circuits.

Most soldering irons require mains voltage or 24 V a.c. from a small transformer run off the mains. Cordless or battery-powered irons are becoming common and are more convenient to use where there is no mains supply. They are powered by batteries fitted in the handle but can also be run continuously for long periods by connecting directly to a 12 V lead–acid battery. A voltage regulator is needed if the iron requires less than 12 V (see Chapter 14).

Solder is an alloy of tin and lead. The percentage mixture should be 60 : 40 for electrical work. Solder with a smaller percentage of tin melts at a higher temperature and is not suitable for electronic circuits. It is meant for heavy-duty work, such as joining power cables and water pipes.

Building the circuits

For each of the circuits in the following chapters, a circuit diagram is given using the circuit symbols introduced earlier in this chapter. To help identify the components, the symbols are summarized in Table 12.5 for easy reference.

A suggested layout of the components is also given with each circuit. For small circuits with few components, the layout is for a tag strip, while more complicated circuits are laid out for a piece of stripboard. Unlike the circuit diagrams, the layouts are drawn as they actually look and a key to the symbols used is given in Table 12.6.

When building the circuits, it is not necessary to understand exactly how each circuit works. However, to build them successfully, it is important to follow the layout of components very carefully so that the components connect to each other in the correct way. It is also important that the joints are soldered properly to make them strong and reliable.

Examples of circuits built on tag strip are shown in Figure 14.4. When mounting the tag strip in a housing, some of the metal tags can be removed, leaving square holes for screws (see Figure 14.6 as an example).

Stripboard

Figures 12.15 and 13.4 show each side of stripboard. The board itself is made of *sandwiched resin bonded paper* (SRBP), *Veroboard*, or *paper phenolic*. These are brown insulating materials that are strong but easily cut with a small hacksaw. Stripboard can also be made of glass fibre in epoxy resin which is slightly stronger than SRBP.

A common size of stripboard has holes of diameter 1.0 mm (0.04 in) arranged in a grid with the rows spaced at 2.5 mm (0.1 in). One side of the board is coated with parallel strips of copper called tracks.

A larger size of stripboard is available with holes of 1.3 mm (0.05 in) diameter spaced at 3.8 mm (0.15 in). However, the wider spacing of the holes makes it difficult to fit some of the small components. The size with 2.5 mm (0.1 in) spacing is recommended and the layouts shown in the following chapters are for this size.

Table 12.5 *Full list of symbols for the circuit diagrams.*

Symbol	Name of component	Page reference
	Resistor	262
	Potentiometer	268
	Diode	270
	Zener diode	272
	LED (light-emitting diode)	275
	npn transistor	277
	pnp transistor	277
	npn Darlington pair	277
	Op-amp IC	283
	Voltage-regulating ICs	284
	Voltmeter	261

Table 12.5 (continued)

Symbol	Name of component	Page reference
	Ammeter	262
	Bulb	268
	One cell of a battery (positive is long side)	38
	Battery of several cells connected in series	38
	Fusible link	312
	Fuse	76
	On–off switch	199
	Spring-loaded on–off switch	360
	One pole, two way, or changeover switch	203
	Switch contacts in a relay	285
	Energizing coil of a relay	285
	External connections to circuit	
	Three wires that connect	
	Two wires that cross and do not connect	
	Earthing connection to metal case	357

Table 12.6 *Full list of components for circuit layouts. The components are scale drawn to show how much space they need in the layout.*

Symbol	Name of component	Page reference
	Resistor (0.5 W)	262
	Potentiometer (miniature horizontal)	268
	Diode (1 A)	270
	Zener diode (0.5 W)	272
A K	Connections to an LED	275
B E C E C B	Low-power transistors[1]	277
E C B	High-power transistor or Darlington pair of transistors in one case[1]	282
	Op-amp IC (including breaks in copper track underneath stripboard)	283
I A	Low-power voltage-regulating IC (arrangement of wires shown as an example)	284
I C O I A O	High-power voltage-regulating ICs (arrangement of wires shown as an example)	284

Table 12.6 (continued)

Symbol	Name of component	Page reference
Battery + / output −	External connections to circuit	
○ ○ ○ / ○ ○ ○ / ○ ○ ○	Unused holes in stripboard	289
●	Used hole in stripboard with the direction of the copper track underneath shown	294
●——●	Link across the top of stripboard connecting two separated copper tracks	294
●– – –●	Link underneath stripboard connecting several adjacent copper tracks	294
⊗	Break in a copper track underneath stripboard	294
	Tag strip	289

¹Arrangement of wires shown as an example. If the actual arrangement is not known, always check the order of BCE before using a transistor in a circuit by following the procedure outlined in this chapter (see Table 12.2).

Mounting components on stripboard

To mount components, the component wires are pushed through the holes from the plain side and soldered to the copper tracks on the other side. The tracks make electrical contact between wires that are soldered in the same line of holes. When mounting the components on stripboard, it is important that the board is first oriented correctly so that the copper tracks connect the correct line of holes. The direction of the tracks is clearly indicated beside each layout.

Different tracks sometimes need to be joined and this is shown by connections on the layout that go across. The connections are formed by links made from pieces of copper wire, such as the strands from 2.5 mm^2 cable.

For some layouts, it is necessary to make breaks in the tracks. A break can be made by carefully scratching the copper off, using any metal tool with a sharp corner. Another method which is quicker and neater is to use a sharp drill of about 3 mm ($\frac{1}{8}$ in) in diameter. A break is made where the track passes around a hole by twisting the drill in this place with fingers. A few turns are sufficient to cut away the copper without drilling all the way through the plastic of the board.

Components with three or more wires have various arrangements of the wires. Transistors have three wires so must be connected to three different tracks. For the low-power transistors, enough space is allowed in the layouts for the wires to go in a choice of six holes. In this way, a transistor with any arrangement of wires can be positioned without having to bend the wires too much.

Potentiometers also have three connections. They are available as standard or miniature sizes and as horizontal or vertical (see Figure 12.4). The space allowed for potentiometers in the layouts is at the end of the board so that the board can be left long for a large horizontal potentiometer or cut short for a miniature vertical one. Panel-mounting potentiometers with solder tags can be attached using short pieces of stiff copper wire to connect the tags to the holes at the end of the board.

Procedure for soldering

Prepare for soldering as follows:

☐ Make sure that all surfaces to be soldered are quite clean without any trace of grease or other dirt. These include the wires on components, the tags on a tag strip, and the copper tracks on stripboard. Carborundum or wet-dry paper may be needed to rub off thick dirt and reveal clean metal.

☐ Clean the tip of the soldering iron with a file before use and 'tin' it by melting some solder on after it has heated up.

Soldering:

1. Tin the wires before joining them together. This means heating each wire so that the solder melts on and coats the parts to be soldered. The wires on new components may be already tinned.

2. Try to join the components by bending their wires together first so that the strength of the completed joint does not depend only on the solder. On tag strip, twist the wire around the tag. On stripboard, bend the wire over by about 45° on the track side. (Solder is only intended to make a good electrical contact between the wires, not for providing the strength of the joint.)
3. Remove old solder from the tip of the soldering iron by quickly wiping across a moist sponge or cloth. Then tin the tip with fresh solder.
4. Hold the tip of the soldering iron against the joint to heat it up.
5. Apply solder directly to the hot wires so that it melts and flows over the wires freely. Hold the iron on the wires for only a few seconds. If the first attempt at making a joint fails, remove the iron to allow the component to cool down. Some components, such as diodes and transistors, are easily damaged by excessive heating.

Removing and recycling components

Components need to be removed if they are put in the wrong position or are faulty.

Components can be recycled from old circuit boards, but this should only be done as a last resort, for example when they are difficult to obtain as new. Always try to use new components when building circuits. If it is necessary to reuse components, they must be removed carefully and thoroughly tested after removal.

The procedure for removing components is as follows:

1. Clamp the circuit board firmly in some way. It can be held in a vice or screwed to the side of a table.
2. Remove old solder from the tip of the soldering iron by quickly wiping across a moist sponge. Then tin the tip with fresh solder.
3. On the component side of the board, grip one wire of the component to be removed with fine-nose pliers.
4. Melt the solder which secures the wire on the other side of the board and pull steadily with the pliers. Avoid heating for too long and bending the wires too much, otherwise the component that is being removed will be damaged.

If a solder sucker is available, it can be used to remove most of the solder in the last step.

13 Expanded-scale voltmeters

Measuring the voltage across a lead–acid battery is a convenient way of estimating its state of charge. Here are the voltages of interest:

☐ Greater than 13.5 V when on charge, showing that the state of charge is above 90 per cent.

☐ Less than 11.5 V when at load supplying a current showing that the state of charge is below about 50 per cent.

These voltages can be measured by a d.c. voltmeter with a range of 0–15 V. However, for an analogue (moving needle) voltmeter covering this range, the scale is too coarse. On a 0–15 V scale, it is difficult to detect small differences in voltage which correspond to significant changes in the state of charge of lead–acid batteries.

What is needed is to expand the scale over the voltages of interest which are those between 10 and 15 V. This can be done by the combination of a 0–5 V d.c. voltmeter with a constant offset voltage of 10.0 V. Together these form an *expanded-scale voltmeter* with the range 10–15 V. (For a system voltage of 24 V, the voltages are doubled. This means that the voltages of interest are in the range 20–30 V and require a 0–10 V d.c. voltmeter with a 20.0 V offset voltage.)

One advantage of using these sizes of voltmeter is that they are common in schools for teaching about electricity. They can be obtained from most suppliers of school equipment and often cost less than voltmeters from electronics shops.

Three designs for providing a stable offset voltage in an expanded-scale voltmeter are given in this chapter and their main details are summarized in Table 13.1. The choice of which design to build mostly depends on the availability of components. Refer to Chapter 12 for background details on all the components used in these designs and advice on how to build the circuits.

A steel junction box is ideal for housing the meter and other components (see Figure 13.3(b)). The '+' and '−' connections to the solar system can be brought out of the box to a connector strip screwed on the top.

Table 13.1 *Details of three circuit designs for providing the offset voltage in an expanded-scale voltmeter.*

Circuit	Main components	Advantages	Disadvantages
Design 1	Diodes	Least number of components	Adjusted by adding diodes 0.4 V change in offset voltage across scale[1]
Design 2	Two transistors	Potentiometer adjustment	Requires stripboard 0.4 V change in offset voltage across scale[1]
Design 3	Op-amp IC	Potentiometer adjustment Stable offset voltage	Requires stripboard IC not always available in some countries

[1]This change in offset voltage does not include inaccuracy of analogue voltmeters.

As a substitute for a digital multimeter, the expanded-scale meter can be converted to a test meter with four scales. This covers most measuring requirements when installing and testing a solar system. Full details for the conversion are given at the end of the chapter.

Scale repainting

It is important that the users of a solar system understand what the position of the needle means since they look at it each day. To help them, the scale can be simplified by repainting it to look like a fuel gauge. An example of a meter with a repainted scale together with two other units that indicate state of charge are shown in Figure 4.4.

In the following instructions, the low band starts at 11.5 V for a 12 V system (23 V for a 24 V system). Other values between 10.8 and 11.8 V can be used instead according to the type of battery and lowest state of charge that is recommended (see Table 11.2).

The items needed to change the scale are shown in Figure 13.1. Proceed as follows for a 12 V system:

1. Carefully dismantle the voltmeter and remove the scale from the meter.
2. For the scale positions of 1.5 and 3.5, scratch long lines leading towards the needle pivot. Also scratch a '1' next to each scale number to make 10, 11, and so on to 15. Blacken the scratch marks with a pen to make them more visible.

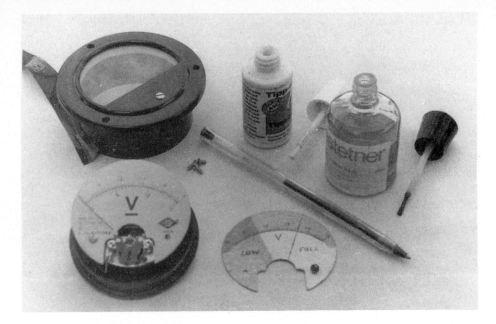

Figure 13.1　Repainting a 0 – 5 V scale for use in an expanded-scale voltmeter. Materials shown are typists' white correction paint and the red varnish for correcting duplicating stencils.

3.　Paint over the bottom half of the scale with white correction paint, as used by typists. (Advantages of this paint are that it is easy to apply, dries quickly, and can be written on.)

4.　Paint the area to the left of the 11.5 line with red correction fluid, as used to correct duplicating stencils.

5.　Write 'low' under the red area on the left and 'full' to the right of the 13.5 line.

6.　Assemble the scale back into the meter taking care that the mechanical adjuster for the needle engages properly.

For a 24 V system, there are some slight differences. For step 2, add a '2' in front of each of the numbers and convert '10' to '30'. When finishing off the scale in step 5, the 'full' region is above 27 V and the 'low' region is below 23 V or some other value from Table 11.2.

Design 1: diodes only

The simplest way of providing a 10.0 V offset is by a reverse-biased 10V0 Zener diode connected in series with a 0–5 V voltmeter (see Figure 13.2).

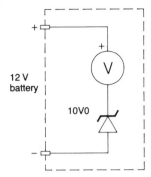

Figure 13.2 Circuit diagram for a design 1 expanded-scale voltmeter using a 10V0 Zener diode.

Zener diodes with this value of breakdown voltage are often not available but they can be substituted for by combinations of lower-voltage Zener diodes, ordinary diodes, and transistors. (A transistor can be used here either as a Zener diode by putting the BE junction in reverse bias or as an ordinary diode by putting the CB junction in forward bias.) An example of one combination is shown in Figure 13.3(a).

Here is the procedure of building this circuit for a 12 V system using a transistor instead of a Zener diode:

1. Collect a number of cheap low-power silicon transistors.

2. Use the procedure in Table 12.2 to measure the breakdown voltage of their BE junctions in reverse bias. Choose one transistor with a BE breakdown voltage of just below 10 V.

3. Ordinary diodes drop 0.7 V when put in forward bias so one or more diodes can be connected in series with the BE junction of the transistor to raise the offset voltage in steps of 0.7 V. Use as many diodes as are needed to set the offset voltage in the range 9.7–10.3 V. (Figure 13.3(a) is an example where the BE junction of an npn transistor has a breakdown voltage of 8.4 V in reverse bias. Therefore two diodes are added to make the voltage up to the required range.)

4. Solder the chain of transistor and diodes onto a tag strip. Leave two spaces in the tag strip where it can be attached to the terminal posts of a 0–5 V meter (see the example of this mounting arrangement in Figure 13.3(b)).

5. Solder on one multi-stranded wire for connection to the negative terminal and another for connection to the outside of the box.

6. Mount the tag strip on the back of the voltmeter and make the connection to the negative terminal.

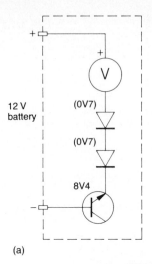

(a)

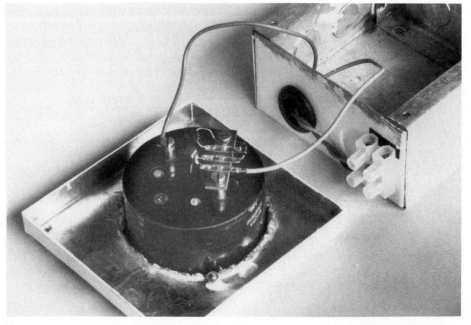

(b)

Figure 13.3   Example of a design 1 expanded-scale voltmeter using two diodes and a transistor.
(a)   Circuit diagram. The BE junction of the npn transistor shown has a breakdown voltage of 8.4 V in reverse bias. Two ordinary diodes are added to make up the voltage to about 10.0 V.
(b)   Complete expanded-scale meter mounted in a steel junction box. The box is open, showing how the components are mounted on the back of the meter using a tag strip.

7. Attach a multi-stranded wire to the positive terminal for connection to the outside of the box. This is now an expanded-scale voltmeter.

8. Using a multimeter, measure the voltage of a 12 V battery as accurately as you can.

9. Connect the expanded-scale voltmeter to the same 12 V battery. Using a small screwdriver, adjust the position of the needle from the front of the voltmeter to give the same reading as the multimeter in step 8 minus 10.0 V. If the range of this mechanical adjustment is not enough, add or remove a diode as required.

For 24 V systems, a 0–10 V meter is needed. The offset voltage is either obtained from a 20V0 Zener diode or made up with lower-voltage Zener diodes, ordinary diodes, and transistors to the range 19.7–20.3 V. A 24 V supply is required when making the final adjustment to the needle and this can be provided by two 12 V batteries connected in series.

Design 2: two transistors

As for design 1, the breakdown voltage of a Zener diode in reverse bias is used as a reference for the 10.0 V offset voltage. One advantage of design 2 over design 1 is that any value of breakdown voltage below 7 V is suitable.

Using a circuit with two transistors, the reference voltage from a Zener diode is 'multiplied' up to the required value simply by adjusting a potentiometer (see Figure 13.4(a)). Once the circuit is complete, adjusting the needle to show the correct value takes a short time and no change of components is necessary. Also the offset voltage can be easily reset later if necessary.

Figure 13.4(b) shows a layout of the circuit on stripboard having a hole spacing of 2.5 mm (0.1 in). The stripboard can be attached directly to the terminal posts on the back of the voltmeter (see Figure 13.4(d)). This arrangement provides both firm support for the board and electrical contact between the circuit and the meter without the need for extra wires.

Building the circuit

The separation of the terminal posts varies between voltmeters. Furthermore dual scale voltmeters generally have three terminals with one of the terminals common to both scales.

The full size of the stripboard is twenty-seven holes along the copper tracks by seventeen holes across the tracks. This should suit all sizes of single and dual scale voltmeters. The board can be shorter or narrower than this depending on the actual positions of the two terminal posts for the relevant scale of the meter (0–5 V scale for a 12 V system and 0–10 V scale for a 24 V system).

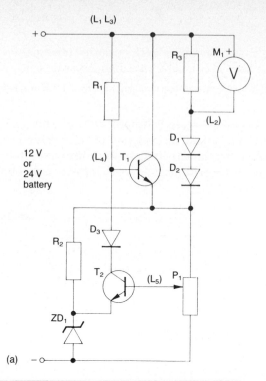

(a)

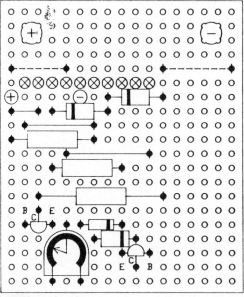

Terminal
posts
of meter
L₁ L₂

X₁ – X₁₀
D₁
L₃ D₂
L₄
R₁
L₅
R₂

R₃

T₁ ZD₁
D₃
P₁ T₂

 Orientation
of copper
tracks

⊕ + of battery

⊖ – of battery

(b)

Component	Position	Specification	
Stripboard		2.5 mm (0.1 in) hole separation, overall dimensions: 27 holes along tracks (71 mm, 2.8 in) by 17 holes across tracks (45 mm, 1.8 in)	
Transistors	T_1, T_2	npn, low-power, silicon	
Diodes	D_1, D_2, D_3	Silicon, 0.5 A	
Zener diode	ZD_1	<7VO or BE junction of a transistor	
Resistors	R_1, R_2	12 V system: $\geqslant$2K2 0.25 W	24 V system: $\geqslant$4K7 0.25 W
	R_3	10K 0.25 W	22K 0.25 W
Potentiometer	P_1	4K7 0.1 W	10K 0.1 W
Meter	M_1	0–5 V d.c.	0–10 V d.c.

(c)

(d)

Figure 13.4 Design 2 expanded-scale voltmeter.
(a) Circuit diagram.
(b) Layout on stripboard. Mounting holes shown for terminal posts separated by 33 mm (1.3 in).
(c) List of component specifications.
(d) A complete expanded-scale voltmeter showing the circuit mounted on the back of the meter.

Figure 13.4(b) shows the arrangement for terminal posts separated by 33 mm (1.3 in) whereas the arrangement in Figure 13.5(c) uses the left and centre posts of a dual scale meter. The board can also be shorter if a vertical potentiometer is used (see Figure 12.4(a)).

The procedure of building a circuit for a 12 V system is as follows:

1. Make two holes at one end of the board for the terminal screws. Dual scale meters have three terminal posts so check that the holes are positioned over the correct pair of posts for the required scale.

2. Make the links L_1 and L_2 which are on the copper track side of the board. These links ensure electrical contact in several places between the copper strips and the terminal posts of the meter. The direction of L_2 to the left or right depends on the position of the hole for the negative terminal.

3. Make the other links L_3, L_4, and L_5 which go across the component side and are only soldered at their ends. To find which position they should be in, count down the rows of holes below links L_1 and L_2. Double check the position of each link before soldering to ensure that it is placed correctly.

4. Solder in all the components after taking note of the following points:
   (a) Transistors (T_1, T_2) – check the order of the C, B, E wires.
   (b) Diodes (D_1, D_2, D_3, ZD_1) – check the cathode ends using a meter.
   (c) Resistors (R_1, R_2, R_3) – check the resistances with a resistance meter.
   (d) Potentiometer (P_1) – Make sure that the leg for the slider contact goes to the middle track.

5. Solder on two multi-stranded wires for the connections to the outside of the meter box.

6. Cut short any excess length of wires on the solder side of the board.

7. Make the line of ten breaks $(X_1$ to $X_{10})$ in the copper tracks.

8. Cut off excess area of the board.

9. Attach the completed circuit board to the terminals of a 0–5 V meter. This is now an expanded-scale voltmeter.

10. Using a multimeter or another voltmeter, measure the voltage of a 12 V battery as accurately as you can.

11. Connect the expanded-scale voltmeter to the same 12 V battery. Using a small screwdriver, adjust the potentiometer to set the position of the needle at the same reading as the multimeter in step 10 minus 10.0 V.

For a 24 V system, the change of components is shown in the component list of Figure 13.4(c). A 24 V supply is required when making the final adjustment to the needle and this can be provided by two 12 V batteries connected in series.

Identifying faults in the circuit

If the expanded-scale voltmeter does not appear to work properly, the causes for this can be poor solder joints, a short circuit across copper tracks, incorrect placement of components, or faulty components. The following procedure of measuring voltages at various points may help to locate the fault (a voltmeter is required with a range of either 0–15 V for 12 V systems or 0–30 V for 24 V systems):

1. Connect the expanded-scale voltmeter to a battery supply of 12 or 24 V, as appropriate for the system.
2. Clip the negative lead of the voltmeter to the negative of the supply.
3. Measure the voltage at the following places by touching the positive lead against the part of the circuit that is being tested. (When taking a measurement, take great care not to touch two metal parts with the positive lead at the same time, otherwise damage may be caused by a short circuit.)
   (a) Cathode of ZD_1 which should be at its breakdown voltage.
   (b) L_5 which should be the same as the previous measurement plus 0.7 V.
   (c) The negative terminal of the meter itself which should be at about 10 V for 12 V systems and 20 V for 24 V systems. This voltage should change as the potentiometer is adjusted.
   (d) L_4 which should be at the voltage measured in the previous step minus 0.7 V.
   (e) The left end of R_2 which should be at the voltage measured in the previous step minus 0.7 V.

Design 3: op-amp

This design uses an op-amp IC (operational amplifier) which sets the offset voltage more accurately than designs 1 or 2. Full details of the circuit are shown in Figure 13.5. It uses a slightly longer size of stripboard than design 2, but the same details apply about attaching the board to single and dual scale voltmeters.

Building the circuit

The procedure for a 12 V system is as follows:

1. Make two holes at one end of the board for the terminal screws. Dual scale meters have three terminal posts so check that the holes are positioned over the correct pair of posts for the required scale.
2. Make the links L_1 and L_2 which are on the copper track side of the board. These links ensure electrical contact in several places between the copper

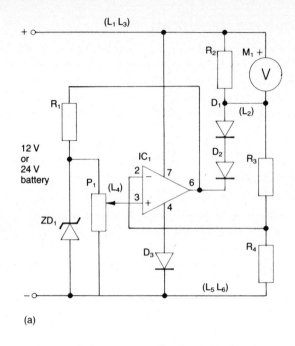

(a)

Component	Position	Specification	
Stripboard		2.5 mm (0.1 in) diameter holes, maximum overall dimensions: 31 holes along tracks (81 mm, 3.2 in) by 17 holes across tracks (45 mm, 1.8 in)	
IC	IC_1	741 op-amp, preferably with DIL socket	
Diodes	D_1, D_2, D_3	Silicon, 0.5 A	
Zener diode	ZD_1	5V6–7V0	
Resistor	R_1	2K2 0.25 W	
	R_2	1K0 0.25 W	
	R_3	330K 0.25 W	
	R_4	100K 0.25 W	
Potentiometer	P_1	10K–22K 0.1 W	
		12 V system:	24 V system:
Meter	M_1	0–5 V, d.c.	0–10 V, d.c.

(b)

Figure 13.5 Design 3 expanded-scale voltmeter.
(a) Circuit.
(b) List of component specifications.
(c) Layout on stripboard.

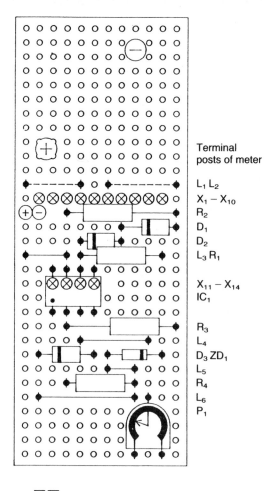

Terminal
posts of meter

L₁ L₂
X₁ – X₁₀
R₂
D₁
D₂
L₃ R₁

X₁₁ – X₁₄
IC₁

R₃
L₄
D₃ ZD₁
L₅
R₄
L₆
P₁

Orientation
of copper
tracks

⊖ – of battery

⊕ + of battery

(c)

strips and the terminal posts of the meter. The direction of L_2 to the left or right depends on the position of the hole for the negative terminal.

3. Make the other links (L_3–L_6) which go across the component side and are only soldered at their ends. To find which position they should be in, count down the rows of holes below links L_1 and L_2. Double check the position of each link before soldering to ensure that it is placed correctly.

4. Solder in all the components after taking note of the following points:
    (a) Op-amp (IC_1) – solder in a DIL socket if available. Otherwise identify the left end of the IC by a dot or a 'U' shaped cutout before soldering in.
    (b) Diodes (D_1, D_2, D_3, ZD_1) – check the cathode ends using a meter.
    (c) Resistors (R_1, R_2, R_3, R_4) – check the resistances using a meter.
    (d) Potentiometer (P_1) – make sure that the leg for the slider contact goes to the middle track.

5. Solder on two multi-stranded wires for the connections to the outside of the meter box.

6. Cut short any excess length of wires on the solder side of the board.

7. Make the two lines of breaks (X_1 to X_{10} and X_{11} to X_{14}) in the copper tracks.

8. Cut off excess area of the board.

9. Attach the completed circuit board to the terminals of a 0–5 V meter. This is now an expanded-scale voltmeter.

10. Using a multimeter or another voltmeter, measure the voltage of a 12 V battery as accurately as you can.

11. Connect the expanded-scale voltmeter to the same 12 V battery. Using a small screwdriver, adjust the potentiometer to set the position of the needle at the same reading as the multimeter in step 10 minus 10.0 V.

For a 24 V system, the change of components is shown in the component list of Figure 13.5(b). A 24 V supply is required when making the final adjustment to the needle and this can be provided by two 12 V batteries connected in series.

Identifying faults in the circuit

If the expanded-scale voltmeter does not appear to work properly, the causes for this can be poor solder joints, a short circuit across copper tracks, incorrect placement of components, or faulty components. The following procedure of measuring voltages at various points may help to identify the fault (a voltmeter is required with a range of 0–15 V for 12 V systems or 0–30 V for 24 V systems):

1. Connect the expanded-scale voltmeter to a battery supply of 12 or 24 V, as appropriate for the system.

2. Clip the negative lead of the voltmeter to the negative of the supply.

3. Measure the voltage at the following places by touching the positive lead against the part of the circuit that is being tested. (When taking a measurement, take great care not to touch two metal parts with the positive lead at the same time, otherwise damage may be caused by a short circuit.)
   (a) Cathode of ZD_1 which should be at its breakdown voltage.
   (b) Left ends of R_3 and R_4 which should be at about 2.3 V for 12 V systems and 4.6 V for 24 V systems.
   (c) The negative terminal of the meter itself which should be at about 10 V for 12 V systems and 20 V for 24 V systems. This voltage should change as the potentiometer is adjusted.
   (d) Left ends of D_2 and R_1 which should be at the voltage measured in the previous step minus 1.4 V.

Conversion to a test meter

An expanded-scale meter can be converted to a multimeter specifically for testing solar electric systems. The additional components required for this conversion are shown in Figure 13.6(a) and they provide four scales for the following measurements:

1. 10–15 V for:
   (a) voltage of battery;
   (b) voltage at appliances when drawing power.

2. 0–5 V for:
   (a) voltage of individual cells in a battery;
   (b) voltage drop across connections.

3. 0–3 A (or higher for brief measurements) for current from individual solar modules.

4. Continuity for:
   (a) wiring;
   (b) fuses;
   (c) identifying the cathode end of diodes.

Any of the three designs given in this chapter can form the basis of this multimeter. (Design 1 is the least suitable because the needle is adjusted to compensate for the offset voltage not being exactly at 10.0 V. When used as a 0–5 V voltmeter or as an ammeter, the needle may not start at zero.)

Figure 13.6(b) shows one way of labelling the switches on the front of the box. If a three-position switch with centre off is available, it can be used in place of the on–off and change-over switches on the right in the circuit.

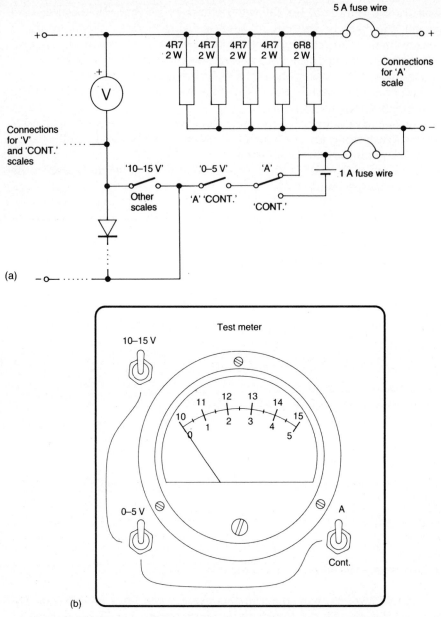

(a)

(b)

Figure 13.6 Modifications to an expanded-scale voltmeter for conversion to a general-purpose test meter.
(a) Circuit diagram of additions.
(b) Labelling of switches on the front of the box.
(c) Connections on one side of the box. This shows how the fusible links and resistors can be mounted on a strip of connector terminals.

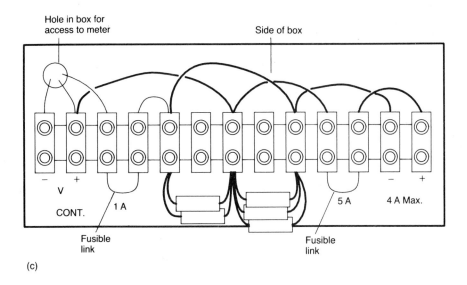

(c)

Voltage scales

The two voltage scales of the multimeter make direct use of the voltmeter. With the first switch up for open, the offset circuit gives the expanded range. For the 0–5 V scale, the first of the three switches is closed to bypass the offset voltage.

Current scale

The current scale works by passing the current being measured through a resistor of 1 Ω and measuring the voltage across this resistor. By Ohm's Law (represented by Formula (12.1)), the choice of 1 Ω means that the 0–5 V scale can be read off directly in amps.

The power rating required for this resistor depends on the maximum current to be measured. For measuring the short circuit current of solar modules, the maximum current is about 3.2 A and this requires a 1R0 resistor of 10 W (calculated from Formula (12.5)). Since this is a high-power rating, it may need to be made up from several resistors and the circuit in Figure 13.6(a) is shown for a combination of five 2 W resistors in parallel. If resistors with the resistances given in the figure are not available, other combinations of resistors can be used, such as ten 10R 1 W resistors in parallel. The total parallel resistance of any combination is calculated using Formula (12.3).

A current higher than 3.2 A can be measured with the 10 W rating but this is only permitted for a few seconds to prevent the resistors becoming too hot. Figure 13.6(c) shows a possible arrangement of mounting five resistors in a strip of connector terminals. The strip is screwed to the outside of the box rather than the inside for effective cooling of the resistors.

The same connections as for voltage could be used for current measurements but it is better to have separate connections, as shown on the right in Figures 13.6(a) and (c). If the negative voltage connection is used for current by mistake, the 1 A fusible link will blow and this protects the switches, wiring and dry cell battery inside the box from damage. If the current connections are used for measuring voltage by mistake, the 5 A fusible link blows to protect the resistors.

When using the current scale, remember that it introduces a voltage drop in the circuit being measured, unlike a proper ammeter. For measuring the current in a load circuit, the appliances may not work as well with a reduction of supply voltage caused by the 1 Ω resistance.

Here is the procedure for testing one solar module out of an array of modules:

1. Disconnect the positive connection to the module.
2. Cover the end of this wire to prevent it shorting against other metal parts.
3. Attach the current connections of the multimeter to the terminals of the module. Record the current measurement together with time of day and weather conditions.

The measurement of current is actually at a load of 1 Ω but this load is low enough for the measurement to be close to the short-circuit current value.

Continuity scale

A dry-cell battery (ordinary torch battery) or nickel–cadmium battery is required with the meter to check for continuity of a circuit.

To select the 'cont.' scale, all the switches are set in the down position and the meter indicates the voltage of the cell showing that it is not flat. A circuit to be tested is connected to the meter terminals. If the circuit being checked is continuous, the needle swings back to the left. If the circuit is not continuous or has a high resistance, the needle stays at the voltage of the battery.

The continuity scale works by comparing the circuit under test to the 1 Ω resistance used for the current scale. When the needle goes more than halfway back to zero, the circuit being checked has a resistance of less than 1 Ω. This system of measurement is like a very low resistance scale on a multimeter, but remember that the needle goes in the opposite direction with zero resistance at the left end.

For checking a diode, the needle moves to 0.7 V when the cathode is connected to the negative terminal. With the cathode connected to the positive terminal, the needle should stay at the voltage of the battery.

14 | Voltage adaptors

Portable appliances are usually powered by dry cells (ordinary torch batteries) which have a voltage of 1.5 V each. These appliances may require a lower voltage than the d.c. operating voltage of a solar electric system. For instance, a radio that normally uses five dry cells operates at 7.5 V (calculated from 5×1.5 V), whereas system voltages are usually 12 or 24 V.

The choice of methods for operating low-voltage appliances in a solar system is summarized in Figure 6.2. This chapter deals with voltage adaptors which reduce the supply voltage at an outlet point in a system so that low-voltage d.c. appliances can be powered at their required voltage.

Voltage adaptors can also be used for charging small lead–acid batteries from the main battery bank in a system. This could be for one 6 V battery or a number of lead–acid cells connected in series. Table 3.2 lists values of charging voltages for maximum and float charging, although reference should be made to the charging conditions specified by the supplier.

When preparing to build a voltage adaptor, the following points should be noted:

☐ The operating voltage required by the appliance or constant charging voltage required by the lead–acid batteries, usually in the range 3–12 V d.c.

☐ The voltage of the solar electric system that needs to be reduced, either 12 or 24 V d.c.

☐ The power or current requirement of the appliance. Low-power appliances which use D-size dry cells draw less than 0.3 A while higher-power appliances can draw over 1 A. For charging lead–acid batteries, check the A h capacity.

☐ The availability of components for building the voltage adaptor. These include diodes, power transistors, voltage-regulating ICs, fixed value resistors, potentiometers, tag strip, and stripboard.

☐ The number of voltage adaptors being made: whether just one for own use or several at once in preparation for future sale.

Table 14.1 *Details of four designs for voltage adaptors.*

Circuit	Main components	Advantages	Disadvantages
Design 1	Diodes	Least number of components Can be easily built on tag strip or a connector strip	Adjusted by adding diodes Voltage output varies with changes in supply Impracticable for use with 24 V supply
Design 2	One transistor and resistors	Output voltage is more stable than for design 1	Requires particular values of resistors Output is fixed unless using a high-power potentiometer
Design 3	Two transistors and potentiometer	Output voltage is easily adjustable Output voltage is stable Easily upgraded for higher output current and 24 V supply	Requires stripboard Uses several components
Design 4	Voltage-regulating IC	Simple to build Output voltage is very stable Internal protection against short circuit of output and over-heating	IC not always available in some countries

☐ The type of connection to the appliance. This can be by a d.c. power-in socket on the case or directly to the contacts in the battery compartment.

Four designs for voltage adaptors are given in this chapter and their main details are summarized in Table 14.1. The choice of which design to build mostly depends on the availability of components. Design 4 has the best features but the least available components in some countries. Refer to Chapter 12 for background details to all the components used in these designs and advice on how to build the circuits.

All the designs described in this chapter are *series regulators*. This means that they are connected in series between the positive of the supply and the positive of the appliance and work by subtracting or 'using up' the excess voltage.

When the voltage they subtract and the current drawn by the appliance are both high, the adaptor itself becomes hot.

For example, a cassette player may require 0.4 A at 9 V d.c. If the system voltage is 24 V, the voltage adaptor must subtract 15 V. At 0.4 A, the adaptor circuit must dissipate 6 W (from 15×0.4). A heat sink may be required to dissipate heat from part of the adaptor.

When using a voltage adaptor to charge small lead–acid batteries, there is a high charging current at the start of charging. The current rating of the voltage adaptor is set by the capacity of the batteries and should be at least 2 C. This means a current equal to two times the battery capacity in A h units. For example, a 1.5 A h battery draws 3 A at the start of charging from a constant voltage supply so the adaptor should be rated for at least 3 A.

Connection to appliance

Portable appliances that use batteries often have a socket on the side for connecting an external source of d.c. power. The socket is marked 'ext. d.c. supply' or words to that effect and an example is shown in Figure 14.1(a). This type of socket should not be confused with sockets for either a.c. mains voltage, marked with '~', or signal connections, such as microphones and headphones. Part 6 in Figure 9.7 has two examples of the plugs used for d.c. power-in sockets.

Next to the socket there should be a picture or some other indication of the polarity of the contacts in the socket (positive and negative parts). An example is shown in Figure 14.1(b) for a power-in plug where the tip of the plug needs to be positive.

Figure 14.1(a) also shows how the wires are folded onto the inside of the plug before soldering. Note that the screwed sleeve of the power-in plug should be slid over the wire first. Do not hold the soldering iron on the connections for too long otherwise the plastic parts of the plug will melt.

When an appliance does not have a power-in socket, the easiest way to connect the wires from a voltage adaptor is directly into the battery compartment. A system for doing this is shown in Figure 14.2.

Design 1: diodes only

When a current flows through a silicon diode, the forward bias or drop in voltage across the diode is about 0.7 V. This voltage stays almost constant over a range of forward currents. The design 1 adaptor simply uses a number of silicon diodes connected in series to reduce the supply voltage in steps of 0.7 V. The number of diodes required for various appliances is summarized in Figure 14.3. Also shown is an example of the circuit for a 9 V appliance that normally uses six batteries.

When building the adaptor, ensure that each diode is connected the correct

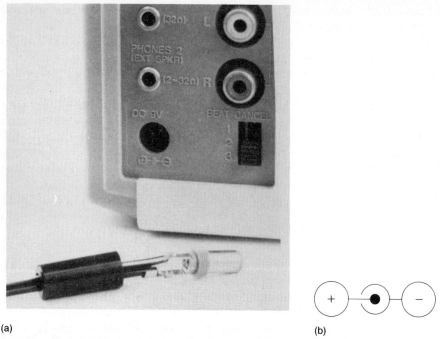

(a)   (b)

Figure 14.1   Example of a d.c. power connection for a low-voltage appliance.
(a)   Close-up view of the socket on a cassette player and the connections in a 2.5 mm power-in plug before they are soldered. (The wire with the white stripe is the positive.)
(b)   Detail of the picture by the socket which shows that the central contact in the socket is the positive polarity.

Figure 14.2   A simple system suggested for making connections directly into the battery compartment of a radio. The negative end on the right is cut away so that the head of the screw is slightly recessed below the end face. This prevents contact to the positive end of the compartment if the rod is put in the wrong way round.

way round otherwise no current will flow to the appliance. (The anode of the first diode should be connected to the positive of the supply. Then the cathode of this diode should be connected to the anode of the next diode, and so on.) One method for mounting the diodes is shown in Figure 14.3(c).

For medium-power appliances, a significant amount of heat is generated in the adaptor. Small diodes of diameter 3 mm and length 5 mm are specified to carry 1 A. When carrying more than about 0.5 A, it is important that air is free to circulate around them freely to prevent them becoming too hot.

Design 1 is suitable for appliances requiring 6–9 V which are run from a 12 V system. It is less suitable for lower-voltage appliances and for running appliances from 24 V systems because of the number of diodes that are needed.

Another disadvantage of this design is that the output voltage is not regulated. The voltage to the appliance increases by the same amount as the supply voltage since the main batteries are charged by the solar array during the day. This increase may damage some low-voltage appliances.

Design 2: one transistor and resistors

For design 2, the chain of diodes of design 1 is replaced by a single high-power transistor. The basic circuit is shown in Figure 14.4(a). It uses a pair of resistors (R_1 and R_2) to set the voltage at the base of the transistor according to the output voltage that is required.

The transistor should have a rating of at least 5 W and be mounted on a heat sink. An LED is included to indicate when the power to the adaptor is on and R_3 is the current-limiting resistor for the LED.

In order to obtain the required output voltage, resistors R_1 and R_2 must be chosen carefully. The table in Figure 14.4(e) gives values of resistors for several output voltages using resistances from the E12 range. If the resistances required are not available, it will be necessary to make them up from two or more resistors connected in series or parallel (see Figure 14.6 as an example).

To improve the stability of the output voltage, resistor R_1 can be replaced by a Zener diode. This is shown in Figures 14.4(c) and (d) with values of breakdown voltage to suit various appliances listed in Figure 14.4(e).

The components can be soldered to a tag strip (see layouts in Figure 14.4) and then mounted inside a box. One example of a finished voltage adaptor is shown in Figure 14.6 where the high-power transistor is directly attached to one side of a metal box. The outside of the box is painted black to help dissipate heat generated by the transistor.

Supply of 24 V and low-power appliances

For a 24 V supply, the resistance of R_2 needs to be increased and appropriate values are listed in Figure 14.4(e). It is advisable to share the heat generated by

Details of appliance		Number of diodes for 12 V supply
Number of batteries	Voltage required (V)	
8	12.0	0
6	9.0	4
5	7.5	6
4	6.0	9
3	4.5	11
2	3.0	13

(a)

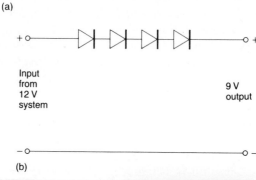

(b)

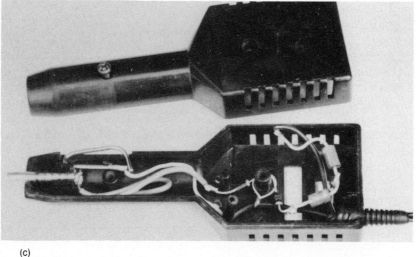

(c)

Figure 14.3 Design 1 voltage adaptor.
(a) Number of diodes required for appliances using different numbers of dry cell batteries.
(b) Example of the circuit for reducing the supply voltage by 2.8 V. This circuit can be used to run a 9 V appliance from a 12 V system.
(c) Four diodes mounted in an old plug that fits into a car's cigarette lighter. The wire on the right leads to the appliance.

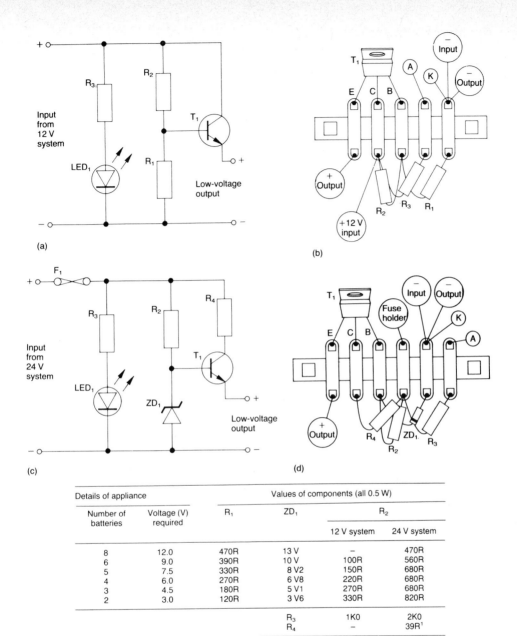

(a)

(b)

(c)

(d)

Details of appliance		Values of components (all 0.5 W)			
Number of batteries	Voltage (V) required	R_1	ZD_1	R_2	
				12 V system	24 V system
8	12.0	470R	13 V	–	470R
6	9.0	390R	10 V	100R	560R
5	7.5	330R	8 V2	150R	680R
4	6.0	270R	6 V8	220R	680R
3	4.5	180R	5 V1	270R	680R
2	3.0	120R	3 V6	330R	820R
			R_3	1K0	2K0
			R_4	–	39R[1]

[1]Power rating 4 W minimum.

(e)

Figure 14.4 Design 2 voltage adaptors for low-power appliances (current requirement less than 0.3 A).
(a) Basic circuit. **(b)** Layout on a tag strip for use in a 12 V system.
(c) and (d) Optional components: fuse (F_1) to protect adaptor; Zener diode (ZD_1) to improve stability of output voltage; resistor (R_4) to share heat dissipation with the transistor when reducing the voltage from a 24 V supply.
(e) List of component specifications for appliances using different numbers of dry-cell batteries.

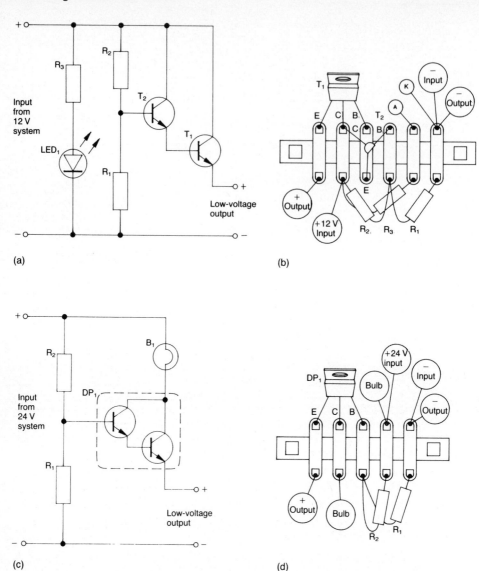

Figure 14.5 Design 2 voltage adaptors for medium- and high-power appliances.
(a) Basic circuit. **(b)** Layout on a tag strip for use in a 12 V system.
(c) and (d) Transistors in (a) replaced by a Darlington pair in one case. A bulb is used to share heat dissipation with the transistor when reducing the voltage from a 24 V supply. (An example of a completed circuit is shown in Figure 14.6.)
(e) List of component specifications for appliances using different numbers of dry-cell batteries.

Details of appliance		Values of components (all 0.5 W)			
Number of batteries	Voltage (V) required	R_1	ZD_1	R_2	
				12 V system	24 V system
8	12.0	560R	13 V	–	390R
6	9.0	390R	10 V	68R	560R
5	7.5	330R	9 V1	120R	560R
4	6.0	270R	7 V5	180R	680R
3	4.5	220R	5 V6	270R	680R
2	3.0	180R	4 V3	330R	820R
			R_3	1KO	2KO
			Bulb	–	12 V[1]

[1] Power rating should be the same or slightly higher than rating of appliance

(e)

the voltage adaptor between the power transistor and another resistor. This is the purpose of R_4 in Figure 14.4(c) and (d). For low-power appliances with a maximum current of 0.3 A, R_4 should be a 39R resistor rated at 4 W or more.

High-power appliances

For high-power appliances that draw more than 0.3 A, an extra transistor is needed to form a Darlington pair with the power transistor (see Figures 14.5(a) and (b)). If a Darlington pair is available as one component, the circuit is simplified to the version in Figure 14.5(c) and (d).

When running a high-power appliance from a 24 V supply, it is preferable to reduce part of the voltage using a bulb rather than a resistor since bulbs can dissipate heat very effectively. Compare Figures 14.4(c) and 14.5(c) which show exchange of R_4 by B_1. The completed adaptor in Figure 14.6 shows how the bulb can be mounted in the lid of a box.

Adjustable version using a potentiometer

One disadvantage of design 2 is that particular values of resistors are required. One solution is to replace R_1 and R_2 in Figures 14.4 and 14.5 by a medium-power potentiometer, as shown in Figure 14.7. Note that the potentiometer must be rated at 0.5 W or more which excludes the miniature sizes shown in Figure 12.4.

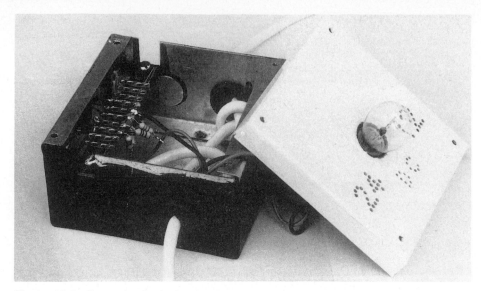

Figure 14.6   Example of a design 2 voltage adaptor based on the circuit in Figure 14.5(c) and using resistor values from Figure 14.5(e). This adaptor supplies 12 V d.c. from a 24 V system for a television rated at 18 W. Component details: bulb is rated at 21 W 12 V; Darlington pair transistor; required resistances made up from pairs of resistors connected in series (560R for R_1 made up from 510R and 51R; 390R for R_2 made up from 330R and 56R). Note that the cables are knotted inside the box to prevent their connections to the tag strip from being pulled on.

Design 3: two transistors and potentiometer

This design is slightly more complicated than design 2 and needs to be built on stripboard instead of tag strip. It is mainly intended for electricians who are making several voltage adaptors to sell. There are no critical values of resistors. Also the basic circuit is easily upgraded for high output current and a 24 V system by adding rather than changing components on the stripboard. The low-voltage output is adjustable by a potentiometer and is more stable than for design 2.

The basic circuits for 12 and 24 V supplies are shown in Figure 14.8 and an example of a completed circuit is shown in Figure 14.9.

Medium- and high-power appliances

For medium- and high-power appliances that draw more than 0.3 A, a Darlington pair of transistors is needed. If a high-power Darlington pair is

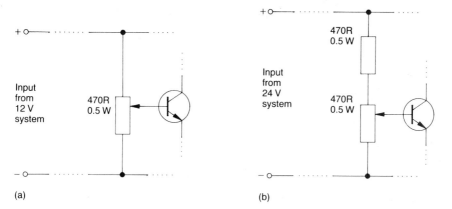

Figure 14.7   Use of a potentiometer with design 2 voltage adaptors of Figures 14.4 and 14.5 to make the output voltage adjustable.
(a) R_1 and R_2 replaced by a potentiometer for a 12 V system.
(b) R_1 and R_2 replaced by a potentiometer and a resistor for a 24 V system.

available as one component, it is simply used instead of T_1 in the circuits of Figure 14.8. Otherwise the alternative is to add a low-power transistor on the stripboard together with an extra break and link (see Figure 14.10).

The Darlington pair enables a wider range of resistances of potentiometer to be used so the circuits in Figure 14.10 are also suitable for low-power appliances.

For a high-power appliance and 24 V supply, a bulb is put in series with the power transistor to help dissipate heat (see Figure 14.10(c) and (d)). A 12 V bulb should be used with a power rating at the same or slightly higher than the power of the appliance.

Building the circuit

The full size of the stripboards shown in Figures 14.8 and 14.10 is fourteen holes along the copper tracks by eleven holes across the tracks. A shorter length can be used if the potentiometer can be mounted vertically. However, a large piece is better because it has more space at the edges for screws to mount the board securely in a box.

The procedure of building the circuit is as follows:

1. On a piece of stripboard, choose the place for the circuit making sure that the copper tracks run the correct way. It is easier to handle a large piece of stripboard when building the circuit so cutting to size should be left until the end.

2. Make the links L_1–L_6 which go across the component side and are only soldered at their ends. Count along the holes in each row very carefully to ensure that the links are put in exactly the right places.

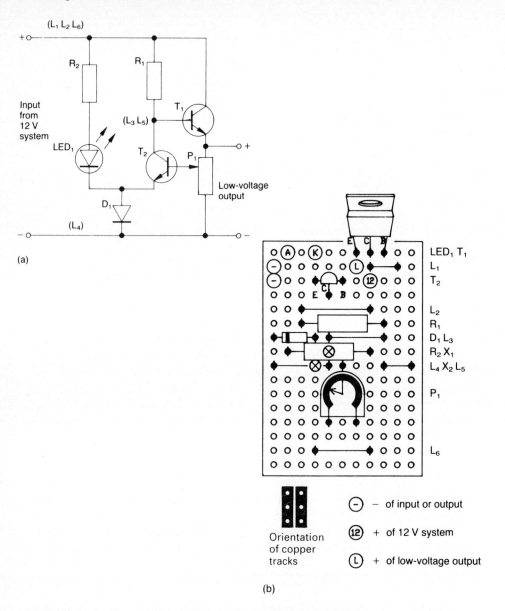

(a)

(b)

Figure 14.8 Design 3 voltage adaptors for low-power appliances.
(a) and (b) Basic circuit for a 12 V system. Output voltage adjustable over the range
3–9 V. (Links L_1 and L_5 are not needed in this circuit but are included in case the
modifications for (b) and Figure 14.10 are done.)
(c) and (d) Additional components (R_3 and R_4) and breaks (X_3, X_4, and X_5) for use with
a 24 V system.
(e) List of component specifications.

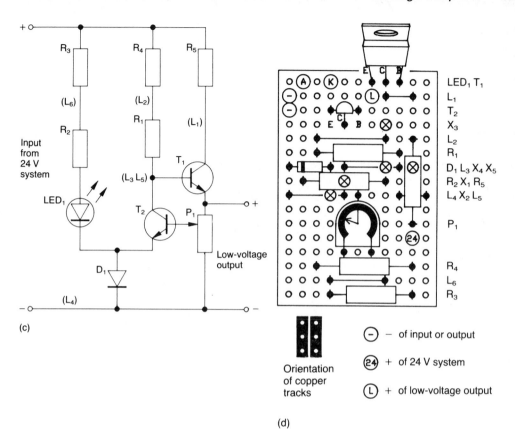

(c)

(d)

Orientation
of copper
tracks

$\ominus$ – of input or output

$\textcircled{24}$ + of 24 V system

$\textcircled{L}$ + of low-voltage output

Component	Position	Minimum specification	
Stripboard		2.5 mm (0.1 in) hole separation, overall dimensions: 14 holes along tracks 38 mm (1.5 in) by 11 holes across tracks 31 mm (1.2 in)	
Transistors	T_1	npn, high-power, silicon	
	T_2	npn, low-power, silicon	
Diode	D_1	Silicon, low current	
Resistors	R_1	270R–330R 0.5 W	
	R_2	1K0 0.25 W	
		12 V system:	24 V system:
	R_3	–	2K0 0.5 W
	R_4	–	1K5 0.25 W
	R_5	–	3R9 4 W
Potentiometer	P_1	470R 0.5 W–1K0 0.25 W	

(e)

Figure 14.9   Example of a design 3 voltage adaptor based on the circuit in Figure 14.8(a).

3. Solder in all the components after taking note of the following points:
    (a) Transistors (T_1, T_2) – Check the order of the C, B, E wires. For the high-power transistor, push just enough of the wires through the holes in the board for soldering so that the transistor stands high.
    (b) Diode (D_1) – check the cathode end using a meter.
    (c) LED (LED_1) – identify the cathode end by the flat.
    (d) Resistors (R_1, R_2) – check the resistance using a meter.
    (e) Potentiometer (P_1) – make sure that the leg for the slider contact goes to the middle track.

4. Solder on multi-stranded wires for the external connections.

5. Cut short any excess length of wires on the solder side of the board.

6. Make the breaks (X_1 to X_6, depending on the particular circuit) in the copper tracks.

7. Cut off excess area of the board.

8. Using a nut and screw, attach the power transistor to the inside of a metal box. Exposed metal on a power transistor is normally connected to the collector wire. The heat sink should be insulated from the metal of the transistor by a mica washer and plastic bush.

9. Put knots in the wires to the supply and the appliance before threading them through the holes in the metal box (see Figure 14.6).

10. Attach a suitable plug to the end of the appliance wire making sure that the positive and negative wires are connected the correct way for the appliance (see Figure 14.1).

Adjusting the low-voltage output

1 Connect a voltmeter to the appliance wires.

2. Connect the supply wires to a 12 or 24 V d.c. supply as appropriate. The voltmeter should now show a voltage at the output.

3. Adjust the potentiometer slider to get the required voltage.

4. Connect the appliance wires to an appliance requiring this voltage.

5. Connect the voltmeter to the appliance wires again and check that the required voltage is maintained.

Identifying faults in the circuit

If the voltage adaptor does not appear to work properly, it can be because of poor solder joints, a short circuit across copper tracks, incorrect placement of components, or faulty components. The following procedure of measuring voltages at various points may help to locate the fault (a voltmeter is required with a range of either 0–15 V for 12 V systems or 0–30 V for 24 V systems):

1. Connect the voltage adaptor to a battery supply of 12 or 24 V, as appropriate for the system.

2. Clip the negative lead of the voltmeter to the negative of the supply.

3. Measure the voltage at the following places by touching the positive lead against the part of the circuit that is being tested. (When taking a measurement, take great care not to touch two metal parts with the positive lead at the same time, otherwise damage may be caused by a short circuit.)
   (a) Anode of D_1 (right end) which should be at 0.7 V.
   (b) Base of T_2 (right end) which should be at 1.4 V.
   (c) L_3 which should be at the output voltage plus either 0.7 V for circuits from Figure 14.8 or 1.4 V for circuits from Figure 14.10.
   (d) L_2 which should be at about 12 V.

Design 4: voltage-regulating IC

The circuit in voltage-regulating ICs works in a similar way to design 3 but using an IC has many advantages: fewer connections to make, stable output voltage, and internal protection against abuse.

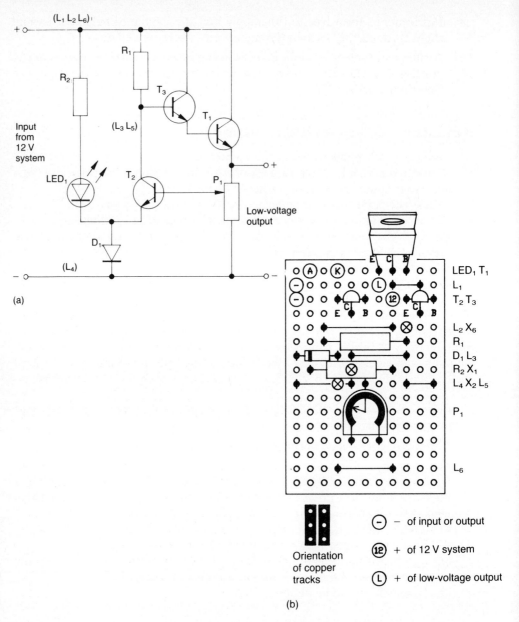

(a)

(b)

Orientation
of copper
tracks

$\ominus$ − of input or output

⑫ + of 12 V system

Ⓛ + of low-voltage output

Figure 14.10   Design 3 voltage adaptors for medium- and high-power appliances. Two separate transistors are used to form a Darlington pair.

(a) and (b)   Basic circuit for a 12 V supply. Output voltage adjustable over the range 3–9 V.

(c) and (d)   Additional components (R_3 and B_1) for use with a 24 V supply.

(e)   List of component specifications.

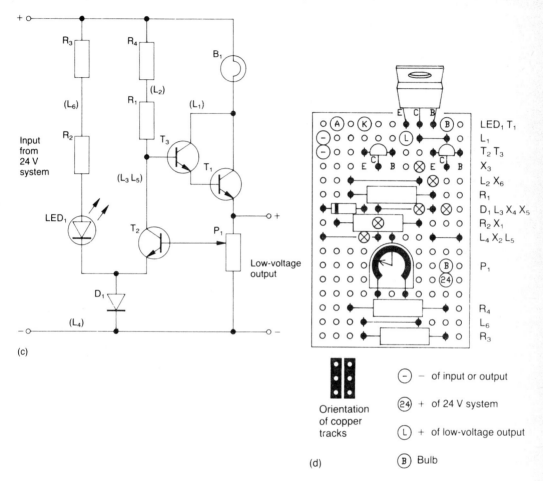

(c)

(d)

Orientation
of copper
tracks

$(-)$ — of input or output

(24) + of 24 V system

(L) + of low-voltage output

(B) Bulb

Component	Position	Minimum specification	
Stripboard		2.5 mm (0.1 in) hole separation, overall dimensions: 14 holes along tracks 38 mm (1.5 in) by 11 holes across tracks 31 mm (1.2 in)	
Transistors	T_1	npn, high-power, silicon	
	T_2, T_3	npn, low-power, silicon	
Diode	D_1	Silicon, low current	
Resistors	R_1	1K8–10K 0.25 W	
	R_2	1K0 0.25 W	
		12 V system:	24 V system:
	R_3	1K0 0.25 W	2K0 0.5 W
	R_4	–	1K5 0.25 W
Bulb	B_1	–	12 V[1]
Potentiometer	P_1	1K–10K 0.25 W	

[1]Power rating should be the same or slightly higher than the rating of appliance.

(e)

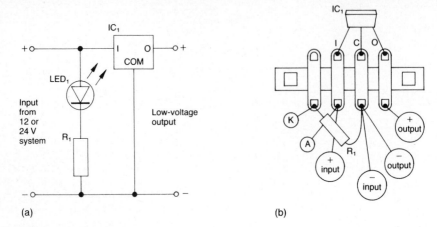

(a)   (b)

Figure 14.11   Design 4 voltage adaptor using a voltage-regulating IC with a fixed output voltage.
(a)   Circuit diagram. R_1 is 1K0 for a 12 V system and 2K0 for a 24 V system.
(b)   Layout on a tag strip.

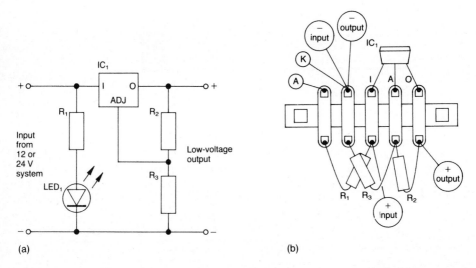

(a)   (b)

Figure 14.12   Design 4 voltage adaptor using a voltage-regulating IC with either an adjustable output voltage or a fixed 5 V output.
(a)   Circuit with fixed resistors. R_1 is 1K0 for a 12 V system and 2K0 for a 24 V system. Values of R_2 and R_3 are given in (c).
(b)   Layout on tag strip for circuit with fixed resistors.
(c)   List of values for R_2 and R_3 according to voltage required and the reference voltage of the regulator.
(d)   Circuit with a potentiometer.

Details of appliance		Value of R_3 (0.25 W)	
Number of batteries	Voltage required (V)	For V_{ref} of 1.25 V and R_2 of 1K2 0.25 W	For V_{ref} of 5 V and R_2 of 4K7 0.25 W
8	12.0	10K	6K8
6	9.0	8K2	3K9
5	7.5	6K8	2K2
4	6.0	4K7	1K0
3	4.5	3K3	–
2	3.0	1K8	–

(c)

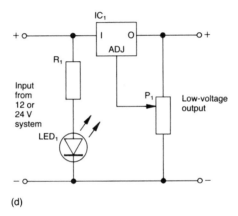

(d)

If too much current is drawn or the output is short circuited, the regulator automatically stops supplying the required voltage and limits the output current to a small value. This is sometimes called *fold-back overload* and it prevents the IC from getting damaged. Regulating ICs switch themselves off if they get too hot and this feature is called *thermal overload protection* or *thermal overload shut down*.

For running a 12 V appliance in a 24 V system, the type of voltage-regulating IC with a fixed voltage output is the simplest to use (see Figure 14.11). For other voltage outputs, the adjustable type of regulating IC is needed and the details are summarized in Figure 14.12 for resistor values. With both circuits, an LED is included to indicate when the power is on.

To make the output voltage adjustable, a potentiometer can be used instead of resistors, as shown in Figure 12.13.

The wire connections on regulators are not standard. Make sure that you find out what they are at the time of buying the regulator. Usually the case is connected to one of the wires so it is best to insulate it from the metal heat sink.

Supply of 24 V

The maximum acceptable voltage at the input of regulating ICs is usually 26 V or higher. This means that the circuits in Figures 14.11 and 14.12 can be used at both supply voltages of 12 and 24 V without any change, except for the LED resistor (R_1). However, more heat is generated by the regulator when connected to a 24 V supply.

If the heat sink attached to the regulator is not large enough, the regulator may overheat and switch itself off automatically. This will not cause any damage but will be inconvenient. One solution is to use a large area of heat sink and ensure that the regulator is firmly attached to it. Alternatively, a high-power resistor or bulb can be put in series with the 'I' connection of the IC to share the power dissipation (specifications as for R_4 in Figure 14.4 or B_1 in Figure 14.5).

15 Charge regulators for sealed nickel–cadmium cells

The recommended value of charging current for a sealed nickel–cadmium cell is marked on the side of the cell case. It is important to maintain this current during charging. Using a lower current results in inefficient charging, while using a higher current results in damage to the cells during over-charging.

The standard charging current is 'C/10', sometimes also written as 'C_{10}'. This means the capacity of the cell in units of A h divided by ten hours. With this charging current, a full charge takes about fourteen hours. Although it is quite safe to over-charge at the C/10 current, manufacturers usually recommend that charging is stopped after sixteen hours. More expensive cells are also available for charging at the higher rate of C/3. These reach full charge from flat in about four hours.

Most charging units available for nickel–cadmium cells are mains powered so cannot be used in solar electric systems operating at 12 or 24 V d.c. In order to charge these cells in a solar system, four methods of regulating a current from a d.c. supply are given in this chapter. Their main details are summarized in Table 15.1.

The first method involves matching a solar module to the requirements of the nickel–cadmium cells so that a regulator is not required. The other three methods use regulating circuits. Design 1 is a simple circuit using only resistors. Design 2 uses transistors and is more versatile. Design 3 uses a voltage-regulating IC which is internally protected against misuse.

In the lists of components for the circuits, three values of charging currents are given. These correspond to an AA-size cell of capacity 0.5 A h and the two common capacities of D-size cells of 1.2 and 4 A h. Examples of these cells are shown in Figures 3.2 and 3.9.

Note that these chargers should only be used with sealed nickel–cadmium cells. Never attempt to charge ordinary torch batteries, even though they may look similar (see warnings in Chapter 3 about trying to charge primary cells).

Table 15.1 *Details of four methods for regulating the charging current to sealed nickel–cadmium cells.*

Circuit	Main components	Advantages	Disadvantages
Self-regulating	Solar module	Simple method with no extra components	Module and nickel–cadmium cells must be matched Inefficient charging at low currents
Design 1	Resistor	Simple design with no special components Enables charging from the main battery of a system	Requires a fixed number of cells Cannot charge more than six cells from a 12 V supply Regulated current varies with supply voltage
Design 2	Transistors	Constant current for any number of cells No limit on current output of solar module Enables parallel groups of cells to be connected to the same appliance circuit	Requires stripboard and special components
Design 3	Voltage-regulating IC	Simple to build Charging current is very stable Internal protection against short circuit of output and over heating	IC not always available in some countries Cannot be used for a 12 V group of cells in a 12 V system

Cell holder

Some sort of container is needed to hold the nickel–cadmium cells and maintain good electrical contact both between each other and the external connections to the charge regulator.

The container part of a mains powered charger could be used with the mains powered circuitry replaced by one of the designs given in this chapter. The connections to the cells should be rewired to put all the cells in series.

Alternatively, a wooden box can be constructed to hold the cells. Springs are used in the battery compartment of a cassette player to make good contact to the ends of the cells. Home-made springs formed by coiling a piece of ordinary wire never last long. When making a box, it is better to use a proper spring, such as from an old car engine. Auto-spares shops usually keep a box of assorted sizes of springs at low prices. Choose a compression type of spring that is parallel sided with a diameter of 10 – 20 mm (⅜–¾ in).

If a charging regulator is being used, such as design 1 or 2, a section can be added at the end of the box to hold the regulator circuit. An example of a box for four cells and a design 1 charging regulator is shown in Figure 15.3(b).

It is normal for nickel–cadmium cells to warm up towards the end of charging. To ensure that they do not become too hot, ventilation holes should be made in the sides and lid of a cell box so that air can flow over the cells freely and keep them cool.

Self-regulating solar module

This method involves charging nickel–cadmium cells directly from a solar module (see Figure 15.1). By choosing the correct size of module to suit the nickel–cadmium cells, a regulator is not needed and the module is said to be *self-regulating*.

The module is chosen so that the maximum current in full sunshine equals the recommended charging current for the cells. The relevant specifications of the module to use are the short circuit current (I_{SC}) or current at load (I_{AL}) under STC.

The size of a solar module that is required can also be calculated from the area of the cells. Solar cells made of single-crystal silicon require about 30 cm^2 of

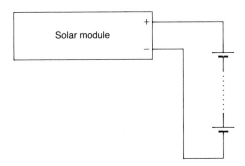

Figure 15.1 Charging a battery of sealed nickel–cadmium cells directly from a solar module. The maximum current output of the module must be matched to the maximum charging current of the cells.

cell area for each amp of current generated under full sun. This figure is used in Formula (15.1):

$$
\boxed{\begin{array}{c}\text{Recommended}\\\text{charging current}\\\text{for each}\\\text{nickel–cadmium}\\\text{cell (A)}\end{array}} \times \boxed{\begin{array}{c}30\\(\text{cm}^2/\text{A})\end{array}} = \boxed{\begin{array}{c}\text{Area of individual}\\\text{single-crystal}\\\text{silicon cells in a}\\\text{solar module}\\(\text{cm}^2)\end{array}} \qquad \textbf{(15.1)}
$$

For the number of cells in a solar module, at least three and a half solar cells are needed for each nickel–cadmium cell that is being charged in series. As an example, a battery of ten nickel–cadmium cells requires a module with thirty-five or more cells (from 3.5×10).

Thin-film silicon modules are also suitable. Use a value of eighty-five for the cm^2/A box in Formula (15.1). For each nickel–cadmium cell in the series group being charged, two and a half thin-film cells or 2 V of V_{OC} are required.

The main disadvantage with this method of charge regulation is having to find a module with the correct size of solar cells to suit the charging current of the nickel–cadmium cells. This is perhaps easier for thin-film modules which are available in a wide range of current capacities.

Note that a module with larger-sized solar cells cannot be used to charge two or more batteries of nickel–cadmium cells that are connected in parallel. This is because the charging current does not divide equally between the parallel lines of cells. Charging in parallel should only be done using a separate regulator for each group of cells (see Figure 15.7(d)).

Another disadvantage of a self-regulating module is to do with the low charging efficiency of sealed nickel–cadmium cells at low charging currents. Below a charging current of about C/40 (a quarter of the standard charging current), the charging efficiency is 0 per cent which means that none of the current is stored and the cells do not charge up.

Design 1: series resistor

In a solar system with 12 V lead–acid or vented nickel–cadmium batteries, the system voltage remains fairly constant. This allows a resistor to regulate the charging current for a fixed number of nickel–cadmium cells connected in series. The circuit for this is shown in Figure 15.2(a).

Series regulation is provided by resistor R_2. The resistance and power rating of R_2 depend on the system voltage, number of cells being charged at the same time, and the charging current required. Details for a number of configurations are summarized by two tables in Figure 15.2(c) and (d). In some configurations,

R_2 is required to dissipate a high power and it may need to be made up from two or more resistors connected in series or in parallel (see resistor section in Chapter 12 and Figure 12.3).

An LED with its own current-limiting resistor (R_1) is included to show when a charging current is flowing. Diode D_1 prevents damage to the cells if the charging unit is connected to the supply unit with the wrong polarity. It also acts as a blocking diode, preventing loss of charge through a solar module at night.

A layout for mounting on a tag strip is shown in Figure 15.2(b). Resistors dissipating a high power should be well spaced so that air can flow over them freely. An example of a complete charger for four nickel–cadmium cells is shown in Figure 15.3.

This design is not suitable for charging more than six cells at once in a 12 V system and design 2 or 3 should be used instead. Design 1 is also not very suitable when the supply voltage varies a lot. Charging is best done overnight to avoid high system voltages which can reach 15 V or more during the day in a 12 V system when the solar modules are in full sunshine.

Dummy cells for charger

The charge regulator is made for a fixed number of nickel–cadmium cells in series. However, when only a few cells need charging, the full number of cells required by the charger may not be available. A simple solution to this problem is to substitute a pair of diodes (connected in series) for each nickel–cadmium cell that is missing. The current rating of the diodes should be higher than the constant charging current for the nickel–cadmium cells. The diodes are mounted on a piece of wood to form a 'dummy cell' which takes up the same space as a real cell in the holder (see Figure 15.4).

Design 2: series transistor

The series resistor of design 1 is replaced by a power transistor and the regulated charging current is set by a low-power transistor and two resistors (see Figure 15.5(a)).

With this design, the regulated current remains constant over a wide range of supply voltages. This has the advantage that different numbers of cells can be charged together in series by the same regulator. In addition, the same charging regulator can be supplied from a 12 V system, a 24 V system, or connected directly to a solar module with no upper limit on the size of individual solar cells.

Two points must be noted when using this design:

1. A minimum voltage drop of 1.8 V is required across the circuit for proper regulation of current.
2. The power rating of the transistor should be more than the maximum power dissipation that is expected.

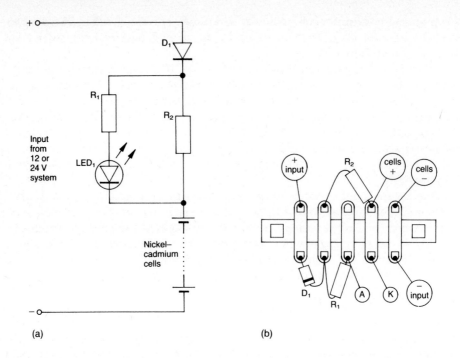

(a)

(b)

Number of cells	R_1 (0.25 W)	R_2 for three regulated currents		
		0.05 A (for 0.5 A h cells)	0.12 A (for 1.2 A h cells)	0.4 A (for 4 A h cells)
1	820R	220R 1 W	100R 2 W	33R 5 W
2	820R	220R 1 W	100R 2 W	22R 5 W
3	820R	150R 0.5 W	68R 2 W	22R 4 W
4	390R	150R 0.5 W	68R 1 W	22R 3 W
5	390R	100R 0.25 W	47R 1 W	15R 3 W
6	390R	68R 0.25 W	39R 1 W	15R 2 W

(c)

Figure 15.2   Design 1 charging regulator for sealed nickel–cadmium cells.
(a)   Circuit diagram.
(b)   Layout on tag strip.
(c)   List of component specifications for 12 V systems and a choice of three charging currents.

Number of cells	R_1 (0.25 W)	R_2 for three regulated currents		
		0.05 A (for 0.5 A h cells)	0.12 A (for 1.2 A h cells)	0.4 A (for 4 A h cells)
5	1K5	470R 2 W	150R 3 W	47R 8 W
6	1K5	330R 1 W	150R 3 W	47R 7 W
7	1K5	330R 1 W	150R 2 W	47R 7 W
8	1K5	330R 1 W	150R 2 W	33R 7 W
9	1K5	330R 1 W	100R 2 W	33R 6 W
10	1K	220R 1 W	100R 2 W	33R 6 W
11	820R	220R 1 W	100R 2 W	22R 4 W
12	680R	220R 1 W	68R 1 W	22R 4 W

(d)

Figure 15.2 (continued)
(d) List of component specifications for 24 V systems and a choice of three charging currents.

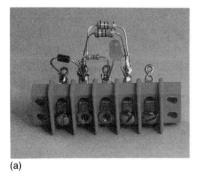

(a)

(b)

Figure 15.3 Example of a design 1 charging regulator for charging four nickel–cadmium cells at 0.12 A from a 12 V system. The table in Figure 15.2(c) specifies 68R 1 W for R_2 so two 100R 0.5 W resistors are connected in parallel to achieve this.
(a) Close-up of circuit.
(b) Complete charger in a wooden box. (Source: Simon Maclaurin)

Figure 15.4 Dummy cells which substitute for D-size nickel-cadmium cells in a charger.

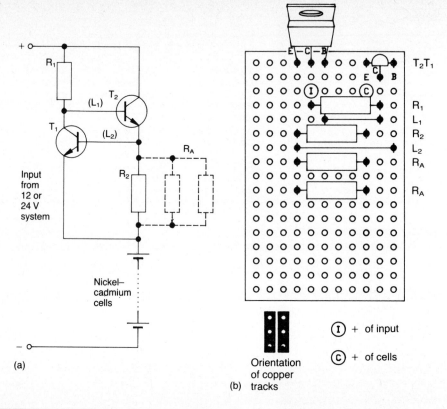

(a)

(b) Orientation of copper tracks

(I) + of input

(C) + of cells

Component	Position	Specifications		
Stripboard[1]		2.5 mm (0.1 in) hole separation, overall dimensions: 17 holes along tracks (46 mm, 1.8 in) by 11 holes across tracks (31 mm, 1.2 in)		
Transistors	T_1	npn, low-power, silicon		
	T_2	npn, high-power, silicon		
		Regulated currents		
		0.05 A (for 0.5 A h cells)	0.12 A (for 1.2 A h cells)	0.4 A (for 4 A h cells)
Resistors	R_1	220R 0.25 W	100R 0.25 W	33R 0.25 W
	R_2	15R 0.25 W	6R8 0.25 W	2R2 0.5 W
	R_A {	33R 0.25 W	15R 0.25 W	4R7 0.25 W
		68R 0.25 W	33R 0.25 W	10R 0.25 W

[1]Size allows for the optional components shown in Figure 15.7.

(c)

Figure 15.5 Basic circuit for design 2 charging regulator for sealed nickel–cadmium cells.

(a) Circuit diagram.

(b) Layout on stripboard. R_2 is used by itself first. After measuring the regulated current (see Figure 15.6), one or two adjustment resistors (R_A) may be needed.

(c) List of component specifications for a choice of three charging currents.

The voltage drop across the regulator is calculated using the following formula:

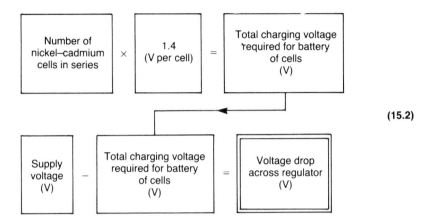

(15.2)

When checking the minimum voltage available across the regulator, the lowest value of supply voltage should be used. For a 12 V system, this may be 11.0 V taking into account a voltage drop from the main battery to the power outlet point. If the answer is less than 1.8, the number of cells must be reduced and the voltage drop recalculated.

To check the maximum power dissipation, the highest value of supply voltage should be used in Formula (15.2). This voltage drop is then used in the following formula:

$$\boxed{\begin{array}{c}\text{Voltage drop}\\\text{across regulator}\\\text{(V)}\end{array}} \times \boxed{\begin{array}{c}\text{Charging}\\\text{current}\\\text{(A)}\end{array}} = \boxed{\boxed{\begin{array}{c}\text{Power dissipated}\\\text{by regulator}\\\text{(W)}\end{array}}} \qquad \textbf{(15.3)}$$

A power transistor must be chosen that has a power rating higher than this answer. If the power dissipation is more than 2 W, the power transistor needs to be mounted on a heat sink.

Example 15.1

A regulator is required to charge six 4 A h sealed nickel–cadmium cells in a 12 V system which has lead–acid batteries as the main means of storage. The charging current is 0.4 A and the supply voltage varies from 11.0 to 15.0 V.

Check the voltage and power conditions for operation of the regulator.
For the minimum voltage drop across the regulator, 11.0 V is used in
Formula (15.2):

$$6 \times 1.4 = 8.4 \text{ V}$$
$$11.0 - 8.4 \text{ V} = 2.6 \text{ V}$$

This is more than 1.8 V so this number of cells can be charged at any time from the
12 V lead–acid batteries. For maximum power dissipation by the regulator, 15.0 V
is used in Formula (15.2):

$$6 \times 1.4 = 8.4 \text{ V}$$
$$15.0 - 8.4 = 6.6 \text{ V}$$

Next, this answer is used together with the charging current of 0.4 A in
Formula (15.3):

$$6.6 \times 0.4 = 2.6 \text{ W}$$

The power rating of transistor T_2 must be at least 3 W, and T_2 should be
mounted on a heat sink since the power dissipation is more than 2 W.

Building the circuit

The minimum size of the stripboard that can be used for the layout shown in
Figure 15.5(b) is ten holes along the copper tracks by eight holes across the
tracks. If the optional features shown in Figure 15.7 are going to be added, the
minimum size increases to seventeen holes along the tracks by eleven holes
across the tracks. However, an even larger piece is better because it has more
space at the edges for screws to mount the board securely in a box.

The procedure for building the circuit is as follows:

1. On a piece of stripboard, choose the place for the circuit, making sure that
   the copper tracks run the correct way. It is easier to handle a large piece of
   stripboard when building the circuit, so cutting to size should be left until the
   end.

2. Make the links L_1 and L_2 which go across the component side and are only
   soldered at their ends. Count along the holes in each row very carefully to
   ensure that the links are put in exactly the right places.

3. Solder in all the components after taking note of the following points.
   (a) Transistors (T_1, T_2) – check the order of the C, B, E wires. For the
       high-power transistor, push just enough of the wires through the holes
       in the board for soldering so that the transistor stands high.
   (b) Resistors (R_1, R_2) – check the resistance using a meter. The adjustment
       resistors (R_A) are added later if required (see next section).

4. Solder on two multi-stranded wires for the external connections.
5. Cut short any excess length of wires on the solder side of the board.

If the power transistor is required to dissipate more than 2 W, use a nut and screw to attach it to a metal plate which acts as a heat sink. Exposed metal on a power transistor is normally connected to the collector wire. The heat sink should be insulated from the metal of the transistor by a mica washer and plastic bush.

Adjusting the regulated current

Although a value for resistor R_2 is given for each charging current, the actual value of the regulated current will be determined by the characteristics of the particular transistor used for T_1.

After building the circuit, the regulated current needs to be measured. If it is necessary to increase the current, this is done by adding resistors in parallel to R_2. The adjustment resistors are marked R_A in the table of Figure 15.5 and they can be added individually or together as a pair to give three different currents.

A 0–0.5 A ammeter is required for measuring the current. If one is not available, the combination of a 0–5 V voltmeter and a 10R 2 W resistor can be used instead, as shown in Figure 15.6(b) and (c). By using a 10 Ω load, 1 V on the voltmeter scale corresponds to 0.1 A (from Ohm's Law).

The procedure for measuring current is as follows:

1. Connect the regulator to a 12 or 24 V supply (as appropriate), a meter system for measuring current, and a few nickel–cadmium cells. (The circuit in Figure 15.6(b) is for a 12 V supply and the combination of a voltmeter with four resistors is for measuring the regulated current.)
2. Measure the regulated current. If the current is correct, no further adjustment is required. However, with resistor R_2 alone, the regulated current is likely to be less than the value required, so proceed to the next step.
3. Taking one of the two R_A resistors, touch its wires against the ends of R_2 while the circuit is still connected to the supply. This should increase the current. Measure the currents for the R_A resistors connected separately and as a pair. Find the arrangement that gives the closest value to the required charging current.
4. Disconnect the regulator from the supply and meter system.
5. If step 3 shows that one or both of the R_A resistors are required, solder them in place now.
6. Repeat steps 1 and 2 to check that the regulated current is now correct.

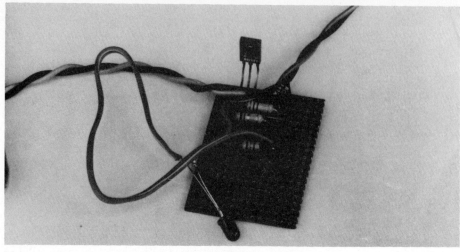

(a)

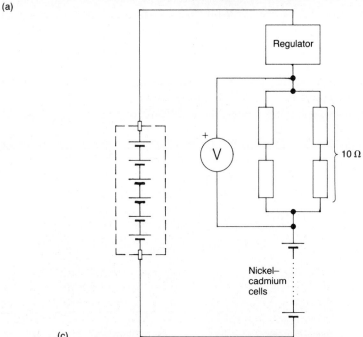

(c)

Figure 15.6 Example of a design 2 charging regulator for sealed nickel–cadmium cells. One R_A resistor is used with R_2.

(a) Close-up of circuit.

(b) Setting the regulated current to 0.12 A with one R_A resistor. The 0–5 V voltmeter works as a 0–0.5 A ammeter by measuring the voltage across a load of 10 Ω. In this example, the load is made up from four 10R 0.5 W resistors connected in series/parallel to achieve a 2 W rating (see Figure 12.3(c)).

(c) Circuit diagram for (b).

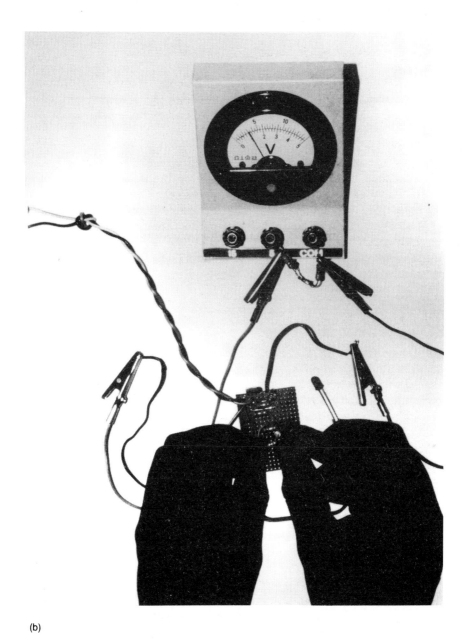

(b)

Figure 15.6 (continued)

LED indicator and parallel connection

An LED is useful for indicating that the cells are being charged and a way of including one is shown in Figure 15.7. The LED is switched on by resistor R_3 and transistor T_3 when current is flowing through the regulator.

A battery of ten cells in series produces about 12 V. This can be permanently connected to both the solar module supply and some appliances. However, the solar module should produce at least 16 V at the charging regulator for proper operation. For modules with single-crystal cells, a module of thirty-six cells is required (see Table 2.1).

Diodes D_1 and D_2 are required when the regulator and battery of cells are permanently connected both to the solar module supply and the appliance circuits. D_1 allows current to the appliances from the solar modules when the appliances are switched on during charging of the cells. The circuit acts as both a current regulator for charging through R_1 and a voltage regulator through D_1. If the appliances use a high current, T_2 must be rated for both charging and appliance currents (check using Formula (15.3)).

When permanently connected to the supply and appliances, the nickel–cadmium cells are on float charge. However, they should not be continually over-charged. To avoid this, regularly discharge the cells completely, perhaps every week.

These diodes are also required when two or more batteries of cells with their own regulator are permanently connected in parallel for charging and supplying appliances (see Figure 15.7(d)). Parallel connection of series groups of cells is one way to increase the total A h storage capacity.

Although nickel–cadmium cells can be deep cycled with no problems, care should be taken with a group of cells connected in series. Differences in the actual capacity of each cell will mean that one of them will reach complete discharge before the rest. Continued use of the battery results in the discharged cell having its polarity reversed by the others. As soon as the V_{AL} of the group drops by about 1.25 V, the loads should be disconnected to avoid repeatedly reversing the polarity of one cell.

Design 3: voltage-regulating IC

A voltage-regulating IC with an adjustable output voltage (see Figure 12.13) can also be used to provide a constant current. This application is shown in Figure 15.8(a) where the regulated charging current is set by resistor R_1.

As for design 2, the regulated current of this design remains constant over a wide range of supply voltages. This has the advantage that different numbers of cells can be charged together in series by the same regulator. In addition, the same charging regulator can be supplied from a 12 V system, a 24 V system, or connected directly to a solar module with no upper limit on the size of individual solar cells. There are some important advantages of using an IC instead of the separate transistors in design 2. The IC is internally protected against damage from reversed polarity of supply, shorted output, and over-heating.

Two points must be noted when using this design:

1. A minimum voltage drop is required across the voltage regulator and resistor R_1 for proper regulation of current.
2. The power rating of the voltage-regulating IC should be more than the maximum power dissipation that is expected.

The total voltage drop across the regulating IC and resistor R_1 depends on the type of regulator. For the IC, the minimum voltage between the input and output terminals ranges from 1 V upwards. The voltage across R_1 is the reference voltage which is 1.25 V for many voltage regulators. Therefore the minimum voltage required is 2.25 V upwards depending on the specification of the IC used.

The difference between the supply voltage and the charging voltage required by the cells is calculated using Formula (15.2) from the previous section on design 2. When checking the minimum voltage available for the regulator, the lowest value of supply voltage should be used. For a 12 V system, this may be 11.0 V, taking into account a voltage drop from the main battery to the power outlet point where the charger is connected. If the answer is less than 2.25, the number of cells must be reduced and the voltage drop recalculated.

The maximum power dissipation for the IC is given in the tables of Figure 15.8(c) and (d) for three charging currents. If other values are required, use the formula method described earlier for design 2.

For a power dissipation of more than 2 W, use a nut and screw to attach the regulating IC to a metal plate which acts as a heat sink. If there is exposed metal on the IC, it should be insulated from the metal of the transistor by a mica washer and plastic bush.

The value of resistor depends on the voltage reference of the regulating IC and the current required. Using the reference voltage specified for the IC, the resistance of resistor R_1 is calculated using the following formula:

$$\boxed{\begin{array}{c}\text{Reference voltage}\\\text{of regulating IC}\\\text{(V)}\end{array}} \div \boxed{\begin{array}{c}\text{Charging current}\\\text{required}\\\text{(A)}\end{array}} = \boxed{\boxed{\begin{array}{c}\text{Resistance of}\\\text{resistor } R_1\\\text{(Ω)}\end{array}}} \qquad \textbf{(15.4)}$$

Many regulating ICs use a reference voltage of 1.25 V. Values for R_1 are given in Figure 15.8(e) for this reference and three charging currents. If resistors of the required value are not available, they can be made up from two or more resistors connected in parallel (see Figure 12.3 and Formula (12.3)).

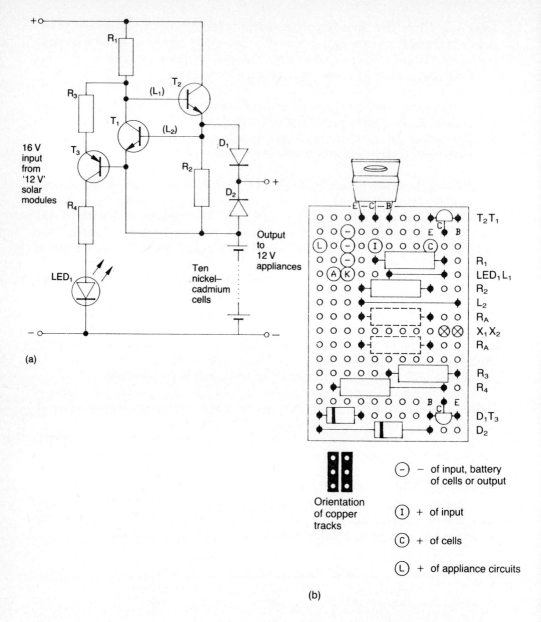

(a)

(b)

Figure 15.7   Additions to the design 2 charging regulator for sealed nickel–cadmium cells of Figure 15.5. The additions are an LED to indicate charging and diodes on the output to enable permanent connection to both supply and appliance circuits.
(a)   Circuit diagram.
(b)   Layout on stripboard.

Component	Position	Specification
Transistor	T_3	pnp, low-power, silicon
LED	LED_1	Standard 5 mm (0.2 in)
Diodes	D_1	Silicon, 1 A or more
	D_2	Silicon, 1 A or more
Resistors	R_3	68R 0.25 W
	R_4	680R 0.25 W

(c)

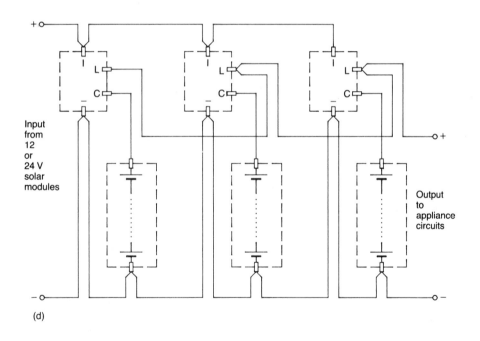

(d)

Figure 15.7 (continued)
(c)   Specifications of additional components. (Specifications of other components listed in Figure 15.5(c).)
(d)   Connection of three 12 V batteries (ten cells each) in parallel for being charged and supplying loads. Each battery has its own regulator with an LED and output diodes.

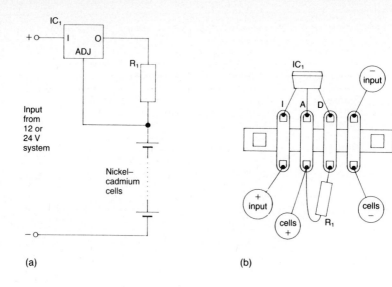

(a)   (b)

Number of cells	Maximum power dissipation of IC_1 for maximum supply of 16 V in a 12 V system (W)		
	0.05 A (for 0.5 A h cells)	0.12 A (for 1.2 A h cells)	0.4 A (for 4 A h cells)
1	1	2	6
2	1	1.5	5
3	0.5	1.5	4
4	0.5	1	4
5	0.5	1	3
6	0.5	1	3
7	0.5	0.5	2
8	0.5	0.5	1.5

(c)

Figure 15.8   Design 3 charging regulator for sealed nickel–cadmium cells.
(a)   Circuit diagram.
(b)   Layout on tag strip.
(c)   Power rating of IC_1 for a 12 V system.
(d)   Power rating of IC_1 for a 24 V system.
(e)   Details of R_1 for a regulator reference voltage of 1.25 V. For other charging currents or a different reference voltage, use Formula (15.4). Power is calculated using Formula (12.5).

Number of cells	Maximum power dissipation of IC_1 for maximum supply of 16 V in a 12 V system (W)		
	0.05 A (for 0.5 A h cells)	0.12 A (for 1.2 A h cells)	0.4 A (for 4 A h cells)
5	1.5	3	10
6	1.5	3	9
7	1	3	9
8	1	3	8
9	1	3	7
10	1	2	7
11	1	2	6
12	1	2	6

(d)

	Regulated currents		
	0.05 A (for 0.5 A h cells)	0.12 A (for 1.2 A h cells)	0.4 A (for 4 A h cells)
Resistance and power rating of R_1	25 Ω 0.25 W	10 Ω 0.25 W	3 Ω 0.5 W

(e)

The circuit can be built on a tag strip, as shown in Figure 15.8(b). After building the circuit, the regulated current can be measured using an ammeter or the procedure described for design 2. If it is necessary to increase the regulated current, this is done by adding resistors in parallel to R_1.

LED indicator and connection to appliances

An LED is useful for indicating that the cells are being charged, and a way of including one is shown in Figure 15.9. The LED is switched on by transistor T_1 when current is flowing through resistor R_1.

A battery of ten cells in series produces about 12 V and requires 14 V for charging. However IC charge regulators with a reference voltage of 1.25 V usually require at least 3 V between their input and output terminals. Therefore the circuit in Figure 15.9 requires at least 18.25 V to charge ten cells and so cannot be used with a '12 V' solar module.

Additional components required are diodes D_1 and D_2. D_1 allows current to the appliances from the solar modules when the appliances are switched on during charging of the cells. The circuit acts as both a current regulator for charging through R_1 and a voltage regulator through D_1. If the appliances use a high current, IC_1 must be rated for both charging and appliance currents (check using Formula (15.3)).

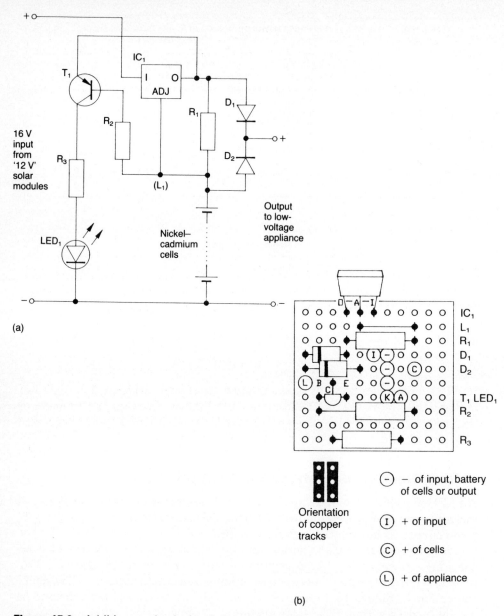

(a)

(b)

− − of input, battery of cells or output

I + of input

c + of cells

L + of appliance

Orientation of copper tracks

Figure 15.9 Additions to the design 3 charging regulator for sealed nickel–cadmium cells of Figure 15.8. The additions are an LED to indicate charging and diodes on the output to enable permanent connection to both the supply and an appliance circuit.
(a) Circuit diagram.
(b) Layout on stripboard.
(c) Specifications of components. (Specifications of other components listed in Figure 15.8.)

Component	Position	Specification
Stripboard		2.5 mm (0.1 in) hole separation, overall dimensions:
		10 holes along tracks (28 min, 1.1 in)
		11 holes along tracks (31 mm, 1.2 in)
IC	IC_1	Voltage regulator with adjustable output, see Figure 15.8 for
		power requirements
Transistor	T_1	pnp, low-power, silicon
LED	LED_1	Standard 5 mm (0.2 in)
Diodes	D_1	Silicon, 1 A or more
	D_2	Silicon, 1 A or more
Resistors	R_1	See Figure 15.8 (e)
	R_2	2K8 0.25 W
	R_3	680R 0.25 W

(c)

When permanently connected to the supply and appliances, the nickel–cadmium cells are on float charge. However, they should not be continually over-charged. To avoid this, regularly discharge the cells completely, perhaps every week.

Although nickel–cadmium cells can be deep cycled with no problems, care should be taken with a group of cells connected in series. Differences in the actual capacity of each cell will mean that one of them will reach complete discharge before the rest. Continued use of the battery results in the discharged cell having its polarity reversed by the others. As soon as the V_{AL} of the group drops by about 1.25 V, the appliances should be disconnected to avoid repeatedly reversing the polarity of one cell.

16 Control units for appliance circuits

Three units are described in this chapter that can be used to improve control of the circuits for appliances in a solar electric system:

1. Relay unit for increasing the current rating of a low-voltage disconnect relay.
2. Distribution unit for separate control of two or more appliance circuits.
3. Switch unit for a reserve battery.

The units are straightforward to build using components available locally. Refer to Chapter 12 for background details to all the components used and advice on how to build the circuits.

Relay unit

Some of the control units described in Chapter 4 feature a low-voltage disconnect which prevents deep discharge of batteries. These control units contain a relay which disconnects the appliance circuits when the batteries are at a low state of charge. The switch contacts in this relay have a maximum current rating. As extra appliances are added to a system, the total current requirement of the appliance circuits may exceed this rating.

To increase the current capacity of the disconnect relay, it is not necessary to add another disconnect unit. Instead a separate relay can be added which is controlled by the relay in the disconnect unit. A circuit for this is shown in Figure 16.1 using a two-pole relay which serves two extra appliance circuits.

The coil which activates the second relay is treated like another appliance in 'circuit 1'. Separate wires are shown connecting the switch contacts of the relay unit to the battery. These are required if the original wires are not thick enough for the higher current. For details about specifying the type of relay, refer to the relay section in Chapter 12.

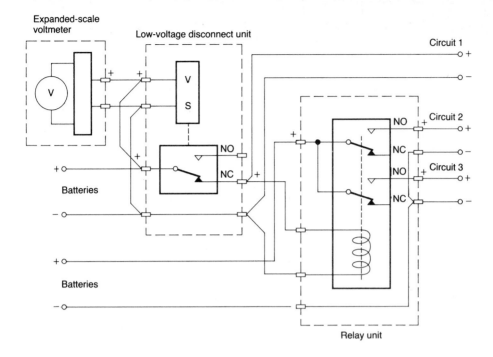

Figure 16.1   Circuit diagram for a relay unit used to extend the current rating of a low-voltage disconnect unit. (VS = voltage sensing circuit.)

Distribution unit

Two distribution units are shown in Figure 4.11 for separate control of appliance circuits. Full details are given in Figure 16.2 for building one type of distribution unit. This unit serves four circuits and includes LEDs to indicate when there is a charging current and when each circuit is on.

All the parts can be obtained from an electronics supplier but alternative sources for the fuse rack and switches are auto-spares shops. The parts can be built in one of the large metal junction boxes used in mains systems.

The rating of the blocking diode should be higher than the maximum current expected from the solar array. This can be calculated using Formula (5.4). Small diodes can be connected in parallel, as shown in Figure 16.2(b), to achieve the required current rating. The switches and fuses should be rated for 10 A.

Switch unit for reserve battery

A reserve battery is useful in a medium-sized system. It enables essential appliances to be used when the main battery bank is automatically disconnected to prevent a deep discharge. Details of a unit for switching in a reserve battery are given in Figure 16.3.

This switch unit is used with a control unit that has switch-over contacts for disconnecting the circuits. These are represented by the 'NO' and 'NC' connections in Figure 4.5 and 4.12. Using the NO connection, the switch unit controls a reserve battery in the following ways:

☐ Kept on float charge through a diode when not required.
☐ Switched in by a key-operated switch (using an ignition switch from a car).
☐ Only serves circuits for essential appliances.
☐ Automatically disconnected from appliance circuits when the main batteries are reconnected by the control unit.

The reason for using a key-operated switch is so that control of the reserve battery is restricted to users who have a key. These users are then responsible for ensuring that the reserve battery itself is not run down too much. They should also find out why the main batteries have become low and take the necessary corrective action.

The rating of the diode should be the same as that of the blocking diode for the whole array. This current can be calculated using Formula (5.4). The switches only carry current for the coil in the relay so can be rated at less than 1 A.

Operation

During normal operation, only the LED for the main batteries is on. The reserve battery is on charge in parallel with the main batteries. However, the diode reduces the voltage so that it charges slowly on float charge while the main batteries are cycling. Turning the switches has no effect.

Operation of the unit is required once the main batteries reach a low voltage and are disconnected from the appliance circuits by the control unit:

1. The LED for 'main' batteries goes off.
2. Set the switch down for 'on'.
3. Insert the key and turn against the spring long enough for the relay to switch over. The LED for 'reserve' battery should go on and the circuits for essential appliances should have power.
4. The key can be removed.
5. At the end of the evening, set the switch to 'off'. The LED for 'reserve' battery goes off and the circuits are disconnected.

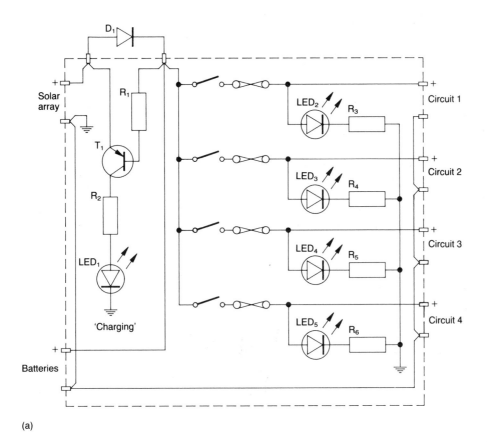

(a)

Figure 16.2 Construction details for a distribution unit with indicator lamps serving four appliance circuits.

(a) Circuit diagram.

(b) Arrangement for labelling the lid of a metal box to which the components are attached. The fuse holder is from a vehicle.

(c) View behind lid showing how components are arranged. Thick wires are required for carrying charging and appliance currents.

(d) List of specifications for electronic components.

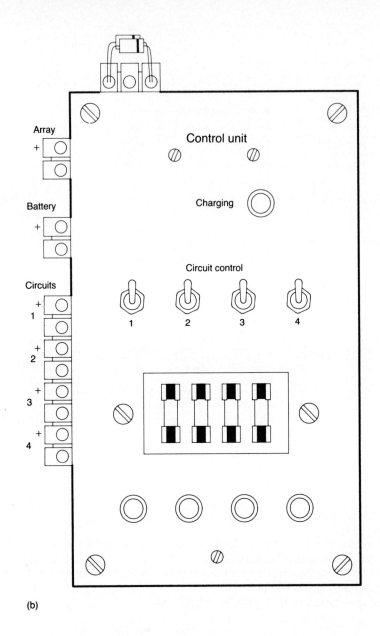

(b)

Figure 16.2 (continued)

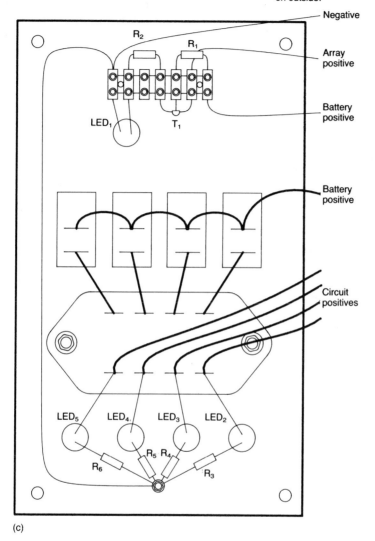

(c)

Component	Position	Minimum specification	
Transistor	T_1	pnp, low-power, silicon	
Diode	D_1	Silicon, current rating greater than total array current (Formula (5.4))	
LEDs	LED_1–LED_5	Standard 5 mm (0.2 in)	
Resistors	R_1	220R–390R 0.25 W	
	R_2–R_6	12 V system: 1K0 0.25 W	24 V system: 2K0 0.5 W

(d)

Figure 16.2 (continued)

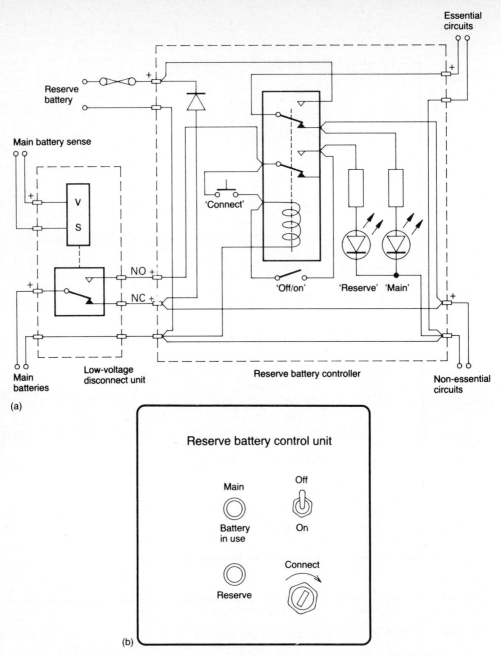

(a)

Figure 16.3 Circuit diagram for a switch unit that controls a reserve battery. The relay should be two-pole with change-over contacts and a switch rating to suit appliance circuits. The 'Connect' key-operated switch is the type from a vehicle. All the wires for carrying charging and appliance currents should be thick. Connections to the LEDs and relay coil can be made using thin wires.

(a) Circuit diagram.
(b) Arrangement for labelling the lid of a metal box to which the components are attached.

Appendices

A | Lighting analysis

Recommended levels of lighting for solar electric systems are given in Chapter 6 and summarized for a few situations in Table 6.3. This appendix describes a formula method for calculating the requirements for lamps which can be applied to any situation. (This method is often taught as part of basic courses for electricians.) The steps involved are summarized in Figure A.1.

According to this method, there are three factors concerning illumination:

1. How effective a lamp is at converting electricity into light.
2. How much of the light from a lamp reaches the area where it is needed.
3. What level of illumination is needed for the activity that requires lighting.

The first factor is to do with efficacy. Table 6.2 lists the efficacy values for four types of lamps that can be used in solar systems.

The second factor is to do with how efficiently light is utilized. The efficiency is measured as a *coefficient* which is a decimal number between zero and one. A coefficient of utilization closer to one than to zero means that most of the light from the lamp reaches the right areas.

To illuminate the floor area or work surface, most of the light from a lamp on the ceiling must be directed downwards. When the ceiling is very high or painted a dark colour, any light going upwards is lost and the coefficient of utilization is less than 0.5. By painting the ceiling white or using a reflector above the lamp, less light is lost. In this way the coefficient is increased and a value of 0.8 or higher might be achieved.

Lampshades block some of the light so should not be used. Diffusers reduce the glare from the bright parts of a lamp. Diffusers allow most light through when new but must be cleaned regularly to maintain this performance.

The level of illumination of the third factor is the amount of visible light that is required on unit area of the floor or work surface. It is called *illuminance* and its units of measure are related to the units of light (lumens or lm) and area (m^2 or ft^2). The SI unit of illuminance is lux (defined as lm/m^2), while the old unit of

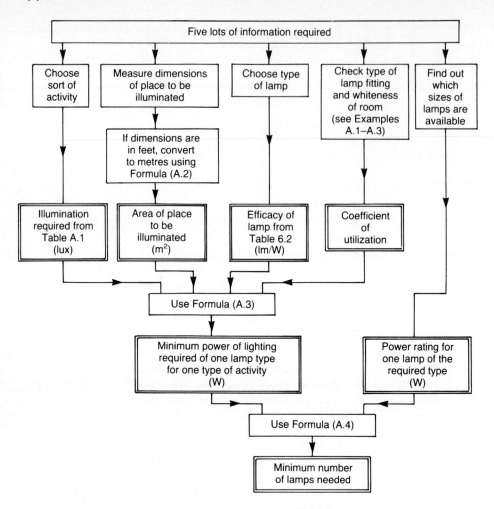

Figure A.1   Summary of steps for selecting the minimum number of lamps needed of one type to illuminate one sort of activity:
☐   steps involved
▣   results at each stage with units in brackets

foot-candles (defined as lm/ft^2) may still be in some use. The conversion from foot-candles to lux is given in Formula (A.1):

$$\boxed{\begin{array}{c}\text{Illuminance}\\\text{(foot-candles)}\end{array}} \times \boxed{0.093} = \boxed{\begin{array}{c}\text{Illuminance}\\\text{(lux)}\end{array}} \qquad \textbf{(A.1)}$$

Table A.1 *Levels of illuminance required for different sorts of activity that need illumination.*

Activity	Levels of illuminance (lux)	
	Minimum acceptable for a solar system	Standard for mains supplied systems
Moving around outside, e.g. when there is no moonlight	0.5	1.0
Moving around inside	10	150
Routine work, e.g. reading a book	20	400
Fine work, e.g. medical care	⩾100	⩾750

When designing a lighting system powered by mains electricity, a list of *standard service illuminances* are available covering a variety of activities. For example, the standard service illuminance for an office according to one code is 500 lux. However, our eyes can become accustomed to doing activities at a much lower illuminance than the standard levels. Table A.1 lists the minimum levels of illuminance that can be used in a solar system together with the levels recommended in mains systems for comparison.

Using the formulas

Since lux is based on square metres as the unit of area, measurements taken in square feet should be converted to square metres using the following formula:

$$\boxed{\text{Area (ft}^2)} \times \boxed{0.093} = \boxed{\text{Area (m}^2)} \qquad \textbf{(A.2)}$$

The three factors concerning illumination are combined in one formula to calculate the minimum lighting power that is needed. The formula applies to one level of illuminance and one type of lamp:

$$\boxed{\begin{array}{c}\text{Illuminance}\\\text{required}\\\text{(lux)}\end{array}} \times \boxed{\begin{array}{c}\text{Area to be}\\\text{illuminated}\\\text{(m}^2)\end{array}} \div \boxed{\begin{array}{c}\text{Efficacy}\\\text{of type of}\\\text{lamp used}\\\text{(lm/W)}\end{array}} \div \boxed{\begin{array}{c}\text{Coefficient}\\\text{of}\\\text{utilization}\end{array}} = \boxed{\begin{array}{c}\text{Minimum power}\\\text{required of one}\\\text{lamp type for}\\\text{one activity}\\\text{(W)}\end{array}} \qquad \textbf{(A.3)}$$

The answer is converted to the minimum number of lamps required using the power rating of each lamp.

$$\boxed{\begin{array}{c}\text{Minimum power required}\\\text{of one lamp type for}\\\text{one sort of activity}\\\text{(W)}\end{array}} \div \boxed{\begin{array}{c}\text{Power rating of}\\\text{one lamp of}\\\text{required type}\\\text{(W)}\end{array}} = \boxed{\begin{array}{c}\text{Minimum number}\\\text{of lamps needed}\end{array}} \qquad \textbf{(A.4)}$$

Application of these formulas according to Figure A.1 is illustrated by the following examples.

Example A.1

Lighting is needed for an outside area of dimensions 130×130 ft using one standard low-pressure sodium (SOX) lamp mounted on a pole.

The area to be illuminated is $16\,900$ ft^2 (from 130×130 ft assuming that the area is rectangular). Since the dimensions are in square feet, they are first converted to units of square metres using Formula (A.2):

$$16\,900 \times 0.093 = 1572 \text{ m}^2$$

This is rounded to 1600 m^2 for the following calculations.

For Formula (A.3), the details required are as follows:

1.   Activity of moving around outside requires a minimum illuminance of 0.5 lux (from Table A.1).
2.   Area to be illuminated is 1600 m^2.
3.   Efficacy of a SOX tube lamp is 120 lm/W (from Table 6.2).
4.   Coefficient of utilization to use is about 0.5 because only about half the light will reach the right area on the ground.

Using these values in Formula (A.3), the minimum power of lamp needed is:

$$0.5 \times 1600 \div 120 \div 0.5 = 13.3 \text{ W}$$

A SOX lamp can be used with the nearest power above this answer. For example, if the only sizes of lamp available are 35 W and 55 W, the 35 W one is suitable although it has spare capacity to light a larger area or provide better illumination for the area specified.

Example A.2

Lighting is needed for doing fine work on a table of 1×1 m. A headlamp fitting containing a tungsten filament lamp can be used (see Item 1 in Figure 6.7). What power is required?

For Formula (A.3), the details required are as follows:

1. Activity requires a minimum illuminance of 100 lux (from Table A.1).
2. Area to be illuminated is $1\ m^2$ (from 1×1 m).
3. Efficacy of a filament bulb lamp is about 15 lm/W (from Table 6.2).
4. Coefficient of utilization to use is about 0.8 because headlamp fittings have a curved reflector to direct most of the light forward.

Using these values in Formula (A.3), the minimum power of lamp needed is

$$100 \times 1 \div 15 \div 0.8 = 8.3\ W$$

The nearest power of lamp available for a headlamp fitting above this answer might be 15 W.

Example A.3

Tube lamps of 20 W are available with an average light output of 1500 lm and fitted with reflectors (as in Figure 6.10(b)). Find the minimum number of these lamps that are needed for a hall of dimensions 10×28 m.

For Formula (A.3), the details required are as follows:

1. Activity requires a minimum illuminance of 20 lux (from Table A.1).
2. Area to be illuminated is $280\ m^2$ (from 10×28 m).
3. Efficacy of these tube lamps is 75 lm/W (from 1500 lm divided by 20 W).
4. Coefficient of utilization to use is about 0.8 as long as the walls are white.

Using these values in Formula (A.3), the minimum power of lamp needed is

$$20 \times 280 \div 75 \div 0.8 = 93.3\ W$$

Using this answer in Formula (A.4) with the power rating of one lamp, the minimum number of lamps needed is:

$$93.3 \div 20 = 4.7$$

The nearest number of lamps above this answer is five but using six lamps may be better. Six lamps can be arranged in three rows along the hall with two lamps in each row to give an even illumination around the whole hall.

B │ Tilt correction for daily insolation

For sizing the number of solar modules in a system, values of daily insolation are required. These can be obtained from the maps in Figure 8.4 as averages over three-month periods. If meteorological records for several years are available from a weather station near the site, they can be used to provide a better estimate of daily insolation. However, measurements of daily insolation are taken for a horizontal surface, whereas modules are always tilted away from horizontal.

This appendix details a procedure which corrects these measurements for a tilted surface. Apart from enabling weather records to be used in sizing, corrected values for different tilt angles can be compared to find the optimum tilt angle. The value of this procedure is emphasized by the graphs in Figure 8.6 showing monthly averages of daily insolation for two sites.

The first section of this appendix explains the information recorded in meteorological records. A brief description is given of the instruments used for measuring daily insolation. The next section describes the correction procedure which uses tilt factors from a set of tables. The procedure is illustrated by one example at the end of the appendix.

Meteorological records

A summary of weather records should be available from the government ministry which is responsible for running the country's meteorological stations. Suppliers of solar equipment may also have a copy of the weather records for your area of interest.

Figure B.1 shows an example of a weather records summary from a meteorological station with the details of daily insolation averaged over separate months. These are called *monthly averages of daily radiation* or *daily radiation means for each month*.

Records are collected at the meteorological station over a number of years and the monthly averages are averaged again over this period. The highest and lowest monthly averages over the years of recording may also be given for each month and are called *maximum means* and *minimum means*.

The lowest minimum mean of daily insolation could be used to size the number of modules. This would ensure that electricity is always available, even for the lowest value of daily insolation on record. However, the extra expense of this approach may not be justified since the full generating capacity of a system sized this way will not be used for most years. The lowest minimum mean does give an indication of how much the shortfall might be.

Units of daily insolation

The daily insolation figures from meteorological records are often measured in units of *langleys*. One langley is another name for one calorie per square centimetre (cal/cm^2) of sunshine energy reaching the ground. Other units also used for this measurement are listed in Table B.1.

The unit of daily insolation used for the sizing procedures in Chapter 8 is peak-hours per day at an irradiance of 1000 W/m^2. Conversion of measurements in other units to peak-hours is done using the appropriate conversion factor from Table B.1 in the following formula:

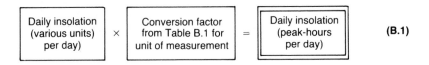

$$
\boxed{\begin{array}{c}\text{Daily insolation}\\\text{(various units)}\\\text{per day)}\end{array}} \times \boxed{\begin{array}{c}\text{Conversion factor}\\\text{from Table B.1 for}\\\text{unit of measurement}\end{array}} = \boxed{\begin{array}{c}\text{Daily insolation}\\\text{(peak-hours}\\\text{per day)}\end{array}} \quad \textbf{(B.1)}
$$

Instruments for measuring daily insolation

The general name for an instrument used to measure irradiance is a *solarimeter*. Two well-known types are the Eppley pyranometer in the United States and the Kipp and Zonen pyranometer in Europe.

The detecting part of a pyranometer is a metal disc with thermocouples attached underneath and a black surface on top. The detector is fixed in a horizontal position facing directly upwards and protected by two glass domes (see Figure B.2(a)).

The back surface of the detector warms up as it absorbs radiation from all parts of the sky. The rise in temperature is sensed by the thermocouples and this gives a measure of the light intensity or irradiance at that particular moment. As the sun passes overhead, measurements are recorded through the day and added up to give a value of total insolation for the day.

Station name: Mombasa, Port Reitz Airport Met. Station
Latitude 04° 02′S.   Longitude 39° 37′E.

Station number: 94.35/021
Altitude 186 feet (57 metres)

Month	Number of days of		Daily sunshine (1949–70)			Daily radiation (1963–70) Instrument GB			Monthly evaporation (1958–70) Pan type A			Cloud amount (1946–70)				Daily wind run ( )	Wind speed (1946–70)		Calms (1966–70)		Visibility (1961–70)			
												Total		Low							Fog		Mist. Haze	
	Rain (>1 mm)	Thunder	Mean	Max. mean	Min. mean	Mean	Max. mean	Min. mean	Mean	Highest	Lowest	0600 GMT	1200 GMT	0600 GMT	1200 GMT		0600 GMT	1200 GMT	0600 GMT	1200 GMT	0600 GMT	1200 GMT	0600 GMT	1200 GMT
	(days)	(days)	(hours)	(hours)	(hours)	(langleys)	(langleys)	(langleys)	(mm)	(mm)	(mm)	(oktas)	(oktas)	(oktas)	(oktas)	(miles)	(knots)	(knots)	(days)	(days)	(days)	(days)	(days)	(days)
January	4	2	8.6	9.6	6.7	530	580	444	220	244	201	5.6	4.1	4.7	2.9		6	12	2	0	0	0	1	1
February	2	1	9.1	10.2	7.5	535	609	423	211	238	173	5.5	3.4	4.3	2.3		5	13	3	1	0	0	1	1
March	6	5	9.0	9.9	7.3	544	618	445	225	261	162	5.3	3.9	4.0	2.5		4	12	9	1	1	0	1	1
April	11	6	7.5	9.8	6.0	453	509	405	184	221	154	5.7	5.2	3.7	3.1		5	13	6	1	0	0	2	2
May	13	1	6.5	9.2	4.4	387	451	326	159	211	129	5.8	5.7	4.1	3.6		7	13	3	1	1	0	2	1
June	9	0	7.5	9.5	5.5	390	450	327	148	187	119	5.2	5.3	3.8	3.8		7	13	3	0	0	0	1	1
July	11	0	7.0	7.9	5.8	386	431	340	144	171	111	5.5	5.6	4.2	4.1		6	13	3	1	0	0	2	2
August	9	0	7.9	9.2	6.4	420	471	352	164	192	136	5.4	5.4	4.4	4.2		6	13	2	0	0	0	1	1
September	9	0	8.5	9.6	7.0	489	550	402	187	218	162	5.5	4.7	5.2	3.7		6	13	2	1	1	0	1	1
October	11	0	8.7	10.0	7.3	506	564	413	200	243	155	5.8	3.9	5.5	3.3		5	12	5	1	0	0	2	1
November	10	2	9.0	10.0	7.0	529	647	433	195	242	148	5.5	3.9	4.9	3.2		3	12	10	1	1	1	2	1
December	6	4	8.8	10.1	7.0	520	589	462	197	213	185	5.5	4.2	4.4	3.2		5	11	3	1	0	0	1	1
Year	101	21	8.2	8.7	7.4	474	517	422	2234	2454	1976	5.5	4.6	4.4	3.3		5	12	51	9	2	1	17	13

Figure B.1   An example of the summary of weather records from one meteorological station. The measurements of use for sizing a system are 'mean' values of 'Daily radiation'.

Month	Atmospheric pressure (1946–70)		Temperature (1946–70)									Relative humidity			Rainfall (1946–70)			
			Means			Extremes		Dry bulb		Dew point								
	0600 GMT	1200 GMT	Max.	Min.	Range	Highest	Lowest	0600 GMT	1200 GMT	0600 GMT	1200 GMT	0300 GMT	0600 GMT	1200 GMT	Mean	Highest	Lowest	Max. 24 hour fall
	(mb)	(mb)	(°C)	(°C)	(°C)	(°C)	(°C)	(°C)	(°C)	(°C)	(°C)	(%)	(%)	(%)	(mm)	(mm)	(mm)	(mm)
January	1006.2	1002.3	32.1	23.2	8.9	36.9	18.4	26.8	30.4	22.6	22.5	92	78	63	35	130	0	49.0
February	1005.8	1001.9	32.4	23.6	8.8	36.1	20.6	27.1	30.9	22.8	22.5	92	77	61	19	90	0	49.9
March	1005.6	1001.9	32.7	24.2	8.5	37.3	20.8	27.6	31.4	23.9	23.3	92	80	63	64	253	1	105.7
April	1006.0	1002.9	31.2	23.8	7.4	35.1	21.1	26.7	29.9	23.8	23.3	94	85	68	171	601	23	119.7
May	1008.2	1005.6	29.2	22.6	6.6	33.8	18.9	25.3	28.0	23.0	22.4	94	87	72	234	772	36	138.9
June	1010.5	1008.1	28.5	21.2	7.3	31.5	17.5	24.1	27.3	21.7	20.7	93	86	68	68	135	6	43.4
July	1011.2	1008.9	27.7	20.3	7.4	31.1	17.6	23.1	26.4	20.8	20.1	94	87	68	66	205	5	37.1
August	1011.2	1008.7	28.0	20.3	7.7	32.0	14.1	23.3	26.7	21.0	21.1	94	87	67	69	216	10	74.5
September	1010.5	1007.6	28.9	20.8	8.1	32.0	17.6	24.3	27.6	21.3	20.4	94	83	65	80	356	10	149.9
October	1009.2	1005.7	29.7	22.0	7.7	32.8	17.7	25.5	28.5	22.3	21.5	94	82	66	98	279	13	103.4
November	1007.5	1003.7	30.6	23.0	7.6	35.7	20.0	26.6	29.4	23.2	22.8	94	81	68	100	316	9	105.4
December	1006.4	1002.7	31.6	23.3	8.3	35.7	19.4	27.0	30.0	23.3	23.1	94	80	67	69	172	2	68.8
Year	1008.2	1005.0	30.2	22.4	7.8	37.3	14.1	25.6	28.8	22.5	21.9	93	83	66	1073	1784	585	149.9

Figure B.1 (continued)

Table B.1 *Conversion factors for use in Formula (B.1).*

Units of daily insolation		Conversion factor to peak-hours at 1000 W/m^2
Abbreviation	Name in full	
peak-hour	Peak-hour at an irradiance of 1000 W/m^2	1
langley	Calorie per square centimetre	0.0116
cal/cm^2	Calorie per square centimetre	0.0116
W h/m^2	Watt-hour per square metre	0.001
kW h/m^2	Kilowatt-hour per square metre	1
W/m^2 averaged over 24 hours	Watt per square metre averaged over 24 hours	0.024
kJ/m^2	Kilojoule per square metre	0.000278
MJ/m^2	Megajoule per square metre	0.278
Btu/ft^2	British thermal unit per square foot	0.0428
kcal/m^2/yr	Kilocalorie per square metre per year	0.00000318
peak-hour/week	Peak-hour per week	0.143
peak-hour/month	Peak-hour per month	0.0329
peak-hour/year	Peak-hour per year	0.00274

A cheaper but less accurate type of solarimeter uses a silicon photocell (small solar cell) for the detecting part (see Figure B.2(b)). It operates on the principle of the photovoltaic effect and this is quite different from the temperature change sensed in a pyranometer.

Photovoltaic solarimeters are also available with integrators that automatically add up the light intensity through the day by an electronic or chemical means. With an integrator, the operator simply records the reading of daily insolation at the end of the day and resets the integrator to zero ready for the next day.

A photovoltaic solarimeter can be used to make a direct check of the performance of a solar module. When used to check modules made of amorphous silicon, a correction filter is required on the solarimeter. This corrects for the different response of the photocell in the solarimeter which is made of crystalline silicon.

Limitations of standard weather records

The measurements of daily radiation in meteorological records are nearly always for a horizontal surface because the detectors are mounted horizontally, as shown in Figure B.2. However, solar modules are always mounted at a certain angle of tilt from horizontal (as defined in Figure 8.3). Therefore the daily radiation figures must be corrected according to the angle of tilt that a module will be at before they can be used to calculate the output expected from the module.

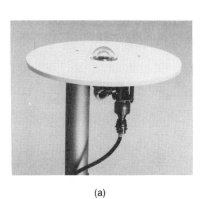
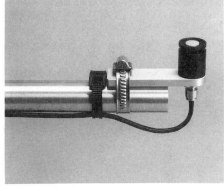

(a)   (b)

Figure B.2   Two types of solarimeter used by meteorologists to measure daily insolation. Both types measure the total of direct and diffuse radiation combined. (Source Didcot Instruments Co. Ltd.)
(a)   Pyranometer.
(b)   Photovoltaic solarimeter.

To calculate the correction for the tilt angle, it is necessary for the measurements of daily insolation to be divided into two components called *direct* and *diffuse*. On a clear day, 80–90 per cent of the insolation comes straight from the direction of the sun in the sky. The remaining 10–15% comes from the remaining area of the sky away from the sun and is called diffuse. On a cloudy day, less light comes from the direction of the sun and most of the daily insolation is diffuse. Tilting a module to increase the electrical output is only really effective when most of the insolation is direct.

A type of solarimeter different from the ones shown in Figure B.2 is needed to obtain values of direct and diffuse light. The solarimeter used is the photovoltaic type with a moving shadow bar. When the shadow bar is out of the way, the total of direct and diffuse is measured. When the shadow bar blocks out the sun, casting a shadow over the detector, only the diffuse part is measured.

However, measurements of daily insolation as direct and diffuse components are not available for all parts of the world. The procedure given in this appendix is for use with the single measurement of total insolation on a horizontal surface. In calculating the tilt factors listed at the end of the appendix, the diffuse part is taken into account in an approximate way which is reliable enough for most applications.

A more thorough analysis of correcting for tilt angle can be provided by some suppliers of solar equipment. They have extensive records of solar data together with computer programs which can estimate the output from their solar modules under various conditions.

Procedure for using tilt factors

For any value of daily insolation averaged over a month, the procedure simply involves multiplying this value by a *tilt factor*. These are listed in Table B.3 at the end of this appendix as twelve tables which cover the following:

1. Latitudes from 60°N. to 60°S. in bands of 5° in separate tables.
2. Twelve months of the year in separate columns of each table.
3. Tilt angles from the latitude minus 35° to the latitude plus 35° in separate rows of each table.

The tilt factors are for correcting measurements of total insolation which are the direct and diffuse parts combined. Tilt factors for tilt angles less than 15° are not included. At lower angles, rain-water cannot run off easily and dirt builds up on the glass. Each table has tilt factors for latitudes both north and south of the equator. Details for south of the equator are at the bottom of each table with the months starting from July.

Times of sunrise and sunset are given to help in estimating the daily requirement for lighting. The actual times at the site will differ slightly from these according to clearness of the local horizon, position east and west in the time zone, and national adjustments, such as a 'summer time' change in the clock.

The tilt factors from Table B.3 are used together with Table B.2 in the following way:

1. Make your own copy of Table B.2 and complete row 1 with details of the name, position, and latitude of the site.
2. Find the table from Table B.3 with the correct range of latitude for the site. Copy the order of months into row 2 of your table. Note that the months start from January for sites north of the equator and from July for sites south of the equator.
3. From the same table of tilt factors, copy the times of sunrise into row 3 starting from January or July according to whether the site is north or south of the equator.
4. As for step 3, copy the times of sunset into row 4.
5. Obtain a summary of weather records from a weather station near the site of interest. In the summary of weather records, find the daily insolation means for each month. Write the name of the unit used in the weather records at the end of row 5.
6. From the weather records that you have, copy the values of daily insolation into row 6 of your table. For sites south of the equator, remember to put the values in your table starting from July.

7. Convert the values from row 6 to units of peak hours per day at 1000 W/m^2 and put the converted values in row 7. The conversion is done using Formula (B.1) with the appropriate conversion factor from Table B.1. Sometimes the insolation values are given as monthly totals. In this case, it is also necessary to divide each value by the number of days in the month for conversion to daily insolation.

8. Choose an angle of tilt for the module and write this angle at the end of row 8. A good angle to start with is the angle of latitude for the site. When the latitude is less than 15° from the equator, use a tilt angle of 15°. For sites north of the equator, the module is tilted towards the south, while for sites south of the equator, the module should be tilted towards the north.

9. From the table of tilt factors, find the row for the tilt angle marked in row 8. (Tilt angles for southern latitudes are on the right side of the table.) Copy the tilt factors for each month into row 9.

10. Multiply the daily insolation for each month in row 7 by the tilt factor for that month in row 9 and write the corrected values in row 10. Look along the values in row 10 and put a circle around the lowest one. Also circle other values in the line that are within 0.2 peak-hour units of the lowest.

To increase the value for the worst month, try a different tilt angle for the module and write this value at the end of row 11. Then repeat the instructions in steps 9 and 10 from row 12 onwards in your table. At the new tilt, some corrected values will be higher than before, while others will be lower. Put a circle around the lowest value and other values which are within 0.2 units of the lowest. Then try another tilt to see whether the lowest values can be increased.

The best tilt angle for the module is usually chosen to increase the value for the worst month. An alternative approach is used for systems in which the solar electricity is required mostly for lighting. For this approach, choose a tilt angle giving the lowest values for months with long hours of daylight when less electricity is needed at night. The time of sunset at the top of the table can be used to calculate how long the evenings are for each month.

For self-regulated systems (see Table 2.1 and Figure 4.6), another aim in comparing different angles of tilt is to reduce the highest value. The reason for doing this is to reduce over-charging of the battery during sunny months which have high levels of daily insolation.

If the lowest months are due much more to cloud cover than short days, the correction will be an over-estimate. After finding the optimum tilt according to the results in the table, use a slightly smaller tilt angle for the modules. This improves the response to diffuse irradiance which comes from all parts of the sky during very cloudy periods.

Table B.2 *Table used to record and correct daily insolation means averaged over months. Insolation values are corrected according to tilt angle of the module using the tilt factors given in the tables at the end of this appendix. The lines of the table are numbered for reference to the instructions in the text.*

1	Site details: Name					Position				Latitude				
2 Month														
3 Sunrise														
4 Sunset														
5	Daily insolation on a horizontal plane in units of													
6														
7 Peak-hour/day[1]														
8	Daily insolation corrected for a tilt angle of													
9 Tilt factor[2]														
10 Peak-hour/day														
11	Daily insolation corrected for a tilt angle of													
12 Tilt factor														
13 Peak-hour/day														
14	Daily insolation corrected for a tilt angle of													
15 Tilt factor														
16 Peak-hour/day														
17	Daily insolation corrected for a tilt angle of													
18 Tilt factor														
⋮	⋮	⋮	⋮	⋮	⋮	⋮	⋮	⋮	⋮	⋮	⋮	⋮	⋮	⋮

[1]At an irradiance of 1000 W/m^2.
[2]From Table B.3.

Table B.3 Tilt factors for correcting monthly averages of daily insolation on a horizontal surface. Twelve separate tables cover angles of latitude over the range 0° to 60° in 5° bands for both north and south of the equator.

Northern hemisphere latitudes 0°–5°N.

Month	Jan.	Feb.	Mar.	Apr.	May	June	July	Aug.	Sept.	Oct.	Nov.	Dec.	
SRi[1]	6.14	6.17	6.10	5.58	5.00	5.55	6.01	6.02	5.55	5.48	5.49	6.00	
SSe[2]	18.04	18.11	18.08	18.02	18.00	18.05	18.11	18.08	17.57	17.44	17.41	17.00	
Tilt[3]													Tilt[3]
40°S	1.12	1.01	0.87	0.71	0.58	0.52	0.55	0.65	0.79	0.95	1.08	1.15	40°N
35°S	1.13	1.03	0.91	0.76	0.65	0.59	0.62	0.71	0.84	0.98	1.10	1.16	35°N
30°S	1.14	1.05	0.94	0.82	0.71	0.67	0.69	0.77	0.88	1.00	1.11	1.16	30°N
25°S	1.13	1.06	0.97	0.86	0.78	0.73	0.75	0.82	0.91	1.02	1.11	1.15	25°N
20°S	1.12	1.06	0.99	0.90	0.83	0.80	0.81	0.87	0.94	1.03	1.10	1.13	20°N
15°S	1.10	1.06	1.00	0.93	0.88	0.86	0.87	0.91	0.97	1.03	1.08	1.11	15°N
15°N	0.84	0.89	0.94	1.01	1.06	1.08	1.07	1.03	0.98	0.91	0.86	0.83	15°S
20°N	0.78	0.84	0.91	1.00	1.06	1.10	1.08	1.03	0.95	0.87	0.80	0.76	20°S
25°N	0.71	0.78	0.88	0.98	1.06	1.11	1.09	1.02	0.93	0.82	0.73	0.69	25°S
30°N	0.64	0.72	0.83	0.96	1.06	1.11	1.08	1.00	0.89	0.77	0.67	0.61	30°S
35°N	0.56	0.66	0.79	0.93	1.04	1.10	1.07	0.98	0.86	0.71	0.59	0.53	35°S

Month	July	Aug.	Sept.	Oct.	Nov.	Dec.	Jan.	Feb.	Mar.	Apr.	May	June
SRi[1]	6.11	6.08	5.57	5.44	5.41	5.00	6.04	6.11	6.08	6.02	6.00	6.05
SSe[2]	18.01	18.02	17.55	17.48	17.49	18.00	18.14	18.17	18.10	17.58	17.00	17.55

Southern hemisphere latitudes 0°–5°S.

[1]Time of sunrise for the middle of the month.
[2]Time of sunset for the middle of the month.
[3]Tilt angle of module from horizontal (see Figure 8.3).

Table B.3 (continued)

Northern hemisphere latitudes 5°–10°N.

Month	Jan.	Feb.	Mar.	Apr.	May	June	July	Aug.	Sept.	Oct.	Nov.	Dec.	Tilt³
SRi¹	6.21	6.22	6.11	5.55	5.45	5.46	5.54	5.57	5.54	5.51	5.56	6.09	
SSe²	17.57	18.06	18.07	18.05	18.07	18.14	18.18	18.13	17.58	17.41	17.34	17.41	
45°S	1.17	1.04	0.88	0.70	0.56	0.50	0.53	0.64	0.79	0.97	1.13	1.21	45°N.
40°S	1.18	1.07	0.92	0.76	0.63	0.57	0.59	0.70	0.84	1.00	1.14	1.22	40°N.
35°S	1.19	1.08	0.95	0.81	0.69	0.64	0.66	0.75	0.88	1.03	1.15	1.22	35°N.
30°S	1.18	1.09	0.98	0.85	0.75	0.70	0.73	0.81	0.92	1.04	1.15	1.21	30°N.
25°S	1.17	1.09	1.00	0.89	0.81	0.77	0.79	0.85	0.94	1.05	1.14	1.19	25°N.
20°S	1.15	1.09	1.01	0.93	0.86	0.83	0.84	0.89	0.97	1.06	1.13	1.17	20°N.
15°S	1.12	1.08	1.02	0.95	0.90	0.88	0.89	0.93	0.99	1.05	1.11	1.14	15°N.
15°N	0.82	0.86	0.92	0.99	1.04	1.06	1.05	1.01	0.96	0.89	0.83	0.80	15°S.
20°N	0.75	0.81	0.89	0.97	1.04	1.07	1.06	1.00	0.93	0.84	0.77	0.73	20°S.
25°N	0.67	0.75	0.84	0.95	1.03	1.07	1.05	0.99	0.90	0.79	0.70	0.65	25°S.
30°N	0.59	0.68	0.80	0.92	1.02	1.07	1.04	0.97	0.86	0.73	0.62	0.57	30°S.
Month	July	Aug.	Sept.	Oct.	Nov.	Dec.	Jan.	Feb.	Mar.	Apr.	May	June	Month
SRi¹	6.18	6.13	5.58	5.41	5.34	5.41	5.57	6.06	6.07	6.05	6.07	6.14	SRi¹
SSe²	17.54	17.57	17.54	17.51	17.56	18.09	18.21	18.22	18.11	17.55	17.45	17.46	SSe²

Southern hemisphere latitudes 5°–10°S.

Northern hemisphere latitudes 10°–15°N.

Month	Jan.	Feb.	Mar.	Apr.	May	June	July	Aug.	Sept.	Oct.	Nov.	Dec.
SRi[1]	6.29	6.27	6.12	5.52	5.38	5.38	5.46	5.52	5.53	5.54	6.03	6.17
SSe[2]	17.49	18.01	18.06	18.08	18.14	18.22	18.26	18.18	17.59	17.38	17.27	17.33
Tilt[3]												
50°S.	1.23	1.08	0.90	0.70	0.55	0.48	0.51	0.63	0.80	1.00	1.18	1.28
45°S.	1.24	1.11	0.94	0.75	0.62	0.55	0.58	0.69	0.84	1.03	1.20	1.28
40°S.	1.25	1.12	0.97	0.81	0.68	0.62	0.64	0.74	0.89	1.06	1.21	1.29
35°S.	1.25	1.13	1.00	0.85	0.74	0.68	0.71	0.80	0.92	1.07	1.21	1.28
30°S.	1.23	1.14	1.02	0.89	0.79	0.74	0.76	0.84	0.95	1.08	1.20	1.26
25°S.	1.21	1.13	1.03	0.92	0.84	0.80	0.82	0.88	0.98	1.09	1.19	1.24
20°S.	1.19	1.12	1.04	0.95	0.88	0.85	0.86	0.92	0.99	1.08	1.16	1.20
15°S.	1.15	1.10	1.04	0.97	0.92	0.90	0.91	0.95	1.01	1.07	1.13	1.16
15°N.	0.79	0.84	0.90	0.97	1.02	1.04	1.03	0.99	0.94	0.87	0.81	0.78
20°N.	0.71	0.78	0.86	0.95	1.01	1.04	1.03	0.98	0.90	0.81	0.74	0.69
25°N.	0.63	0.71	0.81	0.92	1.00	1.04	1.02	0.96	0.87	0.75	0.66	0.60

Southern hemisphere latitudes 10°–15°S.

Month	July	Aug.	Sept.	Oct.	Nov.	Dec.	Jan.	Feb.	Mar.	Apr.	May	June
SRi[1]	6.26	6.18	5.59	5.38	5.27	5.33	5.49	6.01	6.06	6.08	6.14	6.22
SSe[2]	17.46	17.52	17.53	17.54	18.03	18.17	18.29	18.27	18.12	17.52	17.38	17.38

Table B.3 (continued)

Northern hemisphere latitudes 15°–20°N.

Month	Jan.	Feb.	Mar.	Apr.	May	June	July	Aug.	Sept.	Oct.	Nov.	Dec.	
SRi[1]	6.38	6.32	6.13	5.48	5.31	5.28	5.37	5.47	5.53	5.58	6.10	6.27	
SSe[2]	17.40	17.56	18.05	18.12	18.21	18.32	18.35	18.23	18.00	17.34	17.20	17.23	
Tilt[3]													
55°S	1.31	1.13	0.92	0.70	0.54	0.47	0.50	0.62	0.81	1.04	1.25	1.36	55°N.
50°S	1.32	1.16	0.96	0.76	0.61	0.54	0.56	0.68	0.86	1.07	1.27	1.37	50°N.
45°S	1.33	1.18	0.99	0.81	0.66	0.60	0.63	0.74	0.90	1.10	1.27	1.37	45°N.
40°S	1.32	1.19	1.02	0.85	0.72	0.66	0.69	0.79	0.94	1.11	1.28	1.36	40°N.
35°S	1.31	1.19	1.04	0.89	0.78	0.72	0.75	0.84	0.97	1.13	1.27	1.35	35°N.
30°S	1.29	1.19	1.06	0.93	0.83	0.78	0.80	0.88	0.99	1.13	1.25	1.32	30°N.
25°S	1.26	1.17	1.07	0.95	0.87	0.83	0.85	0.91	1.01	1.13	1.23	1.29	25°N.
20°S	1.22	1.15	1.07	0.98	0.91	0.88	0.89	0.94	1.02	1.11	1.20	1.25	20°N.
15°S	1.18	1.13	1.06	0.99	0.94	0.92	0.93	0.97	1.03	1.10	1.16	1.20	15°N.
15°N	0.76	0.82	0.88	0.95	1.00	1.03	1.01	0.97	0.92	0.85	0.78	0.75	15°S.
20°N	0.67	0.75	0.83	0.92	0.99	1.02	1.01	0.95	0.88	0.78	0.70	0.65	20°S.
													Tilt[3]
Month	July	Aug.	Sept.	Oct.	Nov.	Dec.	Jan.	Feb.	Mar.	Apr.	May	June	Month
SRi[1]	6.35	6.23	6.00	5.34	5.20	5.23	5.40	5.56	6.05	6.12	6.21	6.32	SRi[1]
SSe[2]	17.37	17.47	17.53	17.58	18.10	18.27	18.38	18.32	18.13	17.48	17.31	17.28	SSe[2]

Southern hemisphere latitudes 15°–20°S.

Northern hemisphere latitudes 20°–25°N.

Month	Jan.	Feb.	Mar.	Apr.	May	June	July	Aug.	Sept.	Oct.	Nov.	Dec.	
SRi[1]	6.47	6.37	6.14	5.45	5.23	5.18	5.28	5.42	5.51	6.01	6.18	6.37	
SSe[2]	17.31	17.51	18.04	18.15	18.29	18.42	18.44	18.28	18.01	17.31	17.12	17.13	
Tilt[3]													
60°S	1.40	1.20	0.95	0.71	0.53	0.46	0.49	0.62	0.83	1.09	1.33	1.46	60°N
55°S	1.42	1.22	0.99	0.76	0.60	0.52	0.55	0.68	0.88	1.12	1.35	1.47	55°N
50°S	1.42	1.24	1.03	0.82	0.66	0.59	0.62	0.74	0.92	1.15	1.36	1.48	50°N
45°S	1.42	1.25	1.06	0.86	0.72	0.65	0.68	0.79	0.96	1.17	1.36	1.47	45°N
40°S	1.41	1.26	1.08	0.90	0.77	0.71	0.73	0.84	0.99	1.18	1.36	1.45	40°N
35°S	1.39	1.25	1.09	0.93	0.82	0.77	0.79	0.88	1.01	1.18	1.34	1.43	35°N
30°S	1.36	1.24	1.10	0.96	0.86	0.81	0.83	0.92	1.03	1.18	1.32	1.39	30°N
25°S	1.32	1.22	1.10	0.99	0.90	0.86	0.88	0.94	1.04	1.17	1.28	1.35	25°N
20°S	1.27	1.19	1.10	1.00	0.93	0.90	0.91	0.97	1.05	1.15	1.24	1.29	20°N
15°S	1.21	1.15	1.08	1.01	0.96	0.93	0.95	0.99	1.05	1.12	1.19	1.23	15°N
15°N	0.73	0.79	0.86	0.93	0.98	1.01	1.00	0.96	0.90	0.82	0.75	0.71	15°S
													Tilt[3]
	July	Aug.	Sept.	Oct.	Nov.	Dec.	Jan.	Feb.	Mar.	Apr.	May	June	Month
	6.44	6.28	6.01	5.31	5.12	5.13	5.31	5.51	6.04	6.15	6.29	6.42	SRi[1]
	17.28	17.42	17.51	18.01	18.18	18.37	18.47	18.37	18.14	17.45	17.23	17.18	SSe[2]

Southern hemisphere latitudes 20°–25°S.

Table B.3 (continued)

Northern hemisphere latitudes 25°–30°N.

Month	Jan.	Feb.	Mar.	Apr.	May	June	July	Aug.	Sept.	Oct.	Nov.	Dec.	Tilt³
SRi¹	6.56	6.43	6.15	5.41	5.15	5.08	5.19	5.36	5.50	6.05	6.26	6.47	
SSe²	17.22	17.45	18.03	18.19	18.37	18.52	18.53	18.34	18.02	17.27	17.04	17.03	
Tilt³													
65°S	1.52	1.27	0.99	0.72	0.53	0.45	0.49	0.63	0.85	1.15	1.43	1.59	65°N
60°S	1.54	1.30	1.04	0.77	0.59	0.52	0.55	0.69	0.90	1.18	1.45	1.61	60°N
55°S	1.54	1.32	1.07	0.83	0.65	0.58	0.61	0.74	0.95	1.21	1.47	1.61	55°N
50°S	1.54	1.34	1.10	0.87	0.71	0.64	0.67	0.80	0.98	1.23	1.47	1.60	50°N
45°S	1.53	1.34	1.12	0.91	0.76	0.70	0.73	0.84	1.02	1.24	1.46	1.59	45°N
40°S	1.51	1.34	1.14	0.95	0.81	0.75	0.78	0.88	1.04	1.25	1.45	1.56	40°N
35°S	1.47	1.32	1.15	0.98	0.86	0.80	0.83	0.92	1.06	1.24	1.42	1.52	35°N
30°S	1.43	1.30	1.15	1.00	0.90	0.85	0.87	0.95	1.07	1.23	1.38	1.47	30°N
25°S	1.38	1.27	1.14	1.02	0.93	0.89	0.90	0.97	1.08	1.21	1.34	1.41	25°N
20°S	1.32	1.23	1.13	1.03	0.96	0.92	0.94	0.99	1.08	1.18	1.29	1.35	20°N
15°S	1.25	1.18	1.11	1.03	0.98	0.95	0.96	1.00	1.07	1.15	1.23	1.27	15°N
Month	July	Aug.	Sept.	Oct.	Nov.	Dec.	Jan.	Feb.	Mar.	Apr.	May	June	Tilt³
SRi¹	6.53	6.34	6.02	5.27	5.04	5.03	5.22	5.45	6.03	6.19	6.37	6.52	Month
SSe²	17.19	17.36	17.50	18.05	18.26	18.47	18.56	18.43	18.15	17.41	17.15	17.08	SRi¹
													SSe²

Southern hemisphere latitudes 25°–30°S.

Northern hemisphere latitudes 30°–35°N.

Month	Jan.	Feb.	Mar.	Apr.	May	June	July	Aug.	Sept.	Oct.	Nov.	Dec.
SRi[1]	7.07	6.50	6.17	5.36	5.06	4.56	5.08	5.29	5.48	6.10	6.35	6.59
SSe[2]	17.11	17.38	18.01	18.24	18.46	19.04	19.04	18.41	18.04	17.22	16.55	16.51
Tilt[3]												
70°N	1.67	1.37	1.04	0.73	0.53	0.44	0.48	0.63	0.88	1.22	1.56	1.76
65°N	1.69	1.40	1.09	0.79	0.59	0.51	0.54	0.70	0.93	1.26	1.58	1.77
60°N	1.70	1.43	1.13	0.85	0.65	0.57	0.61	0.75	0.98	1.29	1.60	1.78
55°N	1.69	1.44	1.16	0.89	0.71	0.63	0.67	0.81	1.02	1.31	1.60	1.77
50°N	1.68	1.44	1.18	0.93	0.76	0.69	0.72	0.85	1.05	1.32	1.60	1.75
45°N	1.66	1.44	1.20	0.97	0.81	0.75	0.78	0.89	1.08	1.33	1.58	1.72
40°N	1.62	1.43	1.21	1.00	0.86	0.79	0.82	0.93	1.10	1.32	1.55	1.68
35°N	1.58	1.40	1.21	1.02	0.90	0.84	0.87	0.96	1.11	1.31	1.51	1.63
30°N	1.52	1.37	1.20	1.04	0.93	0.88	0.90	0.99	1.12	1.29	1.47	1.57
25°N	1.46	1.33	1.18	1.05	0.96	0.92	0.93	1.01	1.12	1.26	1.41	1.49
20°N	1.38	1.28	1.16	1.05	0.98	0.94	0.96	1.02	1.11	1.22	1.34	1.41
15°N	1.30	1.22	1.13	1.05	0.99	0.97	0.98	1.02	1.09	1.18	1.27	1.32

Southern hemisphere latitudes 30°–35°S.

Month	July	Aug.	Sept.	Oct.	Nov.	Dec.	Jan.	Feb.	Mar.	Apr.	May	June
SRi[1]	7.04	6.41	6.04	5.22	4.55	4.51	5.11	5.38	6.01	6.24	6.46	7.04
SSe[2]	17.08	17.29	17.48	18.10	18.35	18.59	19.07	18.50	18.17	17.36	17.06	16.56
Tilt[3]												
70°S	1.67	1.37	1.04	0.73	0.53	0.44	0.48	0.63	0.88	1.22	1.56	1.76
65°S	1.69	1.40	1.09	0.79	0.59	0.51	0.54	0.70	0.93	1.26	1.58	1.77
60°S	1.70	1.43	1.13	0.85	0.65	0.57	0.61	0.75	0.98	1.29	1.60	1.78
55°S	1.69	1.44	1.16	0.89	0.71	0.63	0.67	0.81	1.02	1.31	1.60	1.77
50°S	1.68	1.44	1.18	0.93	0.76	0.69	0.72	0.85	1.05	1.32	1.60	1.75
45°S	1.66	1.44	1.20	0.97	0.81	0.75	0.78	0.89	1.08	1.33	1.58	1.72
40°S	1.62	1.43	1.21	1.00	0.86	0.79	0.82	0.93	1.10	1.32	1.55	1.68
35°S	1.58	1.40	1.21	1.02	0.90	0.84	0.87	0.96	1.11	1.31	1.51	1.63
30°S	1.52	1.37	1.20	1.04	0.93	0.88	0.90	0.99	1.12	1.29	1.47	1.57
25°S	1.46	1.33	1.18	1.05	0.96	0.92	0.93	1.01	1.12	1.26	1.41	1.49
20°S	1.38	1.28	1.16	1.05	0.98	0.94	0.96	1.02	1.11	1.22	1.34	1.41
15°S	1.30	1.22	1.13	1.05	0.99	0.97	0.98	1.02	1.09	1.18	1.27	1.32

Table B.3 (continued)

Northern hemisphere latitudes 35°–40°N.

Month	Jan.	Feb.	Mar.	Apr.	May	June	July	Aug.	Sept.	Oct.	Nov.	Dec.	
SRi[1]	7.19	6.57	6.17	5.32	4.55	4.43	4.56	5.22	5.47	6.14	6.46	7.12	
SSe[2]	16.59	17.31	18.00	18.28	18.57	19.17	19.16	18.48	18.05	17.18	16.44	16.38	
Tilt[3]													
75°S.	1.85	1.49	1.10	0.76	0.53	0.44	0.48	0.64	0.92	1.31	1.72	1.97	75°N.
70°S.	1.88	1.53	1.15	0.81	0.60	0.51	0.54	0.71	0.98	1.35	1.75	1.99	70°N.
65°S.	1.89	1.55	1.19	0.87	0.66	0.57	0.61	0.76	1.02	1.39	1.77	2.00	65°N.
60°S.	1.89	1.57	1.23	0.92	0.72	0.63	0.67	0.82	1.07	1.41	1.77	1.99	60°N.
55°S.	1.88	1.57	1.25	0.96	0.77	0.69	0.72	0.87	1.10	1.43	1.77	1.97	55°N.
50°S.	1.85	1.57	1.27	1.00	0.82	0.74	0.78	0.91	1.13	1.43	1.75	1.94	50°N.
45°S.	1.81	1.55	1.28	1.03	0.86	0.79	0.82	0.95	1.15	1.43	1.72	1.89	45°N.
40°S.	1.76	1.53	1.28	1.06	0.90	0.84	0.87	0.98	1.16	1.41	1.68	1.84	40°N.
35°S.	1.70	1.49	1.27	1.07	0.94	0.88	0.90	1.01	1.17	1.39	1.63	1.77	35°N.
30°S.	1.63	1.45	1.26	1.08	0.97	0.91	0.94	1.03	1.17	1.36	1.56	1.69	30°N.
25°S.	1.55	1.39	1.23	1.09	0.99	0.94	0.96	1.04	1.16	1.32	1.49	1.59	25°N.
20°S.	1.45	1.33	1.20	1.08	1.00	0.97	0.98	1.04	1.14	1.27	1.41	1.49	20°N.
15°S.	1.35	1.26	1.16	1.07	1.01	0.98	1.00	1.04	1.11	1.21	1.32	1.38	15°N.
Tilt[3]													
Month	July	Aug.	Sept.	Oct.	Nov.	Dec.	Jan.	Feb.	Mar.	Apr.	May	June	
SRi[1]	7.16	6.48	6.05	5.18	4.44	4.38	4.59	5.31	6.00	6.28	6.57	7.17	
SSe[2]	16.56	17.22	17.47	18.14	18.46	19.12	19.19	18.57	18.17	17.32	16.55	16.43	

Southern hemisphere latitudes 35°–40°S.

Northern hemisphere latitudes 40°–45°N.

Month	Jan.	Feb.	Mar.	Apr.	May	June	July	Aug.	Sept.	Oct.	Nov.	Dec.	
SRi[1]	7.33	7.06	6.20	5.26	4.43	4.27	4.42	5.13	5.45	6.20	6.58	7.28	
SSe[2]	16.45	17.22	17.58	18.34	19.09	19.33	19.30	18.57	18.07	17.12	16.32	16.22	
Tilt[3]													
80°S.	2.10	1.65	1.18	0.78	0.54	0.44	0.48	0.66	0.97	1.43	1.93	2.25	80°N.
75°S.	2.13	1.69	1.23	0.84	0.60	0.51	0.55	0.73	1.03	1.47	1.97	2.28	75°N.
70°S.	2.15	1.72	1.28	0.90	0.66	0.57	0.61	0.78	1.08	1.51	1.99	2.29	70°N.
65°S.	2.15	1.73	1.31	0.95	0.72	0.63	0.67	0.84	1.12	1.54	1.99	2.28	65°N.
60°S.	2.13	1.74	1.34	1.00	0.78	0.69	0.73	0.89	1.16	1.55	1.99	2.26	60°N.
55°S.	2.11	1.74	1.36	1.04	0.83	0.74	0.78	0.93	1.19	1.56	1.97	2.23	55°N.
50°S.	2.06	1.72	1.37	1.07	0.87	0.79	0.83	0.97	1.21	1.56	1.94	2.18	50°N.
45°S.	2.01	1.69	1.37	1.09	0.91	0.84	0.87	1.00	1.22	1.54	1.89	2.11	45°N.
40°S.	1.94	1.65	1.36	1.11	0.95	0.88	0.91	1.03	1.23	1.52	1.83	2.03	40°N.
35°S.	1.86	1.60	1.35	1.12	0.98	0.91	0.94	1.05	1.23	1.48	1.77	1.94	35°N.
30°S.	1.77	1.55	1.32	1.13	1.00	0.94	0.97	1.06	1.22	1.44	1.68	1.84	30°N.
25°S.	1.66	1.48	1.29	1.12	1.02	0.97	0.99	1.07	1.20	1.39	1.59	1.72	25°N.
20°S.	1.55	1.40	1.24	1.11	1.02	0.99	1.00	1.07	1.17	1.33	1.49	1.60	20°N.
15°S.	1.42	1.31	1.19	1.09	1.03	1.00	1.01	1.06	1.14	1.26	1.38	1.46	15°N.
Month	July	Aug.	Sept.	Oct.	Nov.	Dec.	Jan.	Feb.	Mar.	Apr.	May	June	Tilt[3]
SRi[1]	7.30	6.57	6.07	5.12	4.32	4.22	4.45	5.22	5.58	6.34	7.09	7.33	
SSe[2]	16.42	17.13	17.45	18.20	18.58	19.28	19.33	19.06	18.20	17.26	16.43	16.27	

Southern hemisphere latitudes 40°–45°S.

Table B.3 (continued)

Northern hemisphere–latitudes 45°–50°N.

Month	Jan.	Feb.	Mar.	Apr.	May	June	July	Aug.	Sept.	Oct.	Nov.	Dec.	
SRi[1]	7.50	7.16	6.22	5.19	4.29	4.07	4.25	5.03	5.43	6.27	7.12	7.48	
SSe[2]	16.28	17.12	17.56	18.41	19.23	19.53	19.47	19.07	18.09	17.05	16.18	16.02	
Tilt[3]													
85°S	2.44	1.85	1.28	0.82	0.54	0.44	0.49	0.68	1.03	1.58	2.22	2.64	85°N
80°S	2.47	1.89	1.34	0.88	0.61	0.51	0.55	0.75	1.09	1.63	2.26	2.67	80°N
75°S	2.49	1.93	1.39	0.94	0.67	0.57	0.62	0.81	1.15	1.67	2.28	2.69	75°N
70°S	2.50	1.95	1.42	1.00	0.74	0.63	0.68	0.87	1.20	1.70	2.29	2.68	70°N
65°S	2.48	1.96	1.45	1.04	0.79	0.69	0.73	0.92	1.23	1.72	2.28	2.66	65°N
60°S	2.45	1.95	1.47	1.08	0.84	0.75	0.79	0.96	1.27	1.73	2.26	2.62	60°N
55°S	2.40	1.94	1.49	1.12	0.89	0.79	0.83	1.00	1.29	1.72	2.23	2.56	55°N
50°S	2.34	1.91	1.49	1.14	0.93	0.84	0.88	1.04	1.30	1.71	2.18	2.49	50°N
45°S	2.26	1.86	1.48	1.16	0.96	0.88	0.92	1.06	1.31	1.68	2.11	2.40	45°N
40°S	2.17	1.81	1.46	1.17	0.99	0.92	0.95	1.09	1.31	1.64	2.03	2.29	40°N
35°S	2.06	1.74	1.43	1.18	1.02	0.95	0.98	1.10	1.30	1.59	1.94	2.17	35°N
30°S	1.94	1.66	1.40	1.17	1.03	0.97	1.00	1.10	1.28	1.54	1.84	2.04	30°N
25°S	1.81	1.58	1.35	1.16	1.04	0.99	1.02	1.11	1.25	1.47	1.72	1.89	25°N
20°S	1.67	1.48	1.29	1.14	1.05	1.01	1.02	1.10	1.21	1.39	1.60	1.73	20°N
15°S	1.51	1.37	1.23	1.12	1.05	1.01	1.03	1.08	1.17	1.30	1.46	1.56	15°N

Month	July	Aug.	Sept.	Oct.	Nov.	Dec.	Jan.	Feb.	Mar.	Apr.	May	June	Tilt[3]
SRi[1]	7.47	7.07	6.09	5.05	4.18	4.02	4.28	5.12	5.56	6.41	7.23	7.53	
SSe[2]	16.25	17.03	17.43	18.27	19.12	19.48	19.50	19.16	18.22	17.19	16.29	16.07	

Southern hemisphere latitudes 45°–50°S.

Northern hemisphere latitudes 50°–55°N.

Month	Jan.	Feb.	Mar.	Apr.	May	June	July	Aug.	Sept.	Oct.	Nov.	Dec.	Tilt³
SRi¹	8.11	7.28	6.25	5.11	4.11	3.43	4.04	4.51	5.40	6.35	7.30	8.12	
SSe²	16.07	16.59	17.53	18.49	19.41	20.17	20.08	19.19	18.12	16.57	15.59	15.38	
Tilt³													
90°S.	2.92	2.12	1.41	0.86	0.56	0.44	0.49	0.70	1.11	1.77	2.61	3.21	90°N.
85°S.	2.96	2.17	1.47	0.93	0.62	0.51	0.56	0.77	1.18	1.83	2.66	3.25	85°N.
80°S.	2.99	2.21	1.52	0.99	0.69	0.57	0.62	0.84	1.24	1.88	2.69	3.27	80°N.
75°S.	2.99	2.24	1.57	1.05	0.75	0.63	0.69	0.90	1.29	1.91	2.70	3.27	75°N.
70°S.	2.98	2.25	1.60	1.10	0.80	0.69	0.74	0.95	1.33	1.93	2.70	3.24	70°N.
65°S.	2.94	2.24	1.62	1.14	0.86	0.75	0.80	1.00	1.36	1.94	2.67	3.20	65°N.
60°S.	2.89	2.22	1.63	1.18	0.90	0.80	0.84	1.04	1.39	1.94	2.63	3.13	60°N.
55°S.	2.82	2.19	1.63	1.20	0.95	0.85	0.89	1.07	1.40	1.92	2.58	3.04	55°N.
50°S.	2.73	2.14	1.62	1.22	0.98	0.88	0.93	1.10	1.41	1.89	2.50	2.94	50°N.
45°S.	2.62	2.08	1.60	1.23	1.01	0.92	0.96	1.13	1.41	1.85	2.41	2.81	45°N.
40°S.	2.49	2.01	1.57	1.24	1.04	0.95	0.99	1.14	1.39	1.80	2.30	2.66	40°N.
35°S.	2.35	1.92	1.53	1.24	1.06	0.98	1.01	1.15	1.37	1.73	2.18	2.50	35°N.
30°S.	2.19	1.82	1.48	1.23	1.07	1.00	1.03	1.15	1.34	1.66	2.04	2.32	30°N.
25°S.	2.02	1.70	1.42	1.21	1.07	1.01	1.04	1.14	1.31	1.57	1.90	2.13	25°N.
20°S.	1.83	1.58	1.35	1.18	1.07	1.02	1.05	1.12	1.26	1.47	1.74	1.92	20°N.
15°S.	1.64	1.45	1.28	1.15	1.06	1.03	1.04	1.11	1.21	1.36	1.56	1.71	15°N.

Month	July	Aug.	Sept.	Oct.	Nov.	Dec.	Jan.	Feb.	Mar.	Apr.	May	June
SRi¹	8.08	7.19	6.12	4.57	3.59	3.38	4.07	4.59	5.53	6.49	7.41	8.17
SSe²	16.04	16.51	17.40	18.35	19.30	20.12	20.11	19.28	18.25	17.11	16.11	15.43

Southern hemisphere latitudes 50°–55°S.

Northern hemisphere latitudes 55°–60°N.

Month	Jan.	Feb.	Mar.	Apr.	May	June	July	Aug.	Sept.	Oct.	Nov.	Dec.	
SRi[1]	8.41	7.44	6.28	5.01	3.46	3.09	3.34	4.35	5.37	6.45	7.55	8.46	
SSe[2]	15.37	16.44	17.50	18.59	20.06	20.51	20.38	19.35	18.15	16.47	15.35	15.04	
Tilt[3]													
90°S	3.71	2.56	1.64	0.98	0.64	0.51	0.56	0.81	1.28	2.10	3.25	4.16	90°N.
85°S	3.74	2.61	1.70	1.05	0.70	0.58	0.63	0.87	1.35	2.16	3.29	4.19	85°N.
80°S	3.75	2.64	1.75	1.11	0.77	0.64	0.69	0.94	1.40	2.20	3.31	4.19	80°N.
75°S	3.74	2.65	1.79	1.16	0.82	0.70	0.75	0.99	1.45	2.22	3.30	4.16	75°N.
70°S	3.70	2.65	1.81	1.21	0.88	0.75	0.81	1.04	1.48	2.23	3.28	4.11	70°N.
65°S	3.63	2.63	1.82	1.25	0.92	0.80	0.85	1.09	1.51	2.23	3.23	4.03	65°N.
60°S	3.54	2.59	1.83	1.28	0.97	0.85	0.90	1.12	1.53	2.21	3.16	3.92	60°N.
55°S	3.43	2.54	1.82	1.30	1.01	0.89	0.94	1.15	1.53	2.18	3.07	3.78	55°N.
50°S	3.30	2.46	1.79	1.31	1.04	0.93	0.98	1.17	1.53	2.13	2.96	3.62	50°N.
45°S	3.14	2.37	1.76	1.32	1.06	0.96	1.00	1.19	1.52	2.07	2.83	3.44	45°N.
40°S	2.96	2.27	1.71	1.31	1.08	0.99	1.03	1.20	1.50	2.00	2.69	3.23	40°N.
35°S	2.77	2.15	1.66	1.30	1.09	1.01	1.05	1.20	1.46	1.91	2.52	3.01	35°N.
30°S	2.55	2.02	1.59	1.28	1.10	1.02	1.06	1.19	1.42	1.81	2.34	2.76	30°N.
25°S	2.32	1.87	1.51	1.25	1.10	1.03	1.06	1.18	1.37	1.70	2.14	2.50	25°N.
20°S	2.08	1.72	1.43	1.22	1.09	1.04	1.06	1.16	1.31	1.57	1.93	2.22	20°N.
Tilt[3]													
Month	July	Aug.	Sept.	Oct.	Nov.	Dec.	Jan.	Feb.	Mar.	Apr.	May	June	
SRi[1]	8.38	7.35	6.15	4.47	3.35	3.04	3.37	4.44	5.50	6.59	8.06	8.51	
SSe[2]	15.34	16.35	17.37	18.45	19.55	20.46	20.41	19.44	18.28	17.01	15.46	15.09	

Southern hemisphere latitudes 55°–60°S.

Table B.4 *Example of entries in Table B.2 for correcting values of daily insolation according to tilt angle of a module. Details are given for São Paulo in the southern hemisphere and are explained in Example B.1.*

#												
1	Site details: Name São Paulo Position Brazil Latitude 24°S.											
2	July	Aug.	Sept.	Oct.	Nov.	Dec.	Jan.	Feb.	Mar.	Apr.	May	June
3	6.44	6.28	6.01	5.31	5.12	5.13	5.31	5.51	6.04	6.15	6.29	6.42
4	17.28	17.42	17.51	18.01	18.18	18.37	18.47	18.37	18.14	17.45	17.23	17.18
5	Daily insolation on a horizontal plane in units of langleys											
6	260	300	380	440	470	470	470	460	390	350	280	270
7	3.02	3.48	4.41	5.10	5.45	5.45	5.45	5.33	4.52	4.06	3.25	3.13
8	Daily insolation corrected for a tilt angle of 25°N.											
9	1.32	1.22	1.10	0.99	0.90	0.86	0.88	0.94	1.04	1.17	1.28	1.35
10	(3.99)	4.25	4.85	5.05	4.90	4.69	4.80	5.01	4.70	4.75	(4.16)	4.23
11	Daily insolation corrected for a tilt angle of 50°N.											
12	1.42	1.24	1.03	0.82	0.66	0.59	0.62	0.74	0.92	1.15	1.36	1.48
13	4.29	4.32	4.54	4.18	3.60	(3.22)	(3.38)	3.94	4.16	4.67	4.42	4.63
14	Daily insolation corrected for a tilt angle of 40°N.											
15	1.41	1.26	1.08	0.90	0.77	0.71	0.73	0.84	0.99	1.18	1.36	1.45
16	4.26	4.38	4.76	4.59	4.20	(3.87)	(3.98)	4.48	4.47	4.79	4.42	4.54
17	Daily insolation corrected for a tilt angle of 35°N.											
18	1.39	1.25	1.09	0.93	0.82	0.77	0.79	0.88	1.01	1.18	1.34	1.43
19	(4.20)	(4.35)	4.81	4.74	4.47	(4.20)	(4.31)	4.69	4.57	4.79	(4.36)	4.48
20	Daily insolation corrected for a tilt angle of 30°N.											
21	1.36	1.24	1.10	0.96	0.86	0.81	0.83	0.92	1.03	1.18	1.32	1.39
22	(4.11)	4.32	4.85	4.90	4.69	4.41	4.52	4.90	4.66	4.79	(4.29)	4.35

Example B.1

Here are monthly averages of daily insolation in langleys per day for São Paulo (the same site as Example 8.1).

Jan.	Feb.	Mar.	Apr.	May	June	July	Aug.	Sept.	Oct.	Nov.	Dec.
470	460	390	350	280	270	260	300	380	440	470	470

Which month has the lowest daily insolation after correcting for the tilt angle of the module?

Table B.4 is a copy of Table B.2 completed for São Paulo using these values. The months start from July since São Paulo is south of the equator. The latitude for São Paulo is in the range 20–25° so this identifies the table to use in Table B.3. The times of sunrise and sunset are copied into Table B.4.

Since the values of daily insolation are given in langleys, they are converted for row 7 of Table B.4 using a conversion factor of 0.0116 in Formula (B.1). The first angle tried for module tilt is 25°N. which is the closest to the latitude and facing towards the equator. At this tilt, the lowest corrected values of daily insolation are 3.99 and 4.16 for July and May in Line 10.

To increase upon 3.99, a much higher tilt of 50°N. is tried. Now the lowest values are 3.22 and 3.38 for December and January in row 13 which are lower than for the first attempt. Angles are tried between 25°N. and 50°N. to find the optimum. A tilt angle of 35°N. has the highest circled values of 4.20 to 4.36 (row 19). If the electricity is required mostly for lighting, the module could be tilted to improve the values for winter months which have late sunrise and early sunset times. However, the results for this site show that at a steeper tilt angle than 35°N., there is only a small gain in peak-hours for winter months compared to a large drop for summer months. Therefore, 35°N. tilt is the optimum.

The answer obtained in Example 8.1 from the maps is 4.1 peak-hours per day at a tilt of 24°N. The calculations in Example B.1 show that a small improvement is achieved by tilting the module at 35°N. as well as evening out the variation through the year.

C | Full worked example of a system design

This appendix shows how the procedures from Chapters 2–6 and Chapter 8 are used when designing a system. The main steps involved are summarized in Figure C.1.

The example is for a school in Bangladesh at a latitude of 22°N. and longitude of 90°E. A scale plan of the buildings and rooms on the site is shown in Figure C.2. The plan also shows possible routes for cables which are described later under the section on 'distribution'.

The school requires power for lighting and small electronic appliances, such as cassette players, torches, and equipment in the science laboratory.

Choice of module

Before selecting the type of solar module, it is necessary to choose the method of regulating battery charging. This is summarized by Figure 4.6. Since the system is large, the result of the first decision recommends using a charge regulator.

Table 2.1 shows which modules can be used. The site has a high temperature so suitable modules are either the crystalline type with a minimum of thirty-four cells or the thin-film type with V_{OC} greater than 23 V.

The choice of suitable modules then depends on their relative price. Table C.1 (from Table 2.2) gives some examples of prices and current outputs under STC. From the last column, the one of best value is module C since it has the lowest value of $ per amp. However, for the values used in this example, the differences in total cost per amp of current between the three modules are small.

In comparing crystalline and thin-film modules, a larger area of thin-film modules is required for the same current output. When comparing the total costs of a full solar array, the extra costs for the type C modules of a larger support structure and additional wiring are likely to out-weigh the small differences of cost per amp in Table C.1. Therefore Module B is selected for the rest of this example.

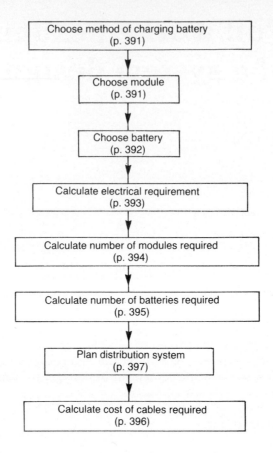

Figure C.1   Summary of the main steps for designing a solar electric system (p. page references to text).

Choice of battery

Details of batteries that may be available near the site are given in Table C.2 (based on Table 3.5).

In order to compare the relative value for money of the three batteries, some of the details from Table C.2 are used for calculations in Table C.3 (from Table 3.6).

The three batteries vary in cost a lot but the relative cost for 'one cycle' is about the same at around 0.3 A h per $. When considered over the 'cycle life', battery F is the best value at 428 A h per $. This is because it is a nickel–cadmium type which can be cycled over its full capacity and has a long cycle life.

Table C.1 *Example of entries for Table 2.2 showing how modules are compared by cost per amp of output current.*

Type of regulation: self-reg. / self-reg. with a diode / charge reg.

Local climate: below 30 °C / above 30 °C

Details of make and model of each module	Cost for one module			Current (A)	Total cost ÷ current
	Price	Other	Total		
Module A (crystalline, 35 cells, 39 Wₚ) $260	$20	$280	2.2	$127/A
Module B (crystalline, 36 cells, 50 Wₚ) $320	$20	$340	2.9	$117/A
Module C (thin-film, 23 V_oc, 12 Wₚ) $ 80	$ 10	$ 90	0.8	$112/A

Table C.2 *Example of entries for Table 3.5 which summarizes the details of available batteries.*

Make and model	Nominal capacity (A h)¹	Voltage (V)	Costs for one battery			Cost for a 12 V battery
			Price	Transport and other	Total	
Battery D (lead-acid, SLI for trucks)	50	12	$80	$10	$90	$90
Battery E (lead-acid, solar, low antimony)	100	12	$220	$50	$270	$270
Battery F (nickel-cadmium, vented)	200	6	$300	$50	$350	$700

¹At C/100 or C_{100} (measured for a full discharge over 100 hours).

However, the full cost advantage of this choice is only gained after a number of years. If funding at the start is limited, battery E may be a better choice.

Sizing the system

The procedure for sizing the minimum number of modules is summarized in Figure 8.2. First the electrical requirement must be calculated.

Using the lighting recommendations from Table 6.3, two 15 W tube lamps

Table C.3 *Example of comparing batteries by value for money using details from Table C.2 and typical specifications from Table 3.7.*

Number	Nominal capacity (A h)	Cost for a 12 V battery	Usable cycle depth (%)	Cycle life[1] (cycles)	Capacity (Ah)		Relative value for money	
					Usable	Total usable[2]	One cycle	Cycle life
D	50	$90	50	200	25	5 000	0.28 Ah/$	56 Ah/$
E	100	$270	80	1200	80	96 000	0.30 Ah/$	355 Ah/$
F	200	$700	100	1500	200	300 000	0.29 Ah/$	428 Ah/$

[1] At usable cycle depth.
[2] Over cycle life.

are used in each of the large rooms and one 8 W tube lamp in each of the small rooms. Four 15 W tube lamps are chosen for the long dormitory because it does not need the same level of illumination as the other rooms. Immediately around each building, illumination is provided by light from the rooms so only a single exterior lamppost is needed in the middle of the site. This contains two 8 W tubes in a weather-proof housing.

Small electronic appliances could be served by a power outlet circuit with one socket in every room. This would be separate from the lighting circuits which are switched off during the day. However, sealed nickel–cadmium cells are more versatile for the different requirements. The cost of the cells and charger is offset by not requiring the extra distribution system.

Table C.4 (based on Table 8.4) shows how the total power requirement is calculated. The electrical requirements for each group of appliances are divided between whether they are essential or non-essential. Each house has one lamp which is always available. The other lamp is on a circuit which is disconnected when the batteries are low.

The guideline in Chapter 8 recommends that the essential total is less than half of the non-essential total. This is not the case in Table C.4. However, the best-value battery from Table C.3 is nickel–cadmium, so deep discharges are not a problem. Note that a low-voltage disconnect does not work well with nickel–cadmium batteries because of the small change in voltage during discharge. Therefore the non-essential circuits must be switched off by hand during cloudy weather to reduce use of electricity. If the batteries are allowed to become completely flat, no electricity is available for any of the appliances.

The maps in Figure 8.4(c) are used to find the variation in daily insolation over the year for the site. The results are summarized in Table C.5 based on the

Table C.4 *Summary of lighting requirements and calculation of total daily electrical requirement for the school.*

Type of circuit	Details of appliances	Total power of circuit (W)	Daily use (hours per day)	Electrical requirement (W h per day)	
				Essential	Non-essential
Lighting	Block A: 5 tubes (15 W each) 2 tubes (8 W each)	91	4	364	
Lighting	Block B, 6 tubes (15 W each)	90	4		360
Lighting	Block C: 8 tubes (15 W each) 1 tube (8 W)	128	4		512
Lighting	Block D, 4 tubes (15 W each)	60	2	120	
Lighting	Block E, 2 tubes (8 W each)	16	6		96
Lighting	Block H, 8 tubes (8 W each)	64	6	192	192
Sockets	Charger for sealed nickel-cadmium batteries	5	16	80	
Sub-totals for each group of circuits (W h per day):				756	1160
Total daily requirement for electricity (W h per day):				1916	

table in Figure 8.5(b). The value of 4.6 peak-hours per day at 12 V is used to size the system since it is the lowest over a three month period.

Using module B from Table C.1, the daily output of one module is calculated from Formula (8.2):

2.9 A × 4.6 peak-hours per day × 12 V = 160 W h per day at 12 V

Using a nickel–cadmium battery, the charging efficiency is about 70 per cent. The minimum number of modules needed is calculated with these values in Formula (8.3):

1916 W h per day × 100% ÷ 160 W h per day at 12 V ÷ 70% = 17

Therefore the minimum number of modules that can be used is 17.

The procedure for sizing the number of batteries is shown in Figure 8.7. Five days is chosen for the storage period of the batteries since the site sometimes has a week of cloudy weather. Using Formula (8.4) the total usable capacity needed is:

1916 W h per day × 5 days ÷ 12 V = 798 A h at 12 V

Table C.5 *Summary of measurements from the maps in Figure 8.4(c).*

Module details: make	Module B	type (conditions:	single crystal at load of 14 V)
current	2.9 A		
Site details: name	a school	position	Bangladesh
latitude	22° N.	longitude	90° E.

	Results from each quarterly period			
	Mar.–May	June–Aug.	Sept.–Nov.	Dec.–Feb.
Average daily insolation (peak-hours per day)	6.2	4.6	5.4	5.4
Daily output of one module (W h per day at 12 V)	216	160	188	188

Table C.6 *Calculating the total cost of cables required in a centralized system operating at 12 V. Required length of cable estimated from the layout in Figure C.2(a). Minimum cable sizes are obtained using the formula method summarized in Figure 5.5 with a voltage drop of 0.6 V. Cable of 10 mm^2 is doubled or tripled where sizes larger than 10 mm^2 are required because thicker cables are difficult to handle.*

Group of buildings	Appliances Total power (W)	Maximum current (A)	Length of cable to last appliance in circuit (m) Horizontal	+ Vertical	= Total	Minimum cable size (mm^2)	Cable requirements (m) 4 mm^2	6 mm^2	10 mm^2
A	91	7.6	68	9	77	39			308
B	90	7.5	55	9	64	32		128	128
C	128	10.7	38	3	41	29			123
D	60	5.0	85	9	94	31		188	188
E	16	1.3	43	11	54	5		54	
H	64	5.3	65	15	80	28			160

Total requirement for each size of cable (m):		370	407
Unit price for each size of cable ($/m):	0.68	0.95	1.55
Cost for each size of cable:		$352	$1406
Minimum total cost of cables:		$ 1758	

Table C.7 *Calculating the total cost of cables required in a centralized system operating at 24 V. Required length of cable estimated from the layout in Figure C.2(a). Table 5.5 is used to obtain the minimum cable sizes following the procedure in Figure 5.4.*

Group of buildings	Total power of appliances (W)	Length of cable to last appliance in circuit (m) Horizontal	+ Vertical	= Total	Minimum cable size (mm^2)	Cable requirements (m) $4\,mm^2$	$6\,mm^2$	$10\,mm^2$
A	91	68	9	77	10			77
B	90	55	9	64	10			64
C	128	38	3	41	10			41
D	60	85	9	94	10			94
E	16	43	11	54	4	54		
H	64	65	15	80	10			80

	$4\,mm^2$	$6\,mm^2$	$10\,mm^2$
Total requirement for each size of cable (m):	54		356
Unit price for each size of cable ($/m):	0.68	0.95	1.55
Cost for each size of cable:	$37		$552
Minimum total cost of cables:		$589	

The details for Battery F are used in Formula (8.5). The type F batteries have a nominal voltage of 6 V so they are required in series-connected pairs to form 12 V batteries. For capacity, 200 A h is used in the formula:

789 A h at 12 V $\times$ 100% $\div$ 200 A h $\div$ 100% = 3.95

Therefore four 12 V batteries are required. Since each 12 V battery is made up from a pair, a total of eight of the type F batteries is required.

Distribution

According to Figure 5.3, the site can be wired as one large system or several small systems. Figure C.2 shows possible routes of cables for both arrangements.

For the single large system, there is a choice of operating at 12 V or 24 V d.c. One aspect of choosing between the three options depends on the total wire cost for each. These costs are calculated in Tables C.6–C.8 using the procedures from Figures 5.4 and 5.5. The batteries are at floor level, and between buildings the cables run underground. Therefore a length of 3 m is added for each place where

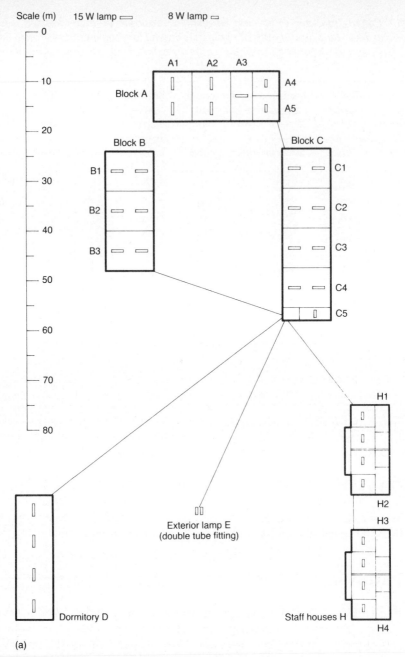

Figure C.2   Scale plan of site showing rooms, lamps, and possible arrangements for wiring.

(a)   Single centralized system for operation at 12 or 24 V.

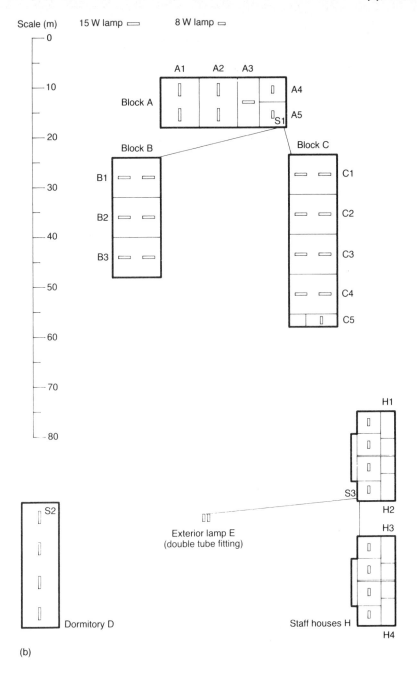

Figure C.2 (continued)
(b) Three separate systems for operation at 12 V.

Table C:8 *Calculating the total cost of cables required in three separate systems operating at 12 V. Required length of cable estimated from the layout in Figure C.2(b). Minimum cable sizes are obtained using the formula method summarized in Figure 5.5 with a voltage drop of 0.6 V. Cable of 10 mm² is doubled or tripled where sizes larger than 10 mm² are required because thicker cables are difficult to handle.*

Battery place	Group of rooms	Appliances		Length of cable to last appliance in circuit (m)			Min. cable size (mm²)	Cable requirements (m)		
		Total power (W)	Maximum current (A)	Horizontal	+ Vertical	= Total		4 mm²	6 mm²	10 mm²
S1	A₁ A₂ A₃	75	6.3	28	3	31	13		62	
	B₁ B₂	60	5.0	45	9	54	18			108
	B₃	30	2.5	53	9	62	10			63
	C₁ C₂	60	5.0	25	9	34	11			34
	C₃ C₄ C₅	68	5.7	45	9	54	21			108
S2	D	60	5.0	25	3	28	9			28
	E	16	1.3	32	11	43	4	43		
S3	H₁ H₂	32	2.7	18	3	21	4	21		
	H₃ H₄	32	2.7	28	9	37	7		37	

	4 mm²	6 mm²	10 mm²
Total requirement for each size of cable (m):	64	99	340
Unit price for each size of cable ($/m):	0.68	0.95	1.55
Cost for each size of cable:	$44	$94	$527
Minimum total cost of cables:			$665

the cable goes up or down a wall. The total vertical length is put in the 'Vertical' column for each circuit.

The most expensive option is the centralized system operating at 12 V. However, this cost must be weighed up against the other factors given in Chapter 5 concerning large systems.

D Testing lead–acid batteries

A procedure for testing the condition of a lead–acid battery is given in this appendix. It can be used to check the performance of batteries from a system and for assessing second-hand batteries that are intended for use in a system.

The sequence of steps involved is summarized in Figure D.1. Measurements

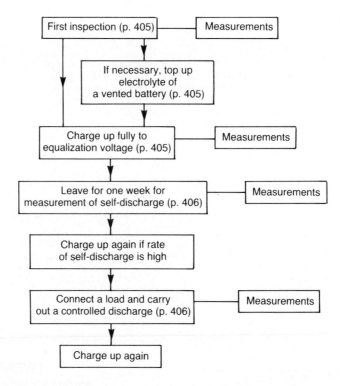

Figure D.1 Summary of steps involved in testing the condition of a lead–acid battery.

are taken of voltage, specific gravity, and temperature. For an accurate assessment of a battery, the full test can take up to two weeks.

A procedure is also given at the end for changing the electrolyte as a last resort for dead batteries.

Deterioration of batteries

Some of the reasons for the deterioration of a lead–acid battery are as follows:

☐ Reduced capacity can be caused by a combination of several factors. Active material shed from the positive plates, corrosion of the grid structure in the positive plates, and sulphation.
☐ Increased self-discharge due to contamination of the negative plates by antimony.
☐ Short circuit failure if plates touch. This can be caused by a build-up of shed material at the bottom, buckling of plates, or growth of plates at the edges and through the separator.
☐ Open circuit failure caused by corrosion or cracking of the grid structure in the positive plates.

Equipment

The following equipment is required for carrying out the tests:

☐ For vented cells, an accurate battery hydrometer with divisions every ten units.
☐ Digital or expanded-scale voltmeter (see Chapter 13).
☐ Mercury-in-glass thermometer with a range of 0–60 °C (30–140 °F).
☐ If available, an ammeter rated up to 5 A.
☐ A load for controlled discharge of batteries. For testing 12 V batteries, this can be provided by a rheostat (12 V, 1 A), resistors (1R 12 W) or a light bulb 12 V 12 W).

If some of the equipment is not available or too expensive, try to do the tests in a school science laboratory which has all the equipment.

It is also necessary to have access to charging facilities. These are required at the start and end of the procedure.

Taking and recording measurements

A full record of the tests should be kept. Table D.1 can be used for recording actions and measurements taken.

Table D.1 *Example of a test sheet for recording measurements while testing a battery. Load current measurements are only needed for the discharge test. If an ammeter is not available, the resistance or power rating of the load for this test must be known in order to calculate the average current.*

Battery type:
Site of system:
Date received: Tested by:

Date	Time	Action	Temperature[1]	Voltage of battery	Load current (A)	Specific gravity[2]					
						1	2	3	4	5	6
		Received									
		Charging started									
		Charging									
		Charging stopped									
		Self-discharge test									
		Self-discharge test									
		Charging started									
		Charging stopped									
		Discharge at 1 A									
		Discharging									
		Discharge stopped									
		Discharge resumed									
		Discharging									
		Discharge Test Completed									

[1]Temperature measured for one cell of battery.
[2]Cell number counting from positive terminal of battery.

Voltages are measured with the test probes connected directly to the terminals of the battery. Measurements should be recorded to an accuracy of 0.1 V or better.

Specific gravity of the electrolyte can only be measured if the battery has vented cells. The procedure for using a battery hydrometer is given in Chapter 11. The measurements should be made carefully to an accuracy of five units.

The temperature of the electrolyte should be measured for one cell in the battery. This enables the measurements of voltage and specific gravity to be corrected to a standard temperature.

To measure the temperature, first make sure that the end of the thermometer is clean. Insert into one cell so that the bulb is fully covered by electrolyte but not pressing against the plates. After waiting for about thirty seconds, read the temperature while the thermometer is still in the cell. Wash the thermometer thoroughly in cool water before storing away safely. Do not clean with hot water which could break the thermometer.

First inspection of battery

Inspect the battery for obvious signs of damage to the case, cover or terminals. Consider replacing the battery if the damage is severe. Next, measure the voltage of the whole battery and of each cell if the interconnections are exposed. If the voltages are less than 1.5 per cell (less than 9 V for a 12 V battery), this shows that the battery is no good.

Measure the specific gravity for each cell. Any cell with less than 1100 is defective.

For batteries in transparent cases, the condition of the plates can be inspected. Here is a list of good features to look for:

- [ ] Small amount of sludge at the bottom and certainly well below the bottom edges of the plates.
- [ ] Plates parallel with no sign of buckling.
- [ ] No sign of corrosion along the edges of positive plates.

If there is a lot of sludge or the plates are buckled and corroded, the battery should be replaced.

In some types of long-life batteries used for stationary applications, the plates can be removed and dismantled from the electrodes. This enables a thorough examination of their condition and replacement of defective plates and separators. This work should be done by a supplier who has access to spare parts.

Topping up and equalization charge

A battery should pass the first inspection before it is worth continuing with the following tests.

Table D.2 *Specific gravity of various types of lead–acid battery at full charge. The value for the particular battery used in a system should be given by the supplier. If possible, measure the specific gravity of a fully charged battery before taking the battery away from the supplier.*

Type of battery	Specific gravity at 25 °C (77 °F)
SLI: temperate climate	1270–1285
tropical climate	1210–1240
Traction	1250–1280
Stationary and PV	1210–1240

For accurate measurements of state of charge, the electrolyte in vented cells must be at the maximum level. Clean the top of the battery and top up with distilled or deionized water, as described in Chapter 11.

The battery should be given an equalization charge. This means charging to above 14 V (see Table 3.2) for about two hours. Gassing at this charging voltage ensures that the electrolyte is evenly mixed by the stirring action of the bubbles. This voltage also ensures that all the cells are fully charged.

Full charge can be confirmed by measuring the specific gravity which should not change over a two-hour period. The specific gravity at full charge is not fixed and a range of values is summarized in Table D.2 for various types of batteries.

Self-discharge

To test the rate of self-discharge, the voltage and specific gravity are measured while there is no current being drawn by a load. Standard procedures for standby batteries specify a test of self-discharge over ninety days. However, one week should be sufficient to show if the rate of self-discharge is too high.

Some changes occur over the first day as the battery settles. After the first day, a drop of 0.2 V for a 12 V battery or ten units of specific gravity over several days is high. When measurements are obtained over a week, they can be converted to the amount of charge lost in A h after the capacity is measured.

Usable capacity

This test requires discharge at a constant current while measuring the voltage and specific gravity of the electrolyte at regular intervals. Discharge is through a fixed load and three suggestions for loads to use are given in the equipment list.

The capacity test should be carried out for a discharge current of about C/100 amps. This means the capacity in A h units divided by 100 hours. If the nominal capacity of the battery is not known, a rough estimate can be obtained

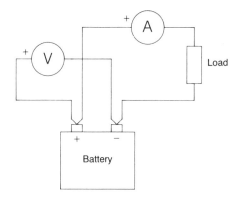

Figure D.2   Circuit for controlled discharge of battery while monitoring the voltage across the battery terminals and the current through the load.

for a 12 V battery by multiplying the battery weight in kilograms by 3 (or weight in pounds by 6). Otherwise use a current of about 1 A.

The current should be measured by an ammeter during the test and the test circuit is shown in Figure D.2. If an ammeter is not available, use a 12R resistor or a 12 W bulb which both draw 1 A at 12 V.

By discharging a 12 V battery to a voltage of 10.8 V, the full capacity of the battery can be calculated. However, it is not really necessary to do a full discharge since the main aim of this test is to measure the usable capacity.

Discharge is only necessary to 50 per cent state of charge. Unfortunately the relationship between state of charge and measurements of voltage and specific gravity is not the same for all lead–acid batteries. Stationary-type batteries for solar, standby and starting generators have an excess of electrolyte around the plates. The specific gravity falls by a small amount of about 100 units during full discharge. In SLI batteries, the plates are fitted closely together inside each container and the specific gravity falls by about 300 for a full discharge.

The discharge test is stopped under the following conditions:

☐ For batteries with excess electrolyte as in solar and standby batteries, continue the discharge for a drop in specific gravity of 50.
☐ For closely spaced plates as in most SLI batteries, carry out the discharge for a drop of 150 in specific gravity.
☐ For all types of 12 V batteries including sealed batteries, stop the discharge before the voltage reaches 11.0 V.

Take measurements of voltage, specific gravity, and temperature at the start and end of each day. Record the values in Table D.1.

At the end of the discharge test, take the battery for charging to full capacity.

Temperature correction and calculation of charge

For these calculations, make a copy of Table D.3 and fill in the measurements for the discharge part of the test. Some values are included in Table D.3 as examples.

To calculate the amount of 'Charge used' in A h units, add up the 'Elapsed time' in hours to each measurement and multiply it by the 'Average discharge current' in amps.

The standard reference temperature is 25 °C (77 °F). Measurements of specific gravity and voltage are corrected to this temperature using Table D.4. Proceed as follows:

1. Find the column with the closest temperature to the value measured in the battery.
2. Look down this column to the closest specific gravity to the value measured.
3. Look along this row to the specific gravity at 25 °C. Write this value in your table.
4. Look down the column found in Step 1 to the appropriate voltage row at the bottom for the type of battery being tested. This gives the voltage correction which should be copied, together with its '+' or '−' sign, into your table.
5. Add or subtract the voltage correction from your voltage measurement to give the corrected value for 25 °C.

Conclusion from discharge test

The usable capacity of the battery is obtained from the three columns on the right in Table D.3. The usable capacity can then be used in Table 3.6 to calculate the relative value for money of the battery, and Figure 8.7 for sizing the number of batteries required in the system. The values to use from Table D.3 are as follows:

1. For batteries with excess electrolyte, the usable capacity to about 50 per cent state of charge is the 'Charge used' when the specific gravity is reduced by 50 units.
2. For SLI-type batteries, the usable capacity should be to a state of charge above 50 per cent. Therefore use the value of 'Charge used' when the specific gravity is reduced by 100 units.
3. For sealed batteries, the usable capacity to 50 per cent state of charge is for a voltage drop of about 0.6 V for 12 V batteries (0.1 V per 2 V cell in a battery).

Table D.3 *Table for summarizing measurements from the discharge test, as recorded in a copy of Table D.1. Values are included as an example of how the corrections are made. The example is for a 100 A h solar battery, so the discharge test is ended after the specific gravity reduces by fifty units (see text). The charge by the end is 55 A h. This is about half of the expected capacity showing that the battery is still in good condition.*

Nominal voltage of battery: 12 V   Average discharge current: 1.2 A

Date[1]	Time[1]	Elapsed time (hours)[2]	Temperature[1] (°C)	Battery voltage (V)[1]	Voltage correction (V)[3]	Average specific gravity of cells[1]	Charge used (A h)[4]	Corrected measurements	
								Voltage at load (V)	Specific gravity[3]
11/9	10:00	0	21	13.1	−0.15	1225	0	12.95	1220
11/9	17:00	7	28	12.4	+0.15	1205	8	12.55	1210
12/9	8.00	22	26	12.3	0	1190	22	12.30	1190
12/9	17:00	31	34	11.9	+0.30	1175	37	12.20	1180
13/9	8.00	46	22	12.2	−0.15	1175	56	12.05	1170

[1]From Table D.1.
[2]From the 'Date' and 'Time' values.
[3]Using Table D.4.
[4]Elapsed time multiplied by 'Average discharge current'.

Table D.4 *Temperature corrections for specific gravity and voltage measurements of lead–acid batteries.*

	Specific gravity at various temperatures											
	0 °C 32 °F	5 °C 41 °F	10 °C 50 °F	15 °C 59 °F	20 °C 68 °F	**25 °C** **77 °F**	30 °C 86 °F	35 °C 95 °F	40 °C 104 °F	45 °C 113 °F	50 °C 122 °F	55 °C 131 °F
	1325	1320	1315	1310	1305	1300	1295	1290	1285	1280	1275	1270
	1315	1310	1305	1300	1295	1290	1285	1280	1275	1270	1265	1260
	1305	1300	1295	1290	1285	1280	1275	1270	1265	1260	1255	1250
	1290	1290	1285	1280	1275	1270	1265	1260	1255	1250	1245	1245
	1280	1275	1270	1270	1265	1260	1255	1250	1250	1245	1240	1235
	1270	1265	1260	1260	1255	1250	1245	1240	1240	1235	1230	1225
	1260	1255	1250	1250	1245	1240	1235	1230	1230	1225	1220	1215
	1250	1245	1240	1240	1235	1230	1225	1220	1220	1215	1210	1205
	1240	1235	1230	1230	1225	1220	1215	1210	1210	1205	1200	1195
	1225	1225	1220	1215	1215	1210	1205	1205	1200	1195	1190	1190
	1215	1215	1210	1205	1205	1200	1195	1195	1190	1185	1180	1180
	1205	1205	1200	1195	1195	1190	1185	1185	1180	1175	1170	1170
	1195	1195	1190	1185	1185	1180	1175	1175	1170	1165	1160	1160
	1185	1185	1180	1175	1175	1170	1165	1165	1160	1155	1150	1150
	1175	1175	1170	1165	1165	1160	1155	1155	1150	1150	1145	1140
	1165	1165	1160	1155	1155	1150	1145	1145	1140	1135	1135	1130
	1155	1155	1150	1145	1145	1140	1135	1135	1130	1125	1120	1120
	1145	1140	1140	1135	1130	1130	1125	1125	1120	1115	1115	1110
	1135	1130	1130	1125	1125	1120	1115	1115	1110	1110	1105	1100

Voltage correction to 25 °C (77 °F) for four nominal battery voltages

	0 °C 32 °F	5 °C 41 °F	10 °C 50 °F	15 °C 59 °F	20 °C 68 °F	25 °C 77 °F	30 °C 86 °F	35 °C 95 °F	40 °C 104 °F	45 °C 113 °F	50 °C 122 °F	55 °C 131 °F
2 V	−0.12	−0.10	−0.07	−0.05	−0.02	0	+0.02	+0.05	+0.07	+0.10	+0.12	+0.15
6 V	−0.37	−0.30	−0.22	−0.15	−0.07	0	+0.07	+0.15	+.0.22	+0.30	+0.37	+0.45
12 V	−0.75	−0.60	−0.45	−0.30	−0.15	0	+0.15	+0.30	+0.45	+0.60	+0.75	+0.90
24 V	−1.5	−1.2	−0.9	−0.6	−0.3	0	+0.3	+0.6	+0.9	+1.2	+1.5	+1.8

Changing 'exhausted' electrolyte

Changing the electrolyte is advised against by all battery manufacturers. Nevertheless it is regularly done in countries where batteries are relatively expensive and are worth treating in this way to obtain a little extra use.

The particular application is where the lowest-cost SLI batteries are used for running televisions so are regularly subjected to deep discharges. Changing the electrolyte is sometimes called a 'battery service' and is performed when a battery will not charge up. If a battery reaches this condition, there is nothing to lose by replacing the electrolyte.

Before proceeding, refer to Chapter 10 and follow the safety precautions on handling electrolyte. These are very important to avoid skin burns and prevent electrolyte entering eyes which could cause blindness. Also, the electrolyte is very damaging to clothes and tools.

The procedure for changing exhausted electrolyte is as follows:

1. Check that the battery will not charge up and that the specific gravity is very low. (A simple test is to drop a little electrolyte from a battery hydrometer or the end of a glass rod onto some rough ground. The cell is dead when there are no signs of fizzing.)
2. Empty out all the electrolyte into a bowl and dispose of the old liquid safely (well away from sources of water for drinking, washing, and irrigation).
3. Replace vent caps and put the empty battery on charge for about fifteen minutes. (Any current that flows will burn out internal short circuits between the plates if they are small. Vent caps prevent any electrolyte from spitting out.)
4. Fill up the battery with fresh electrolyte.
5. Charge up to full capacity.

$\boxed{\text{E}}$ Solutions

Chapter 3

18. **(a)** Usable capacity is calculated from Formula (3.2):

$90 \times 60 \div 100 = 54$ A h

(b) Total usable capacity over the cycle life is calculated from Formula (3.3):

$54 \times 1200 = 64\,800$ A h

Chapter 5

5. **(a)** Maximum current is calculated from total power using Formula (5.2). Total power is calculated as follows:

$20 + 20 + 20 = 60$ W

Using Formula (5.2)

$60 \div 12 = 5$ A

(b) Since the system voltage is 12 V, Figure 5.4 shows that Table 5.4 should be used. Looking down the column for 60 W and 5 A, the cable length larger than 15 m is 19 m. This corresponds to a minimum cable size of 6.0 mm^2.

6. Figure 5.6 is used to check the size of cable from the array to the batteries. The first step is using Formula (5.4):

$3.2 \times 2 \times 12 \div 24 = 3.2$ A

The next step is using Formula (5.5). A cable size of 1.5 mm^2 is chosen first:

$3.2 \times 18 \times 0.04 \div 1.5 = 1.54$ V

This voltage is greater than 1 V specified. The next cable size up of 2.5 mm^2 is tried:

$3.2 \times 18 \times 0.04 \div 2.5 = 0.92$ V

The smallest cable size for keeping the voltage drop below 1 V is 2.5 mm^2.

Chapter 8

3. Total daily electrical requirement can be calculated using a copy of Table 8.3 (see Table E.1).
'Electrical requirement' for each appliance is calculated using Formula (8.1).

Table E.1 *Calculation of total daily electrical requirement for appliances listed in Question 3 of Chapter 8.*

Appliances	Appliance power (W)	Expected daily use (hours per day)	Electrical requirement (W h per day)
Inside lamp 1	8	4	32
Inside lamp 2	8	4	32
Outside lamp	12	12	144
Television	20	3	60
Total daily requirement of electricity (W h per day):			268

7. The position of 8°N. and 81°E. is on the maps of Figure 8.4(c). The measurements are:

March–May	6.5 peak-hours per day
June–August	5.0 peak-hours per day
September–November	5.9 peak-hours per day
December–February	6.3 peak-hours per day

Therefore the lowest value of daily insolation is 5.0 peak-hours per day.

8. Figure 8.2 is followed to find the number of modules. The first step of using Formula (8.2) is not required because the daily output of one module is already given. The next step is using Formula (8.3). A charging efficiency of 80 per cent is used because most batteries in solar systems are lead–acid.

$$900 \times 100 \div 130 \div 80 = 8.7$$

The minimum whole number above 8.7 is 9. However, the system requires an even number for 24 V operation so the minimum number is 10.

Chapter 9

6. The smallest cable size for the input to a power inverter is calculated using Formula (9.1):

$$5 \times 200 \times 100 \times 0.04 \div 12 \div 70 = 4.76 \, \text{mm}^2$$

The smallest standard size of cable above 4.76 mm^2 is 6 mm^2.

F Recommended books

Solar cells

Green, M. A., *Solar cells: operating principles, technology and system applications*, Prentice Hall (1982) pp. 274, ISBN 0 13 822270 3.

☐ Good for background details on solar cells.

Hu, C. and White, R. M., *Solar cells: from basic to advanced systems*, McGraw-Hill (1983) pp. 294, ISBN 0 07 030745 8.

☐ Full details on principles of operation of solar cells, how they are made, and developments being worked on.

Kirkby, N. and Kirkby, B., *RVers' guide to solar battery charging*, Aatec Publications, P.O. Box 7119, Ann Arbor, Michigan 48107.

Komp, R. J., *Practical photovoltaics: electricity from solar cells*, Aatec Publications, P.O. Box 7119, Ann Arbor, Michigan 48107 (1984) pp. 196.

☐ Includes practical details on assembling solar modules from separate solar cells.

Batteries

Barak, M. (ed.), *Electrochemical power sources: primary and secondary batteries*, Institution of Electrical Engineers Energy Series 1, Peter Peregrinus (1980) pp. 498, ISBN 0 906048 26 5.

☐ Full background detail on all types of rechargeable batteries.

Crompton, T. R., *Small batteries: volume 1 secondary cells*, Macmillan (1982) pp. 226, ISBN 0 333 26418 5.

☐ Covers sealed types of rechargeable batteries but only up to a capacity of about 30 A h. Specifications given for the main makes.

General components for solar systems

Derrick, A., Francis, C. and Bokalders, V., *Solar photovoltaic products: a guide for development workers*, Intermediate Technology Publications (1989) pp. 127, ISBN 1 85339 002 X.

□ Extensive list of suppliers and prices (current in 1988) for devices that can be powered by solar electricity.

'EPI technical series' of booklets from the World Health Organization written for field workers and non-technical staff. Programmes for training courses are also covered. They are available free of charge and in English, French, or Spanish from:

Expanded Programme on Immunization	*Tel.* +41 22 912111
World Health Organization	*Telex* 27820 OMS
1211 Geneva 27	
Switzerland	

United Nations Children's Fund	*Tel.* +1 212 326 7000
UNICEF House	*Telex* 175989 TRT
3 United Nations Plaza	
NY 10017	
USA	

Kenna, J. and Gillett, B., *Solar water pumping: a handbook,* Intermediate Technology Publications (1985) pp. 123, ISBN 0 946688 90 7.

□ Very good guide to comparing and costing different methods of pumping water. Includes fifteen pages of tables and maps for accurate estimates of daily insolation averages over months for all parts of the world.

McNelis, B., Derrick, A. and Starr, M., *Solar-powered electricity: a survey of photovoltaic power in developing countries*, Intermediate Technology Publications (1988) pp. 87, ISBN 0 946688 39 7.

□ Covers the many ways that solar electricity is used in developing countries such as water pumps, refrigerators, lighting, and rural electrification. Lots of examples of actual installations.

Real Goods Trading Co. Inc., *Alternative energy sourcebook,* Jade Mountain Import-Export Co., California (1985).

□ Large number of goods listed with lots of personal experiences included in technical advice.

Electricity and electronics

Bernard, J., *The electronic project builder's reference: designing and modifying circuits,* Tab Books, Blue Ridge Summit, PA (1990) pp. 180, ISBN 0 8306 3260 3.

□ Very practical book which expands on Chapter 12. For example, there is detailed advice on how to solder, using different circuit boards and choosing components such as transistors.

Burdett, G., revised by Turner, W., *The Newnes guide to home electrics*, Heinemann (1987) pp. 120, ISBN 0 434 90199 7.

    ☐ Covers basic details of installing mains wiring for home systems.

Jackson, A. and Day, D., *Wiring and lighting: Collins DIY guide*, Collins (1988) pp. 64, ISBN 0 00 412340 9.

    ☐ Good diagrams and in colour, although only intended for the British type of domestic wiring systems.

Jones, M. H., *A practical introduction to electronic circuits*, Cambridge University Press (1985) pp. 278, ISBN 0 521 31312 0.

    ☐ Covers many types of circuits but assumes some knowledge of electronics.

Vaughan, P., *Systematic electronics*, Edward Arnold (1987) pp. 216, ISBN 0 7131 7615 6.

    ☐ Suitable for beginners with good introduction to electricity and electronic components.

Alternative energy systems to solar electricity

Deuss, B., *The zig zag collector*, TOOL (1987), pp. 94, ISBN 9 07 085713 8.

    ☐ Describes the construction and installation of a solar water heater based on a hot water project for hospitals in Indonesia.

Fulford, D., *Running a biogas programme: a handbook*, Intermediate Technology Publications (1988) pp. 160, ISBN 0 946688 49 4.

    ☐ The design of biogas units is given with full technical details. Economic and social effects of biogas programmes are described and advice is given in the problems of management.

Harvey, A. and Brown, A., *Micro-hydro power: a design guide*, Intermediate Technology Publications (1989) pp. 200, ISBN 1 85339 029 1.

    ☐ A wide-ranging guide covering design, economics, purchase, installation, and maintenance of equipment.

Inversin, A. R., *Micro-hydropower sourcebook: a practical guide to design and implementation in developing countries*, NRECA (1986) pp. 285, ISBN 0 946688 48 6.

    ☐ Includes case studies of cost-effective schemes operated within local constraints in developing countries.

Johnston, G. L., *Wind energy systems*, Prentice Hall (1985) pp. 360, ISBN 0 13 957754 8.

    ☐ Covers many aspects of wind generators but not very practical.

Lancashire, S., Kenna, G. and Fraenkel, P., *Windpumping handbook*, Intermediate Technology Publications (1987) pp. 88, ISBN 0 946688 34 6.

    ☐ Mostly about pumping water and aimed at non-technical readers. Includes sections on choosing a wind pump according to technical and economic factors.

McVeigh, J. C., *Sun Power*, Pergamon (1983), pp. 259, ISBN 0 08 026147 7.

    ☐ A general introduction to solar heating of domestic hot water with details on technical aspects and economics.

Malik, M. A. S., Tiwari, G. N., Kumar, A. and Sodha, M. S., *Solar Distillation*, Pergamon Press (1982) pp. 175, ISBN 0 08 028679 8.

☐   A practical study of a wide range of stills and their optimum design, construction and performance.

Rose, *Solar Boat Book*, Ten Speed Press (1983), pp. 181, ISBN 089 815 0868.

☐   Includes plans for heating, cooling, producing fresh water from salt water and cooking.

G Manufacturers of solar modules

This is a list of contact details for some of the main manufacturers of solar modules. These companies can supply both details of their products and a list of local representatives.

The telephone (Tel.) and telefax (Fax) numbers start with the international dialling code for the country. When calling from within the country, the numbers before the number area (up the first space) are usually replaced by '0'. When making an international call, replace the '+' sign with the code for dialling out of the country.

For example, to 'phone Ansaldo S.P.A. from India, the code to dial out of India is 900. Therefore the number to dial is 900 39 10 6556570.

To 'phone Ansaldo S.P.A. from within Italy, area codes for Italy start with 0. Therefore the number to dial is 010 6556570.

Ansaldo S.P.A.	*Tel.*	+39 10 6556570
Via N. Lorenzi, 8	*Fax*	+39 10 445820
16152 Genova	*Telex*	270318 ANSUSE I
Italy		
BP Solar International Ltd	*Tel.*	+44 372 377899
36 Bridge Street	*Fax*	+44 372 377750
Leatherhead	*Telex*	263220 BPSIL
Surrey KT22 8BZ		
United Kingdom		
Central Electronics Ltd	*Tel.*	+91 132 86157
Site 4	*Telex*	592203
Industrial Area		
Sahibabad 201010		
Uttar Pradesh		
India		

Chronar Ltd
Unit 1
Waterton Industrial Estate
Bridgend
Mid Glamorgan CF31 3YN
United Kingdom

Tel.   +44 656 661211
Fax   +44 656 663182
Telex.   498012 CHRNAR

Helios Technology
Via Po, 8
35015 Galliera Veneta
Padova
Italy

Tel.   +39 49 5965655
Fax   +39 49 595 8255
Telex   431591 HELIOS I

Italsolar
Via A d'Andrea, 6
00048 Nettuno
Rome
Italy

Tel.   +39 6 9850246
Fax   +39 6 9850269
Telex   612441

Kyocera Corporation
5-22 Kita Inoue-cho
Higashino
Yamashina-ku
Kyoto 607
Japan

Tel.   +81 75 42221
Fax   +81 75 501 4880
Telex   5422479 KCJPNJ

Mobil Solar
4 Suburban Park Drive
Billercia
MA 01821
United States

Tel.   +1 617 667 5900

Photowatt International S.A.
131 Route de l'Empereur
F-92500 Rueil
Malmaison
France

Tel.   +33 1 47 08 05 05
Telex   202084

R&S Renewable Energy Systems BV
PO Box 45
5600 AA Eindhoven
Netherlands

Tel.   +31 40 520155
Fax   +31 40 550625
Telex   59030 RES NL

Siemens Solar GmbH
Buchenallee 3
D-5060 Bergisch-Gladbach 1
West Germany

Tel.   +49 2204 4060
Fax   +49 2204 40666
Telex   884891 SSOL

Siemens Solar Industries   *Tel.*   +1 805 482 6800
4650 Adohr Lane   *Fax*   +1 805 388 6395
PO Box 6032   *Telex* 6716260
Camarillo 93010
California
United States

Solarex Corporation   *Tel.*   +1 301 948 0202
1335 Piccard Drive   *Fax*   +1 301 948 7148
Rockville   *Telex* 248359 SOLX UR
MD 20850
United States

Index

Main references are given in bold type.
Page numbers for figures, tables and formulas
are in italic type.